P9-EMM-946

Penguin Book 2552
Italian Writing Today

ITALIAN
WRITING
TODAY

EDITED BY
RALEIGH TREVELYAN

PENGUIN BOOKS
BALTIMORE · MARYLAND

Penguin Books Ltd, Harmondsworth,
Middlesex, England
Penguin Books Inc., 3300 Clipper Mill Road,
Baltimore 11, Md, U.S.A.
Penguin Books Australia Ltd, Ringwood,
Victoria, Australia

First published 1967
Copyright © Raleigh Trevelyan, 1967

Made and printed in Great Britain by
Hazell Watson & Viney Ltd,
Aylesbury, Bucks
Set in Linotype Juliana

This book is sold subject to the condition that
it shall not, by way of trade or otherwise, be lent,
re-sold, hired out, or otherwise circulated without
the publisher's prior consent in any form of
binding or cover other than that in which it is
published and without a similar condition
including this condition being imposed on the
subsequent purchaser

Contents

6 Contents

Introduction

The aim of this book is to provide some idea of the kind of writing that the intelligent Italian is reading today. Thirty-four authors – novelists, critics, poets – are represented, many of them writers of importance but whose work has scarcely, if at all, been translated into English. None of the contributions have appeared in English before, and the translations have all, except one, been specially commissioned for *Italian Writing Today*.

One or two 'names' among fiction-writers, such as Moravia, Pratolini and Soldati, have been deliberately left out, simply because they are well known, or because they have not been writing fiction for some while. Amongst those included Bassani, Calvino and Cassola are the three who stand out as having reached the largest reading public of this country. Maraini, with her first translated novel, had something of a *succès de scandale*. Ginzburg and Silone are always respectfully received. Gadda, since his Formentor award, and Pasolini, chiefly because of his work in films, have had personal publicity, but their books until very recently have been considered too difficult for translation. The rest, although nearly all of them have had a novel translated, are still probably only familiar to the specialist few.

Compagnone's *L'amara scienza*, Dusi's *La moglie*, Malerba's *Il serpente* and Patti's *La cugina* were among the more outstanding recent novels, but they were published too late for extracts to be included in this book. The collections by Delfini, Palazzeschi, Rea and Tobino would also have provided suitable stories. Indeed there is a long list of authors who might have been eligible: for instance, Berto, Bigiaretti, Buzzati, Cassieri, Chiara, Cicognani, Comisso, del Buono, Landolfi, Piovene, Prisco, and Testori; and among the women writers Banti, Cialente, Corti, Manzini, Morante (especially), Romano and de Cespedes (more highly regarded abroad than in Italy).

Of the six critics Milano and Chiaromonte are, to our way of thinking, the ones who write more on traditional lines, no doubt because both have lived for long periods in the United States. Arbasino is Italy's Ronald Bryden or Bernard Levin, on theatre, though far more self-consciously outrageous. Barilli and Eco are leading lights in the avant garde movement. Fortini writes as an engaged Marxist; his two pieces are typical of the uncompromisingly intellectual approach, now fashionable in Italy. Other important critics, of either literature or contemporary art, are Arcangeli, Antonielli, Argan, Aristarco, Brandi, Citati, Contini, Dorfles, Longhi, Ragghianti, Siciliano, Solmi and Zolla.

As with the fiction-writers most of the best known poets, in fact the elder generation, have been purposely omitted: Quasimodo, because a volume of his work has just appeared from Penguin; Montale, because he also has been published in volume form by the Edinburgh University Press in the excellent translation by George Kay; Ungaretti, because he has apparently stopped writing poetry and in any case he has been widely translated into English; Saba, because – although we await a volume of the collected poems in translation by this major ranking poet – his work too has appeared extensively in anthologies and magazines both here and in America. Betocchi, Leonetti, Penna and Roversi were possibles for inclusion as were Caproni and Cattafi, who have recently brought out books, *Il congedo del viaggiatore cerimonioso* and *L'osso, l'anima*. In this anthology Risi and Vivaldi are representatives of the avant garde. Gatto, Luzi and Sereni belong to the middle generation. Erba, Pasolini and Pennati cannot be labelled and write as individuals.

Some of the authors chosen here are versatile and well known in other fields. Arbasino, for instance, is not just an opera or theatre critic. Pasolini is a major novelist, critic and film director as well as poet. Sanguineti is a poet and critic. Villa and Volponi are poets. Silone is famous as a novelist. Calvino is represented by two pieces: an extract from an essay and one of his latest short stories. This may well be considered favouritism (and he is one of the Editor's favourite authors); however, by way of contrast, there is Barilli's slightly critical, though very penetrating essay on his work. Assessments (those by Fortini) also appear of two other writers in this book, Luzi and Sereni.

Regionalism has always been an important feature of Italian letters. Sciascia is pre-eminently a Sicilian author. Gatto is 'southern'. Gambini and Rosso are from Trieste and write in a very definite tradition. Indeed schools, groups and movements are much more a part of literary life in Italy than they are in Britain. Sometimes they can be extremely select and ingrowing. Italians are far more interested than we are in cultural debates, specialized literary controversy and the significance of prizes. This may be because of a certain lack of narrative and linguistic tradition, due to the fact that – with two exceptions – there were no great Italian nineteenth-century novels, as there were in France or England (*The Leopard* was really a novel out of its time and this accounted for some of the initial excitement on its discovery). Writers in Italy are constantly striving for the right expressive or stylistic medium. Thus, in a country where at least one third of the adult population is said never to read even a newspaper, despite the great post-war increase in the book-buying public, they tend to form themselves into a would-be intellectual élite instead of making literature more attractive to the people. Some Italian critics seem, indeed, to take almost a delight in being obscure or belonging to an in-group, even though it is true that the high standard of literary criticism is one of the features of Italian writing in the 1960s.

After the war there was a 'neo-realist' phase, a craze for absolute realism and objectivity, especially in depicting working-class or slum life. This was often the excuse for much slipshod writing. Now things have moved to an opposite, experimentalist extreme, especially with the formation of the avant garde group, the *avanguardia*, consolidated in 1963 at the Palermo festival. Barilli, Eco, Risi, Sanguineti, Villa and Vivaldi are representatives here of this group. Life in industry (now in any case an outmoded theme), science fiction, strip cartoons, James Bond, poetry by the electronic brain and, in 1965, 'visual' poetry are some subjects that have been taken up by the *avanguardia*, who also have their own magazines such as *Malebolge, Marcatre* and *Il Verri. Il Menabò,* edited by Calvino and – until his death in 1965 – Vittorini, also publishes much of their writing, and there have been three notable avant garde anthologies, *Gruppo '63, La scuola di Palermo* and *I Novissimi.*

A reference must also be made to the influence of films on Italian writing. Most leading authors have become involved in film-making or script-writing in some way or other. Personality cults and the glamour of publicity have had their appeal and their distractions. Thus a special intelligentsia connected with this world – which geographically and mentally means Rome – has grown up, Pasolini and Soldati being obvious examples. Then, for instance, there are writers such as Ottieri, and several of the younger generation, who produce novels partly in the form of film-scripts.

Finally, the authors who have not so far been mentioned in this introduction: Fenoglio, Fonzi, Meneghello, Ortese and Parise. Each is a highly interesting and original writer, not especially 'aligned'. Fenoglio in fact died recently. All are novelists, though Ortese's contribution is an essay. The number of authors of stature or potential importance in Italy is, indeed, remarkably large when compared with that in most other European countries. Surprisingly few of the novelists, however, seem to have the gift for telling a story, or even the desire to tell one. British publishers – who these days are forced to think ever more in commercial terms – are therefore, and unfortunately, wary about commissioning translations of more or less 'plotless' books, however brilliant, especially if they are specifically national in appeal or too boldly experimental. Admittedly the lack of plot in novels is not just an Italian failing, if it is a failing, but this does help to prevent new Italian fiction from being more widely read over here.

Short biographical notes on authors whose work is represented in *Italian Writing Today* will be found at the end of the book. Sometimes, and particularly when extracts from novels are given, it has been found necessary to insert introductory notes before the pieces concerned.   RALEIGH TREVELYAN

Acknowledgements

I am grateful to the following publishers for permission to use work by their authors: Valentino Bompiani & C., Milan, for Chiaromonte, Eco, and Ottieri; Guilio Einaudi Editore, Turin, for Calvino, Cassola, Fortini, Gambini, Ginzburg, Sereni, and Villa; Giangiacomo Feltrinelli Editore, Milan, for Meneghello, Parise, Rosso, and Sanguineti; Aldo Garzanti Editore, Milan, for Fenoglio, Pasolini, and Volponi; Guiseppe Laterza e Figli, Bari, for Sciascia; C. M. Lerici Editore S.p.A., Milan, for Maraini; Arnoldo Mondadori Editore, Milan, for Arpino, Erba, Gatto, Pennati, and Risi; U. Mursia and C. Editore, Milan, for Barilli; Rizzoli Editore S.p.A., Milan, for Vivaldi; Edizioni di Vanni Scheiwiller, Milan, for Luzi; Vallecchi Editore, Florence, for Silone; both Einaudi and Garzanti for Gadda.

For help in obtaining these permissions I am also grateful to Gerda Andrew, Franziska Becker, Charles G. Bode, Elaine Greene and Celina Wieniewska. I dealt direct with Arbasino, Bassani, Calvino (for his short story), Fonzi, Milano, Ortese and Silone and thank them for their contributions. The extract from *Il padrone* (*The Boss*) by Parise is from William Weaver's forthcoming translation of the book, to be published by Jonathan Cape. Peter Owen is to publish a translation of Gadda's *La cognizione del dolore* (*The Knowledge of Grief*) and Alan Ross a translation of Rosso's *La dura spina*; both will be by William Weaver.

I am particularly indebted to Gavin Ewart, who has translated all the poetry in this book as well as the articles by Fortini. I am also grateful to Nicoletta Coppini for her help, and to Professor Filippo Donini and other members of the Italian Institute of Culture in London. Camillo Pennati was responsible for assisting me in making the selection, and he also worked with me at every stage of the book's preparation; he has my deepest gratitude.

RALEIGH TREVELYAN

Natalia Ginzburg

HE AND I

He's always warm; I'm always cold. In summer, when it is really hot, he never stops complaining how hot he is. If he sees me putting on a jersey in the evening, he's scornful.

He speaks several languages well; I don't speak a single one properly. Even languages he doesn't know he manages to speak in a way of his own.

He has a good sense of direction; I have none. After a day in a town abroad he gets about as carefree as a butterfly. I get lost in my own town, and have to ask how to get myself home. He hates asking the way; when we drive about towns we don't know he refuses to ask the way and tells me to look at the map. I can't read maps, I get all tangled up in those little red circles and he gets angry.

He loves the theatre, painting and music; music especially. I don't understand a thing about music, care little for painting, and am bored at the theatre. One thing alone in the world I love and understand, and that's poetry.

He loves museums, and I visit them reluctantly, feeling dutiful, disgruntled and weary. He loves libraries, and I hate them.

He loves travelling, unknown foreign towns, restaurants. I'd gladly stay at home forever and never move.

All the same, I trail after him on a great many journeys. I trail after him to museums, and churches, and to the opera. I even trail after him to concerts, and fall asleep.

As he knows conductors and singers, he likes going to congratulate them after the performance. I follow him down the long passages leading to the singers' dressing rooms, and listen to him talking to people dressed as cardinals and kings.

He isn't shy; and I am. Sometimes I've seen him shy, though.

With policemen, when they come up to our car armed with note-book and pencil. With them he turns shy, feeling he's in the wrong.

And even not feeling in the wrong. I think he feels respectful towards established authority.

I'm scared of established authority, and he isn't. He respects it. That's different. If I see a policeman coming along to fine us, I think straight away he's going to drag me off to prison. Prison doesn't enter his head; but out of respect he grows timid and agreeable.

This respect of his for established authority made us quarrel violently at the time of the Montesi affair.

He likes tagliatelle, lamb, cherries, and red wine. I like mine-strone, bread-soup, omelettes, and green vegetables.

He's always telling me I know nothing about food; and that I'm like those big fat friars gobbling up vegetable soup in their monas-tery shades; whereas he, he's an epicure, with a sensitive palate. In restaurants he has endless chats about the wine; has two or three bottles brought, looks at them, and ponders, gently stroking his beard.

In England, there are some restaurants where the waiter per-forms a small ceremony: he pours a little wine into the customer's glass, so that he can see whether he likes it. He hated this small ceremony; and stopped the waiter performing it every time, by taking the bottle away from him. I would reproach him, pointing out that everyone should be allowed to get on with his job.

In the same way at the cinema he never lets the usherette take him to his seat. He tips her straight away, but dashes off to seats quite different from those she's pointing out with her torch.

At the cinema he likes sitting right up near the screen. If we go with friends and, like most people, they want to sit back from the screen, he goes off on his own into one of the front rows. I can see quite well near or far, it's all the same to me; but when we're with friends I stay with them, out of politeness; but I'm unhappy in case he's annoyed with me for not sitting with him, jammed up against the screen.

We both love the cinema; and we're quite ready to see any sort of film at any time of day. But he knows the history of the cinema down to the smallest detail; he remembers directors and actors, even the oldest, vanished and forgotten for ages; and he's prepared to trek miles to the remotest suburbs to seek out old silent films, where an actor he loved years ago as a child may appear for a few seconds. I remember one Sunday evening in London; in a faraway suburb, practically in the country, a film he had seen as a child was being shown; it was about the French Revolution, and made in 1930, and an actress who was famous at the time appeared in it for a few minutes. We drove out in search of that distant street; it was raining and foggy, we had wandered for hours and hours through suburbs that were all alike, between rows of small grey houses, gutters, street lamps and gates; I had the map on my knee and couldn't read it, and he was getting cross; at last we found the cinema, and sat there in a completely empty hall. But after a quarter of an hour he wanted to be off again, straight after the brief appearance of the beloved actress; whereas, after such a long journey, I wanted to see how the film ended. Whether he got his way or I did I don't remember; perhaps he did, and we left after a quarter of an hour; it was late, in any case, and although we had gone out in the early afternoon it was now supper time. But when I asked him to tell me how the story ended, I got no satisfactory answer; because he said the story didn't matter in the least, and the only things that mattered were those few minutes, the actress's profile, and her movements, and her curls.

I never remember the names of actors; and as I'm no good at faces I sometimes find it hard to recognize even the most famous. This annoys him terribly; I ask him who so-and-so is, and he's scornful. 'You're not going to tell me,' he says, 'you're not going to tell me you didn't recognize William Holden!'

Exactly. I didn't recognize William Holden. Yet I love the cinema too; but although I've been going to it for so many years I've never managed to become cinematically learned. Whereas he has: he's learned about everything that arouses his curiosity; and I haven't managed to become learned about anything, even the things I've loved most in life: in me they remain scattered images, which admittedly feed my life of memories and feelings, but fail to fill my empty cultural waste-land.

He tells me I lack curiosity: but that's not true. I feel curious about a few, a very few things; and when I've known them, I retain a few scattered images of them, the cadence of a sentence, or of a word. But my universe, where these cadences and images bloom, isolated from one another and unconnected except in some secret way that is unknown and invisible even to me, is dry and melancholy. Whereas his universe is richly green, richly peopled and tilled, a fertile well-watered country of woods and pastures, gardens and villages.

To me, every activity is extremely hard, wearisome, uncertain. I'm very lazy, and if I want to get through anything I've simply got to spend long hours lazing on a sofa. He never lazes, he's always doing something; he types at top speed with the wireless on; when he goes to lie down in the afternoon, he takes along proofs to correct or a book full of notes; on the one day he wants us to go to the cinema, then to a party, then to a theatre. In a single day he manages to do, and to make me do as well, any number of different things; to meet the most disparate people; and if I'm alone and try to do as he does, I can't manage anything, because I stay stuck for the whole afternoon where I meant to stop for half an hour, get lost and can't find the way, or because the dreariest person I least want to see drags me off to the place I least want to go to.

If I tell him what I've done with my afternoon he thinks it completely wasted, he's amused, teases me, and gets annoyed; and says I'm hopeless without him.

I can't arrange my time. He can.

He likes parties. He goes to them in light clothes when everyone else is in dark ones; the notion of changing his suit for a party never crosses his mind. He even turns up in his old raincoat and crumpled hat: a woollen one he bought in London which he wears rammed down over his eyes. He stays only half an hour, he likes chatting and holding a glass for half an hour; he eats lots of small cakes, and I eat hardly any, because when I see him putting away so much I feel that, out of tact or politeness, I at least ought to refrain from eating; after half an hour, when I'm starting to settle down and feel comfortable, he grows impatient and drags me away.

I can't dance and he can.

I can't type and he can.

I can't drive a car. If I suggest getting a licence myself, he says no. He says that in any case I'd never manage it. I think he likes me to be dependent on him for all sorts of things.

I can't sing, and he can. He's a baritone. If he'd learnt singing he might have been a famous singer.

If he'd studied music he might have become a conductor. When he listens to records he conducts the orchestra with a pencil. At the same time he's typing and answering the telephone. He's a man who can do all sorts of things at once.

He teaches and I think does it well.

He could have done all sorts of jobs. But he doesn't regret any of the jobs he didn't do. I could have done only one, a single one: the job I chose, and that I've been doing almost from childhood. Nor do I regret any of the jobs I might have done: but in any case I couldn't have done any of them.

I write stories, and for years I worked at a publisher's. My work wasn't bad, nor was it good. Yet I realize I mightn't have succeeded in working anywhere else. With my colleagues and my boss I was friendly. I felt that if I hadn't had these friendly relationships, I'd have been exhausted and unable to continue working.

For a long time I had an idea that I would some day work on scripts for the cinema. But I never had a chance to, or didn't know how to seek it. I've now lost hope of ever working on film scripts. He worked on film scripts at one time, when he was younger. He worked at a publisher's too. He's written stories. He's done everything that I've done, and a great deal more.

He can flatter people, and an old countess best of all. Maybe he could have been an actor as well.

Once in London he sang in a theatre. He was Job. He had to

hire evening dress; and there he was, in evening dress, at a kind of lectern, singing. He sang Job's words, half speech and half song. I was in a box, dying of fright. I was terrified he'd get flustered, or that his trousers would fall off.

He was surrounded by men and women in evening dress, who were angels and devils and other characters in Job.

He was a great success, and was told how clever he was.

If I'd loved music I'd have loved it passionately. Whereas I don't understand it; and at concerts, which he sometimes makes me go to, I'm distracted and think my own thoughts. Or else I fall fast asleep.

I like singing. I can't sing and I'm completely out of tune; yet sometimes when I'm alone I sing, very softly. I know I'm out of tune because people have told me so; my voice must be like the howling of a cat. But I notice none of this myself; and enjoy myself enormously, when I'm singing. When he hears me he teases me; he says my singing is something beyond music; something I've invented.

When I was a child I used to mutter tunes I'd invented myself. It was an endless moaning counterpoint, that brought tears to my eyes.

The fact that I don't understand painting and the figurative arts doesn't worry me; but it hurts me not to love music, because I feel my spirit is hurt by not loving it. But there's nothing to be done about it; I shall never understand music, and never love it. If I occasionally hear music I like, I can't remember it; so how could I love a thing I can't remember?

I remember the words of a song. Words I love I can repeat for ever. I can repeat the tune that goes with them in my own way too, in my own howling; and howling like that I feel a kind of happiness.

As I write I feel I'm following a tune or a musical metre. Maybe music is very close to my world, and my world, for some unknown reason, doesn't hear it.

All day you hear music, in our house. He has the radio on all day. Or he puts on records. I protest occasionally, and ask for a little silence to work in; but he says such beautiful music must be good for work of any kind.

He's bought an incredible number of records. He says he owns one of the finest record collections in the world.

In the morning, in his dressing gown, dripping bath water, he turns on the radio, sits down at his typewriter and starts his busy, stormy, noisy day. He's superabundant in everything: he fills the bath till it overflows, the teapot and his tea-cup until they're overflowing. He has an outrageous number of shirts and ties. Whereas he very seldom buys shoes.

His mother says that as a child he was a model of tidiness and precision; and it seems that once, when he had to cross some muddy streams in the country, on a rainy day, all in white and with white boots on, at the end of the walk he was spotless, without a trace of mud on his suit or his boots. Nowadays there's no sign of that far-away spotless child in him. His clothes are always spotty. He's grown terribly untidy.

But he still keeps, punctiliously, all the gas company's receipts. In drawers I find ancient gas receipts, from places we left long ago, which he refuses to throw away.

I find very old, wrinkled Tuscan cigars, as well, and cherry-wood cigar holders.

I smoke Stop cigarettes, which are long and not filter-tipped. He sometimes smokes those Tuscan cigars.

I'm terribly untidy. But with the years I've grown nostalgic about tidiness, and sometimes tidy cupboards enthusiastically. In this, I think, I am recalling my mother. I tidy the linen and blanket cupboards, and in summer line all the drawers with clean paper. I very rarely tidy up my papers, because my mother, as she wasn't in the habit of writing, had no papers. My tidiness, and my untidiness, are full of regret and remorse and complex feelings. As for him, his untidiness is triumphant. He has made up his mind that a learned man like himself can quite rightly and properly have an untidy desk.

He does nothing to improve my irresoluteness, the way I hesitate over every action, my feeling of guilt. He laughs and teases me over the smallest thing I do. If I go out shopping in the market, he sometimes follows me, and spies on me unseen. Then afterwards he teases me about my way of shopping, the way I held the oranges and pondered over them, carefully choosing the worst in the whole market (so he says), sneers at me for taking an hour over the shopping, for buying the onions at one stall, the celery at another, and the fruit at another. Sometimes he does the shopping to show me how it can be done fast: he buys everything at a single stall, not hesitating at all; and manages to get them to deliver the basket to the house. He doesn't buy celery because he can't bear it.

This makes me feel more than ever that everything I do is wrong. But if I occasionally find he's made a mistake I keep telling him till he's fed up with me. Because I can be remarkably tiresome at times.

He has sudden rages that overflow like froth on a glass of beer. My tempers are sudden as well. But his pass off quickly; whereas mine leave a complaining, insistent trail behind them, which I think is tremendously irritating, a sort of bitter whine.

Sometimes, in the whirlwind of his temper, I weep; and far from softening and soothing him, my tears make him angrier than ever. He says they're all play-acting; and maybe he's right. Because, in the midst of my tears and his rages, I am completely calm.

Over my real sorrows I never weep.

At one time I would hurl plates and crockery on the floor in a rage. No longer now, though. Perhaps because I've grown older, and my rages are less violent; and then I wouldn't dare touch our plates now, as I'm fond of them and we bought them in London, one day, in Portobello Road.

The price of these plates, and of all sorts of other things we have bought, is reduced remarkably in his memory. Because he likes to think he spent very little and got a bargain. I know the price of that dinner service, it was £16; but he says £12. So too with the picture of King Lear, that's in our dining-room: he bought that in Portobello Road as well, and cleaned it with onion and potato; and now he says he paid a sum for it that I remember as being much larger.

Years ago, at Standards, he bought twelve small bedside mats. He bought them because they were cheap and he thought we should have them in hand; he bought them polemically, thinking I was no good at buying things for the house. They were made of rush-matting the colour of vinegar, and soon became repulsive: they grew stiff as corpses, and I loathed them as they hung on the wire clothes-line on the kitchen balcony. I used to throw them up at him as an example of bad shopping; but he would say they cost very little, very very little, practically nothing. It was some time before I managed to throw them away: because there were so many of them, and because when the moment came to throw them out I wondered whether they mightn't do as rags. We both of us have difficulty in throwing things away: in me it must be a Jewish form of conservation, and the result of my lack of resoluteness; in him it must be a defence against his lack of meanness and his impulsiveness.

He buys bicarbonate and aspirin in large quantities.

Sometimes he's ill, mysteriously unwell; he can't explain what he feels; he stays in bed for a day, bundled up completely in the bedclothes; all that appears is his beard, and the tip of his red nose. Then he takes outsize doses of bicarbonate and aspirin; and says I don't understand, because I'm always well, I'm like those big fat friars who can stand up to wind and weather without danger; whereas he's refined and delicate, and suffers from mysterious illnesses. Then in the evening he's cured, and goes into the kitchen to cook himself tagliatelle.

As a boy he was handsome, thin, slender, without a beard but with a long soft moustache; and he looked like the actor Robert Donat. This was how he was twenty years ago, when I met him; and he wore, I remember, very smart tartan shirts, made of flannel. One evening, I remember, he took me home to the boarding house I was then living in; we walked along the Nazionale together. I already felt very old, weighed down with experience and mistakes; and he seemed to me a boy, millenniums away. What we said to each other that evening along via Nazionale, I can't remember; nothing important, I suppose; the idea that we should one day become husband and wife was millenniums away from me. Then we lost sight of each other; and when we met again he no longer looked like Robert Donat, but rather more like Balzac. When we met again he still had those tartan shirts, but they now looked, on him, like clothes for an arctic expedition; he wore a beard, and a crumpled woollen cap, and everything about him made one think he would soon be off to the North Pole. Because, though he's always so hot, he often dresses as if surrounded by snow and ice and polar bears; or else like a Brazilian coffee planter; but always unlike everyone else.

If I remind him of that distant walk of ours along via Nazionale, he says he remembers, but I know he's lying and can't remember a thing; and sometimes I wonder if we were those two people nearly twenty years ago along via Nazionale; two people who talked so politely, so urbanely, in the sunset; who chatted about everything, and nothing; two pleasant talkers, two young intellectuals out for a walk; so young, so polite, so distracted, so ready to judge each other with absent kindliness, so ready to say goodbye for ever, in that sunset, on that street corner.

Translated by Isabel Quigly

Renzo Rosso

Below is a passage from *La dura spina*, a study in advancing senility. Trieste is under Allied occupation, just after the Second World War. Ermanno Cornelis, a fifty-seven-year-old concert pianist, returns from Vienna. Age is beginning to tell both on his playing and on his sexual prowess. For some years he has desperately sought his vanished youth in affairs with young girls – his pupils. This weakness has caused him to be dismissed from the Munich State Conservatoire. At a café in Trieste he is approached by Cheremísi, a violin teacher, who begs him to give his daughter Giuliana piano lessons. Just before this point in the book Cornelis has been visited in his hotel room by Marta, the chambermaid, but he is too obsessed by the idea of Giuliana to take advantage of her generous advances.

THE PAINFUL THORN

Those were dark times for the city, a late medieval age of violence which it was ill-equipped to face, because despite the many warning signs it had been unable to anticipate the situation even in the last year of war. Foreign detachments of troops were garrisoned there and another army, after making a victorious entry, stood angrily at the gates, expelled by virtue of official documents. Split into two unequal, crazy factions, the townspeople disputed every street and district; and while the smaller party was bent on avenging the wrongs suffered under the previous tyranny by savage reprisals upon the larger faction which had become identified with that tyranny, the latter defended its survival with the old reasons, so that the evil of the recent past reappeared as a lost boon and former crimes were cancelled out by the present excesses of the opposition.

'The same old rumpus – they're giving each other hell, as usual,'

Alfonso replied to Cornelis who had asked him about the noise that could be heard coming from the distant street.

Alfonso had come into the room, unannounced – Lord knows what tale he had spun the night porter. On waking up, Cornelis saw him standing there, his pale, flabby face beaming forth with eager hypocrisy in a room so flooded with dazzling light that he had no idea of the time until he remembered the shutters which had been left open the night before.

Alfonso said that he felt sure he had gone but was ever so glad to find him still there and hoped he, Alfonso, was not bothering him too much, and Cornelis, echoing the deferential irony in the other's tone, replied that he had not left on account of him, because he hadn't seen him and couldn't possibly go before his little farewell visit, telling himself at the same time, to ease his own conscience, that the fellow had come as usual to ask for money.

'When will they stop it?' exclaimed Cornelis, pressing the service bell at the head of the bed.

'It's all the fault of those infernal Slavs,' said Alfonso and his eyes held an accusation which stretched beyond the bed far into the mists of history, transferring his servility to Cornelis to see if he had guessed his political and racial feelings. Cornelis sat up in bed and, looking blindly from the clock on his bedside table to the window and the two sea-gulls momentarily framed in it, he puzzled over the day that had exploded on his awakening, trying to grasp the key to its significance. An uncertain beginning of alarming reality with that sot standing by the bed, wearing a threadbare coat and a demand for charity on his lips – a second cousin, that's to say Aunt Esther's son, certainly a worse violinist than Cheremísi, a rotter and a failure from birth, with pouches under his eyes when he was ten years old. And yet, with no thought of persecution or victimization but a short day's span of carefree indolence – after all not an unpleasant encounter, really, and at worst, a morning exercise in permissible paternal tyranny.

'True, but it's your fault, too,' he snapped.

'Ours.'

Suddenly, in his stomach, the revelation of an appetite.

'Well, you could only be a Fascist, my boy. Did you wash, at least, this morning?'

'I used one of those bidets,' Alfonso replied, glad that they had assumed their usual roles of master and buffoon, though Cornelis was staring at his face where, hidden between the adenoidal mouth and the cockle eyes, lurked a smile of sly dishonesty – maybe the essence of his pauper's irresponsible cunning. A chambermaid – not Marta – appeared at the door. Cornelis ordered breakfast for himself and added, 'For my guest a *quarto* of wine.'

Alfonso protested that he never drank wine so early in the day as it only made him worse than he really was. He'd already eaten and wanted nothing more. Then he stood behind the half-open bathroom door and said that he had never imagined Cornelis to be interested in politics.

'But I'm not in the slightest,' Cornelis retorted from the shower. Like him then, for he hadn't been in the party since '38.

'They threw you out, eh? Is there anything you haven't been thrown out of?'

'Yes, they did. That's why I'm not an anti-Fascist,' and he laughed.

'I've plenty to think about without dabbling in politics, a musician should steer clear,' said Cornelis. But Alfonso had the impression that most of them, more or less . . .

'That's true, take Strauss, for example. The noblest minds often conceal baser souls – those of serfs, in fact. Then, they know little about music – I don't mean Strauss – let alone politics. . . . It's a question of where there's more gain.'

What about him?

'I, too, perhaps a little less than so many others. But on the whole, no. I've always tried to mind my own business and that's all.'

And what about art? Alfonso asked the question just to start an argument.

'It can be achieved in all ways: dignity, opportunism, courage, quiet living, and more by the last. On the other hand, morality lies within, not outside. Don't you think?'

By the way, what was he doing?

'A concert in Zurich at the beginning of March; then two in Berne, one in Milan.'

Marvellous to tour the world. He envied him.

'At one time, maybe, but now it's so exhausting, Germany is destroyed and then I'm getting tired of being a roamer.'

And his lessons? Everyone spoke of him as an extraordinarily fine teacher.

He emerged from the shower and replied that that was his job and his pupils were bright; he had had to refuse a lot of applications. But still people insisted, begged – this was true: for instance only three days before a man called Cheremísi had pleaded with him to take his daughter as a pupil. Perhaps Alfonso knew him.

He felt frozen to immobility in his bath-robe because that name had spread everywhere, a vast, tender anxiety pressing on nerves, palate and avid hearing. Of course he knew Cheremísi – replied Alfonso – he was worse than him, considering the esteem that his distinguished cousin had for him; he'd sell his wife and daughter if there were no risks, out of sheer ambition and greed – a petty, despicable bourgeois.

Cornelis had his breakfast tray put on the little table by the window and sat down with his back to Alfonso.

'What a splendid tie, where did you buy it?' Alfonso asked.

With his mouth full Cornelis told him to keep it. The coffee and milk, good. Bread, excellent. The day was fine, the quay blue, white, yellow, red-lead, bathed in horizontal shafts of sunlight from behind the city. A solitary dirty grey rat of a warship with a large black number painted on the bows. He wondered about the real motive of Alfonso's visit behind the appearances. Butter like cream and exceptional voracity brought him complete pleasure. A boat tacking in the fish-market harbour, the fish-market with a bell-tower, a red-grey church of sea-bars and cuttle-fish. A whole world in the mouth and the perfume of bread and creamy butter. A mass of clouds on the horizon across the bay and haze out to sea towards Pisano, but very slight. My city, he thought, the dialect of my childhood up along via Molino to Vento, as if the city were preparing to come and meet him. When he had finished he asked Alfonso:

'How is your father? Still loitering around the urinals?'

'I wish he were, from my point of view, especially,' his cousin replied, 'but he can hardly move now. Arterio-sclerosis,' he added. It had started two or three years before with a buzzing in his ears, and now he wept continually, thought of nothing but eating, was as greedy as a suckling, never remembered what he had eaten at lunch, became furious and brought it all back. He often spoke of Cornelis and a trip they had once taken together – to Postumia, he said first, then changed his mind and said that the place was Abbazia. But had they really made this trip?

'In 1910 or 1911 – to Abbazia,' he replied, 'he had pestered me for a whole year, it was awful.'

Alfonso quite believed it. Now the old man was always in the kitchen, licking plates which he never washed.

'By the window. That window,' said Cornelis.

'Which window?'

'The geraniums in tin cans.'

'We haven't lived at San Giusto for at least five years. Surely I told you? Since Mother ... d'you remember that?'

Cornelis had begun to dress. Aunt Esther with his mother, in the kitchen at home in via Crispi and before in all the others, the willing, silent shadow of a poor relation, washing plates or sewing, smelling of sweat and damp cotton and sadness, who broke up after his mother's death.

'How is she?' Cornelis asked.

'Well, quite well, she has everything she needs.'

'Do you go to see her sometimes?'

'Well, you know how it is, and then she doesn't recognize me at all. It would distress me to see her, you understand?'

'Of course. You couldn't be a more unfortunate family!'

He heard Alfonso agree with a loud sigh – no, they couldn't; and as he searched in the wardrobe for his light check double-breasted jacket, he decided to banish all ideas and thoughts of grief and unhappiness which were true up to a point knowing as he did that reality was divided into so many little atoms of adaptation of the good in life, and so he said:

'You're a homosexual, too, aren't you?'

But no, what was he thinking of, replied Alfonso.

He went on undaunted:

'Aren't you ashamed?'

'A bit,' said the other, still undecided how much to admit.

'Really?'

'Come on, why should I be ashamed in my situation? What do I care what people think or say? Anyway I feel I don't have long to live!'

Cornelis had turned to the mirror and was looking at himself. He looked well, fresh-complexioned, clear-eyed, smart bearing. He glanced away, not so much because of Alfonso's presence as for something around him, a sense of excitement and nervous agitation, but tremendously powerful. He felt an inclination towards basic actions and thoughts, not elegance – quite simply, health: life and destiny in his grasp, something of the sort. And Alfonso said to him:

'What marvellous shape you're in! I look older than you,' probably feeling as the other did, that his heart was melting at the compliment – a well-worn but ever effective expedient – vanity like oxygen, outside thought, conscience, the more mature stratagems, and so he persisted:

'Damn it, you're still a youngster. I bet the women have to watch out!'

'Yes, yes, the women. Here, pass me my shoes. No, down there on the bottom shelf.'

In the hall the porter said to him:

'I shouldn't go out, *maestro*, it's not a good day for you, something unpleasant might happen to you.'

From the veranda a spring light filtered through and although the radiators were on, a dark-chill draught from the closed dining-room, together with the sickly colour of the lamps lit in the porter's cubby-hole, combined to give the impression that outside the temperature was higher and the atmosphere in a ferment.

'A magnificent day like this,' he replied. 'What could possibly happen to me, and anyway I very much want to take a stroll. Come on, Alfonso.'

Just outside the hotel while he was absorbing the slight swell of the sea, mottled by the mobile polygonal surfaces of the waves —

'The de Berg woman is wrong to live alone and reject everything en bloc. Look at the people, see how excited they are, they don't know each other, but they're talking and laughing together.'

'It might be chaos, too,' Alfonso suggested cautiously.

'No, it's youth, my dear chap, vitality within easy reach. For these people, a day like this must be worth a whole life.'

Walking briskly, they reached via Cavana. Gaps in the crowd alternated with dense, jostling knots of humanity, and it seemed as though the individual could no longer hope to exist. Groups of people tangled and unravelled only to bunch together again at the entrances to bars or the front doors of houses. Women at the windows, boys shouting and chasing each other as they darted amongst the grown-ups with little paper flags in their hands.

'You see how chancy everything is. Young people can have brief, secret love affairs, even in the sunlight. A furtive embrace in a doorway. Look at that woman laughing. Isn't it a pleasure to see her?'

They went on their way and Alfonso said:

'Actually she must have been a prostitute,' but Cornelis gave no sign that he had heard him. Lost in reflection and looking up at the buildings in Piazza della Borsa and the roofs above, half a pace in front of Alfonso to spur him on and feel the crowd flowing around him and closing in behind, he was thinking of ancient streets and houses. He felt driven, unnatural, something uncontrollable inside, but was unable to stop or keep silent and said:

'Here there was a store and a coffee-shop, and over there, carpets. Through a subway ("It's still there," the other man interjected) you could get to via delle Beccherie, and any number of small streets fanned out, via delle Ombrelle, del Pane, dei Vitelli and the Corso seemed narrower by half. The Stock Exchange; the house with the floral mosaics and right there was a music shop.'

Then he realized that with his hands clasped behind his back and a beaming smile on his upturned face, the mood of his carefree stroll struck an almost provocative contrast with that rushing stream.

Alfonso must have noticed it, too, because he came up to his side and pretended to talk to him, moving his lips slightly with a serious expression on his face. Suddenly taking him by the arm and saying, 'Let's go this way, you'll see behind here that it's all still the same,' he led him off the Corso into a side street. From here they turned into Artist's Street, an old acquaintance because of certain rooms that could be rented by the hour, and then up the steep slope of via del Monte, as silent as a theatre corridor.

Cornelis started boldly up the hill, urging on Alfonso who was finding it difficult to keep up. The air was so fresh and dry that it intoxicated him, a boy with an unbridled imagination climbing the steep streets of his city in pursuit of unusual colours, designs and thoughts. But when he came within sight of the top he found it terribly hard to breathe; he could not stop even though it became steadily worse and a noise hammered in his temples and clouded his brain. After he dragged himself the last few yards and leaned on the balustrade of the terrace of the Giants (meanwhile he could hear behind him the breathless Alfonso) the azure magnificence of the sun coursed through his veins like a repulsive yellow sand and bent in half, his mouth wide open, gulping in the air he lacked, he felt his legs buckle under him, his sight and stomach swam and he slumped down.

Alfonso, standing over him, must have looked around bewildered at not finding anyone. He knelt by him and lifting him to a sitting position, propped him against the marble balustrade.

From below rose the din of the crowd and he asked in a whisper why they were shouting so loud. He felt his eyes open, close and re-open and heaved a sigh. He felt warm threads on his cheeks and brow, the blood flowing through his veins again.

It was nothing, all over, said Alfonso but for God's sake, did he think it intelligent to strain his heart like that?

'You're right,' Cornelis muttered. 'I won't do it again.'

Facing him was a double symmetrical flight of steps, mock rustic like a Christmas crib. On the left the portal of the Capucin church. On the right, a grey, unfinished façade and the first houses' tiny windows, small askew walls under large tiles, in the via del Monte which sloped down abruptly.

'It never happened to me before,' he said, calmer now. 'What can it be? Am I going to die?'

And while he listened to Alfonso's words of encouragement that death's warnings were more ambiguous and much less superficial and its lease began when one began to abandon life and this didn't seem to be the case for he was obviously still full of it, Cornelis kept on thinking that this unsavoury individual had only shown up to be present at this harmless lapse and spread the word around. He was now helping him to his feet, brushing off his overcoat, picking up and handing him his hat. Useless to ask him not to mention it to anyone.

'Thanks,' he said. Then:

'Do you remember Aunt Teresa, my mother?'

'Of course I do.'

'How well do you remember her?'

'Very well.'

'What colour were her eyes?'

'What colour?' Alfonso repeated, stupidly, frowning in the effort to recall something which evidently he was expected to know before he could have the necessary.

'Green. No? How odd,' he said, more relieved now that Cornelis had taken out his wallet. He gave him two thousand lire notes.

'Is that enough?'

'But yes, of course. Thanks.'

'Enough for two hundred litres, eh?'

A cheek that curved in a respectful grin:

'The good stuff costs a lot.'

They stood for a moment, embarrassed, a tangle of affection, remorse and nausea against a false, lazy resignation, the encounter almost ended.

'Shall I take you back to the hotel?'

'No, I'm all right. Don't worry.'

'Do you want me to go?'

'I hear that they've slung you out of the orchestra.'

'You've heard, eh?' he replied and looked him straight in the eye. 'Now tell me I'll come to a bad end and that'll be that.'

He bent forward and slipped the money in his pocket. Cornelis turned and looked down into Piazza Goldoni, jammed with people.

'Then goodbye and thank you,' said Alfonso.

Cornelis called him back after he had gone ten yards.

'Yes?'

'Why couldn't Aunt Teresa, my mother, stand you?'

'I don't know, how should I?' Alfonso replied, laughing heartily, 'but anyway, the feeling was mutual.' And went on his way, more quickly now, almost at a run down the slope: a squalid fellow, but young and still free with his hair blowing bravely in the wind.

My God, he thought, when Alfonso had disappeared, each existence was a walnut with the kernel enclosed and to ask why was merely indecent curiosity.

Translated by Gwyn Morris

Italo Calvino

A PREFACE

This novel[1] was the first I wrote; I might almost say the first thing I ever wrote, apart from a few stories. What impression do I get when I pick it up now? More than a work of my own, I read it as a book born anonymously of the general atmosphere of a period, of a moral tension and a literary vogue with which our generation identified itself at the end of the Second World War.

The literary explosion of those years in Italy was not so much artistic as a physiological, existential, collective fact. We had lived through the war and the younger of us – who had just been in time to serve as partisans – did not feel in the least crushed, defeated, 'burnt out', but victorious, propelled by the impetus of the recent battle, sole trustees of its inheritance. This, however, was not easy optimism or gratuitous euphoria; on the contrary, what we felt responsible for was a sense of life as starting from scratch, a general, problematic fury and our ability to survive agony and danger; but our attitude was one of defiant gaiety. Many things sprang from that atmosphere, including the tone of my first stories and my first novel.

This affects us today, in particular: the anonymous voice of the period, stronger than our individual, still uncertain inflections. Having emerged from an experience – war, civil war – which had spared no one, established an immediacy of communication between a writer and his public: we were face to face, on equal footing, bursting with stories for the telling; each had his own, each had lived an irregular, dramatic, adventurous life, and snatched the very words from his neighbour's mouth. Newly-found freedom of speech was for people in the beginning a mania for narrating

1. *Il sentiero dei nidi di ragno* (1947, reissued 1964; *The Path to the Nest of Spiders*, 1956).

their experiences: in the trains that were beginning to run again, crammed with people, bags of flour and cans of oil, each passenger told complete strangers about the things that had happened to him, and so did every customer at the tables of the 'People's restaurants', and every woman in the shop-queues; the greyness of everyday life seemed a thing of the past: we were moving in a multi-coloured universe of stories.

Anyone sitting down to write at that time found himself using the same material as the anonymous oral storyteller: the tales that we had lived or witnessed personally were supplemented by stories told with a particular voice, cadence or mimicked expression. During the partisan war fresh experiences were transformed and transmitted into tales repeated around the fire at night, and these acquired a style, a language, a touch of bravado, a taste for painful or aggressive effects. Some of my stories, some pages of this novel with regard to facts and language stem from this new-born oral tradition.

'Neo-realism' was not a school (let us try to be precise). It was a chorus of voices, mainly peripheral, a manifold discovery of the different Italys – especially the Italys which had hitherto received little publicity in literature. Without the variety of Italys, unknown or supposedly unknown to each other, without the variety of dialects and slang to leaven and mix in with the literary language, there would have been no 'neo-realism'. But it was not 'countrified' in the sense of nineteenth-century regional *verismo*. Local characterization was employed to give a ring of truth to situations recognizable as universal: like American provincial life in those writers of the thirties who, so the critics complained, influenced us directly or indirectly.

And so language, style, rhythm had immense importance for us and hence our realism which was to be as different as possible from naturalism. We had drawn a line or rather a kind of triangle: *I Malavoglia, Conversazione in Sicilia, Paesi tuoi*, as a departure point, basing our work on the local dialect and countryside in each case.

My countryside was something I considered jealously mine – a countryside that no one had really ever written about before. (Except Montale – though he was from the other coast – Montale who has always given me the impression in his images and vocabulary of drawing upon his local memories.) I came from the Western Riviera; from the landscape of my town – San Remo – I deliberately obliterated the whole tourist seaboard – the promenade with its palm trees, casinos, hotels, villas – almost as if I were ashamed of them : I started from the alleys in the old town, followed the torrents upstream, avoided the geometrical fields of carnations, preferred the strips of vineyards and olive groves with their rambling old dry-stone walls, climbed the mule-tracks over the fertile ridges to the edge of the pine-woods, then the chestnuts and so I left the sea – still visible from above, a narrow band between two green borders – for the tortuous valleys of the Ligurian Alpine foothills. I had a landscape. But before it could be depicted it had to be subordinated to something else – people and stories. The Resistance represented the fusion between landscape and people. The novel which otherwise I should never have been able to write is here. The everyday scenery of my whole life had become remarkable and romantic : a single story unfolded from the gloomy arches of the old town right up to the woods; armed men pursued and in hiding; I could include the villas, too, now that I had seen them requisitioned and turned into guard-houses and prisons, the carnation fields, as well, when they became open country, dangerous to cross, where the air was often rent by a hail of machine-gun fire.

In this novel, the signs of the literary period merge with those of the author's youth. The insistence on themes of violence and sex in the end seems naïve (nowadays the reader's palate is accustomed to much hotter food) and contrived (that the author treated them as purely external, temporary themes is borne out by his later works).

Just as naïve and contrived may seem his mania for inserting an ideological discussion into the story, in a story like this of quite a different order – immediate and objective in language and situation. To work in the ideological argument satisfactorily, I had the idea of concentrating the theoretical reflections in a chapter separate from the others, chapter 9, containing the reflections of the commissary, Kim – a kind of preface in the middle of the novel. My earliest readers criticized the idea, advising me to cut the chapter out; but although I realized that the homogeneity of the book suffered (at that time, stylistic unity was one of the few reliable aesthetic criteria; the association of different styles and idioms which triumph today had not yet returned to favour) I held firm: the book had been born like that with its composite, sometimes spurious elements.

The other great future subject of critical discussion – dialect, language – is also here in a simple form: dialect in clots of colour (while in my later stories I tried to absorb it into the language, like a vital but hidden plasma), uneven writing, at times verging on the precious, or else hurriedly spontaneous with only the immediate effect in mind: a documentary style (slang, popular songs) bordering on folklore. . . .

And then (continuing the signs of the times, mine and in general, a written preface only has any sense if it is critical), the way of representing humanity: exasperated, grotesque features, contorted grimaces, dark visceral-collective dramas. The appointment with Expressionism that Italian literary and artistic culture had missed in the period after the First World War had its great moment after the Second. Perhaps it should really be called '*neo-expressionism*' and not '*neo-realism*'.

The distortion of the expressionistic lens in this book deforms the faces of those who had been my dear comrades. I studied to make them counterfeit, unrecognizable, 'negative' for only in their negativeness could I find a sense of the poetic. Yet at the same time I felt remorse when I thought of the reality so much warmer, more varied and indefinable, and the real people whom I knew to be so much better and more richly human. And I was to carry that remorse with me for years.

This novel is the first I wrote. What effect does it have on me when I re-read it now? (Now I have found the crucial point – this remorse. I must start my preface from here.) The uneasiness which

this book has caused me for so long has partly gone, partly remains: a link with something so much bigger than me, with
emotions that involved all my contemporaries, and tragedies,
heroism, generous and brilliant ventures and sombre dramas of
conscience. The Resistance; how does this book figure in the 'literature of the Resistance'? At the time it was written, the creation of
a 'literature of the Resistance' was still an open question, but to
write 'the novel of the Resistance' was a 'must'; scarcely two
months after the Liberation, Vittorini's *Uomini e no* was already
in the bookshop windows, containing our primitive dialectic of
death and happiness: the partisans of Milan had had their novel
immediately, a tale of rapid sorties in the concentric plan of the
city: we who had been partisans in the mountains wanted our
own story with our own rhythm, our different comings and
goings. . . .

Not that I was so culturally impoverished as to ignore the fact
that the influence of history on literature is indirect, slow and
often contradictory; I was well aware that so many great historical
events had passed by without inspiring a great novel, even during
the 'century of the novel', par excellence; I knew that the great
Risorgimento novel had never been written. . . . We knew everything, we were not so ingenuous as all that: but I believe that
whenever we are witnesses or actors in a historical epoch, we are
seized by a special responsibility. . . .

In my case, this responsibility eventually made me see the theme
as too demanding and solemn for my talents. And then, unwilling
to be defeated by the subject I decided to tackle it not directly,
but indirectly. Everything would have to be seen through the
eyes of a child in a world of urchins and vagabonds. I thought
up a story on the fringe of the partisan war, its heroism and
sacrifices, but at the same time sharing its colour, harsh tang and
rhythm. . . .

This novel was the first I wrote. How can I describe it now
after so many years? In the very choice of theme there is an
almost provocative arrogance. Against whom? I should say that
I wanted to fight simultaneously on two fronts challenging

on the one hand the detractors of the Resistance, and on the other the high priests of a hagiographic and sickly sentimental Resistance.

The first front: little more than a year after the Liberation 'righteous respectability' was up in arms and took advantage of every emergency of the time – the demoralization of post-war youth, the recrudescence of crime, the difficulty of establishing a new code of laws – to exclaim: 'There, we told you so, those partisans, they're all the same, don't talk to us about the Resistance, we know too well what their ideals were. . . .' It was in this atmosphere that I wrote my book, in which I intended to reply paradoxically to the 'righteous': 'Very well, I'll assume you're right, I'll not depict the best partisans, but the worst possible, I'll put in the centre of my novel a group of rather crooked types. Well, does that change anything? Even a man who throws himself into the fray with no clear motive is prompted by an elementary urge of human redemption, an urge which makes him a hundred thousand times better than you, which has made him become an active historical force such as you can never hope to be!' The sense of this argument, this challenge is now remote: and even then, I admit, the book was read simply as a novel and not as a controversial contribution to a historical argument. And yet, if there are still traces of a provocative sting, they originate from the controversy of the time.

From the double controversy. Inasmuch as the battle on the second front, within the 'Leftish Culture' also now seems remote. Then began the first attempts at a new 'political direction' of literary activity: the author was expected to create 'the positive hero', to give a lead for education in social conduct, and revolutionary warfare. I said that this was a beginning but I must add that neither then nor later did similar pressures come to anything. But there was danger in the air that the new literature might be allocated a purely official and instructional role: when I wrote this book I had just noticed it and was ready to fight tooth and nail against the rise of a new rhetorical style.

With polemic fury I set to work and altered the faces and

characters of people who had been my dearest comrades, with whom for months and months I had shared a mess-tin of chestnuts and the risk of death, for whose safety I had trembled, whose coolness in cutting bridges behind them I had admired, as well as their way of life, free of egoism, and I made masks contracted by perpetual grimaces, grotesque little 'characters', enveloped their stories in hazy *chiaroscuros* – or what in my youthful simplicity I imagined to be hazy *chiaroscuros* – only to be torn with remorse for years . . . .

It was Pavese who first spoke of a fairy-tale quality in my writing and I, who until then had not realized it, knew it only too well from that moment and tried to confirm the definition. My story had begun and now seems entirely contained in that beginning.

Perhaps, basically, the first book is the only one that counts, perhaps you should write that and finish, you only make the great effort then, the opportunity of self-expression only comes once, and you can only untie the knot within you then or never again. Perhaps poetry is possible only at a moment in life that for most people coincides with extreme youth. Once that moment is past, whether you have expressed yourself or not (and you'll only know after a hundred and fifty years – your contemporaries cannot be good judges), henceforth the game is over, you can only imitate others or yourself, you will never be able to say another true, irreplaceable word. . . .

And so the symbolic hero of my book was a figure of regression: a child. To Pin's childish, jealous gaze, weapons and women seemed distant and incomprehensible : what my philosophy exalted, my poetry transfigured into hostile apparitions, my excess of love tinged with hellish desperation.

In writing, I had to keep my style below the facts, the Italian I wanted was that of a man who 'does not speak Italian at home', I tried to write as a hypothetical, self-taught myself might have written.

Il sentiero dei nidi di ragno sprang from this sense of absolute destitution, half excruciatingly suffered, half imagined and affected. I feel that if the book has any merit today, it is this: the representation of a still obscure vital force in which the poverty of the 'too young' and the poverty of pariahs and outcasts merge into one. Some writers followed the path of that first fragmentary epic: in general, they were the most isolated, less assimilated authors who retained this strength. And it was the most solitary of all who succeeded in writing the novel we had all dreamt about, when we least expected it, Beppe Fenoglio, who left it unfinished (*Una questione privata*[1]) when he died at the age of forty or so before even seeing it published. The book which our generation wanted to write now exists, and our work has achieved completion and sense, and only now, thanks to Fenoglio, can we say that a period is over, only now can we be sure that it really existed – the period from *Il sentiero dei nidi di ragno* to *Una questione privata*. *Una questione privata* (which is included in Fenoglio's posthumous volume *Un giorno di fuoco*) is constructed with the geometrical tension of a novel of amorous madness and knightly pursuit like *Orlando furioso*, and at the same time the Resistance is there as it was inside and out, more faithfully portrayed than ever before, clearly recalled after so many years, with all the moral values, the stronger for being implicit, and the emotion and the fury. And it is a book of landscapes, a book of rapid-moving figures, marvellously alive, a book of precise, true words. And it is an absurd, mysterious book in which people follow one thing to follow another and then another and never reach the real truth.

And so I look back on that period which was so full of colour and significance: the partisan war, the months that seemed years, from which all one's life one should be able to evoke faces and warnings and landscapes and thoughts and exploits and words and emotions: and all is remote and misty and the pages are there in their impudent assurance which I know to be deceptive, those pages I wrote polemically from memory that was still present reality, massive, apparently permanent, once and for all, *experience* – and they are of no use to me. I need all the rest, all that

1. For an extract from *Una questione privata*, see p. 44 (Ed.).

is missing. A finished book will never console me for what I have destroyed in writing it: that experience which I nursed throughout my life might perhaps have helped me to write the last book, but in fact was only sufficient for the first.

Translated by Gwyn Morris

Beppe Fenoglio

A PRIVATE QUESTION

The caretaker peered round the corner. 'A partisan!' she exclaimed. 'What do you want? Who are you looking for? But you're...'

'It's me all right.' Milton was unsmiling, too taken aback at finding her so aged. Her figure had thickened, her face was drawn, and her hair gone white.

'The signorina's boyfriend,' said the woman, and left the shelter of the corner. 'One of her boyfriends. Fulvia isn't here, she's gone back to Turin.'

'I know.'

'She left more than a year ago, when you boys started this war of yours.'

'I know. Haven't you heard from her since?'

'From Fulvia?' She shook her head. 'She promised to write to me but she never did. But I'm still hoping for a letter and one of these days I'll get one.'

'This woman,' Milton was thinking as he stared in amazement, 'this old insignificant woman will get a letter from Fulvia. With her news, her greetings, and her signature.'

She used to sign herself $\frac{Fu}{vi} \Big| \frac{l}{a}$, at least to him.

'Perhaps she's already written and the letter's got lost.' She lowered her glance and continued: 'She was a dear girl, Fulvia. Impulsive, a bit harum-scarum perhaps, but a very dear girl.'

'Certainly.'

'And beautiful, very beautiful.'

Milton didn't answer, only stuck out his lower lip. It was his way of meeting pain and enduring it – Fulvia's beauty had always caused him more pain than anything else.

She gave him a sidelong glance and said: 'And to think that she's not even eighteen yet. She was barely sixteen then.'

'I want to ask you a favour. Let me look at the house again.' His voice came out unintentionally hard, almost harsh. 'You can't imagine . . . it would be such a help.'

'Of course,' she answered, twisting her hands.

'Let me just see our room again.' He had tried, without much success, to speak more gently. 'It won't take you more than a couple of minutes.'

'Of course.'

The woman was going to open the door from the inside, which meant she would have to go right round the villa, so he would have to be patient. 'And I'll tell the peasant's son to stay in the backyard[1] and keep watch.'

'Tell him to watch the far side, please. My comrade is keeping an eye on this side.'

'I thought you were alone,' said the woman, again alarmed.

'It makes no difference.'

The caretaker went round the corner and Milton reappeared at the front. He clapped his hands at Ivan and then signalled with an open hand. Five minutes, he was to wait five minutes. Then he stared at the sky, impressing another great element on his memory of this stupendous day. A fleet of blackish clouds scudded westwards across that grey sea, bearing down with their prows on some little white clouds that disintegrated immediately. A sudden gust of wind shook the trees, and the raindrops pattered on to the gravel.

Now his heart was thumping, his lips were suddenly parched. Through the door he could hear the strains of *Over the Rainbow*. The record had been his first gift to Fulvia. After he bought it he'd gone for three days without smoking. His widowed mother used to give him a lira a day, and he would spend the lot on cigarettes. The day he'd taken her the record they'd played it twenty-eight times. 'Do you like it?' he asked tensely, glowering with anxiety

1. 'Aia': literally 'threshing-floor' – an area at the back of most country dwellings and farms in Italy, used for such work as husking maize, etc.

because what he really wanted to ask was 'Do you love it?' 'You can see I keep playing it again,' was her answer. And then: 'I like it so much I could swoon. When it finishes I feel as if something really has finished.' And then, a few weeks later: 'Fulvia, what's your favourite song?' 'I couldn't say. I've got three or four favourites.' 'Isn't it —?' 'Maybe – but no. It's a lovely song, it really makes me swoon, but there are three or four others I like as much.'

The caretaker was coming. As she walked over the parquet it squeaked unnaturally, emitting a resentful malicious creaking noise. Just as if, thought Milton, it didn't like being disturbed from its sleep. He hurried under the porch and scraped first one muddy shoe then the other on the edge of the step. He could hear the woman switching on the light and fumbling at the keyhole. He was half-way through cleaning himself up.

The door was held ajar. 'Come in, come as you are, get inside quickly.'

'The parquet . . .'

'Oh, the parquet,' she repeated with a kind of gentle despair. But she let him finish, and whispered: 'We've had a lot of rain, and the peasant says it's going to rain a lot more. In all my life I don't remember such a wet November. How do you partisans dry your clothes, living out in the open?'

'They dry on our backs,' Milton answered, still not daring to look inside.

'That's enough now. Come in, come just as you are.'

The woman had lit one of the lights in the chandelier. It shone directly on an inlaid table, illuminating nothing else, and in the surrounding darkness the white covers on the armchairs and sofa loomed like ghosts.

'Don't you feel you're visiting a tomb?'

He laughed foolishly as people do when they want to cover up some deeper thought. He certainly couldn't tell her that for him this was the brightest spot in all the world, that for him it meant life or resurrection.

'I'm afraid . . .' the woman quietly began.

He paid no attention to her, probably he didn't even hear her, he could once more see Fulvia huddled in her favourite corner of the sofa, her head thrown back a little so that one of her plaits swung loose, shining and heavy. And he could see himself sitting at the other end, with his long thin legs stretched out, while he talked and talked for hours on end, she listening so intently that she hardly breathed, her gaze nearly always directed elsewhere than at him. Her eyes would readily fill with tears. And when they were brimming over she would toss her head on one side, withdrawing from him, rebelling. 'Stop. Don't say any more. You make me cry. All your fine words are good for nothing but to make me cry. You're mean. You go on talking like this, choosing subjects and dwelling on them just so you can see me cry. No, you're not mean. But you're sad. Worse than sad, you're gloomy. You might at least cry too. You're sad and ugly. I don't want to get sad like you. I'm beautiful and gay. Or I used to be.'

'I'm afraid,' the caretaker was saying, 'that Fulvia will never come back here after the war.'

'She'll come back.'

'I'd be glad if she did, but I'm afraid she won't. As soon as the war is over her father will sell the villa again. He only bought it for Fulvia, so she could be evacuated here. He'd have sold it already if there was anyone who'd buy it in these times, and in this area. I'm really afraid we'll never see her again on these hillsides. Fulvia will go to the sea, like she did every summer before the war. She's quite mad about the sea and I've often heard her talking about Alassio. Have you ever been to Alassio?'

He had never been there, and was suspicious of the place, he suddenly hated it, he actually hoped the war would reduce it to such a state that Fulvia would never be able to go there again or even want to.

'Fulvia's people have a house at Alassio. Whenever she was bored or depressed she always used to talk about Alassio and the sea.'

'I tell you she'll come back.'

He crossed over to the little table against the far wall, next to the fireplace. He leant over slightly and with his finger traced the shape of Fulvia's gramophone. *Over the Rainbow, Deep Purple, I Cover the Waterfront*, Charlie Kunz at the piano, and *Over the Rainbow, Over the Rainbow, Over the Rainbow*.

'The work that gramophone did,' the woman said, flapping her hand.

'Yes.'

'There was always dancing, too much of it. And dancing was strictly forbidden, even at home. Do you remember how often I had to come in and tell you not to make so much noise, because you could be heard halfway up the hill?'

'I remember.'

'But you didn't dance. Or am I wrong?'

No, he hadn't danced. He'd never tried it, never even learnt. He used to stand and watch the others, Fulvia and her partner, and he would change the records and wind up the gramophone. In fact he was a kind of machine operator. The definition was Fulvia's. 'Wake up, operator! Long live the operator!' Her tone of voice was not really very pleasing, but to hear it he was willing to become deaf to all other voices of humanity and nature. Fulvia very often danced with Giorgio Clerici, they would keep it up for five or six records in a row, holding each other almost as close in the pauses. Giorgio was the most handsome boy in Alba as well as being the richest, and certainly the smartest. There wasn't a girl in Alba good enough to pair with Giorgio Clerici. Then Fulvia came from Turin and they made a perfect couple. His hair was honey-blond, hers chestnut brown. Fulvia was keen on Giorgio as a dancing partner. 'He dances divinely,' she used to proclaim, and of her Giorgio would say: 'She's . . . she's indescribable,' and turning to Milton: 'For all you're so clever with words, even you couldn't say . . .' And Milton would smile at him, quiet, unruffled, confident, almost kindly. They never talked while they were dancing. Let Giorgio dance with Fulvia, let him do what little he was able and destined to do. Only once was he irritated, one time when Fulvia had forgotten to remove *Over the Rainbow* from the dance records. He said as much to her during a pause, and she immediately dropped her eyes and murmured: 'You're right.'

But one day, when they were alone, Fulvia wound up the gramophone with her own hands and put on *Over the Rainbow*. 'Come on, dance with me.' He had said – perhaps shouted – no. 'You must learn, you absolutely must. With me, for me. Come on.' 'I don't want to learn . . . with you.' But she'd already taken hold of him, pushing him into the empty space, steering him round as she danced. 'No!' he protested, but he was so desperately confused that he couldn't even attempt to free himself. 'And especially not that song.' But she wouldn't leave go of him, and he had to take care not to stumble and fall down on top of her. 'You must,' said she, 'because I want you to. I want to dance with you, get it? I'm tired of dancing with boys who leave me cold. I won't put up with not dancing with you any longer.' Then, suddenly, just as Milton was giving in, she left him, violently flinging his arms back against his body. 'Go and drop dead in Libya,' she threw at him as she went back to the sofa. 'You're a hippopotamus, a skinny hippopotamus.' But a second later he felt Fulvia's hands caressing his shoulders and her breath on the nape of his neck. 'You really ought to try and pull your shoulders back and stand up straight. You're very round-shouldered. Truly, straighten your shoulders. You must keep your mind on it, see? And now come and sit down and talk to me.'

He crossed to the bookcase, drawn by the faint glimmer of the glass panes. He had already noticed that it was practically empty, containing at the most about ten forgotten abandoned books. He leant over the shelves, but suddenly straightened up again, as if he'd received the opposite of a blow in the pit of the stomach. He was pale and breathing fast. Among those few neglected books he had seen *Tess of the d'Urbervilles*, which he had given to Fulvia at the cost of leaving himself penniless for a fortnight.

'Who chose which books should be taken away and which should be left? Was it Fulvia?'

'Fulvia.'

'She personally?'

'But of course,' said the caretaker. 'She was the only one who was interested in books. She took them out and packed them herself. But she was chiefly concerned about the gramophone and the records. As you see, she left a few books, but she didn't leave a single record behind.'

Ivan's head appeared framed in the doorway. It looked round, pale and disembodied, like a moon.

'What is it?' said Milton. 'Are they coming up the hill?'

'No, but let's get away from here. It's time.'

'Another two minutes.'

With a sigh and a grimace, Ivan withdrew his head.

'You don't mind if I stay a couple more minutes do you? I'll not be troubling you again, I shan't come back until the war's over.'

The woman gestured with open arms. 'Of course I don't mind. So long as there's no danger. I remember you very well. Did you notice how I recognized you immediately? And I'll tell you something . . . I used to be glad you came to call on the signorina. You more than the rest of the gang. More than Signor Clerici to be honest. Incidentally, I haven't seen young Signor Clerici since. Is he a partisan too?'

'Yes, we're together. We've been together all along, but recently they've transferred me to another group. But what makes you say you preferred me to Giorgio? As a visitor, I mean.'

She hesitated, sketching a gesture as if she would like to take back what she'd just said or at least modify it, but Milton was urging 'Come on, tell me' with every taut nerve in his body.

'You won't mention it to young Signor Clerici when you see him again?'

'Do you think I would?'

'Young Signor Clerici,' she said then, 'used to worry me and even make me angry. I can tell you because I have a good opinion of you, you look a very serious boy, if you'll allow me to say so I've never seen such a serious reliable-looking boy. You know what I mean. I counted for little or nothing, I was only the caretaker of the villa, but Fulvia's mother had asked me, when she brought her here, she'd asked me especially . . .'

'To be a bit of a governess,' Milton suggested.

'Exactly, not to wish to use too strong a word. So I had to keep a bit of an eye on the girl and her goings-on. You know what I mean. With you I had nothing to worry about, nothing at all. You always used to talk to each other, for hours on end. Or to be more exact, you would talk and Fulvia would listen. Am I right?'

'You're right. You were right.'

'But with Giorgio Clerici on the other hand . . .'

'Yes.' Milton's mouth was dry.

'In the end, I mean the last summer, the summer of '43, you were in the army I think.'

'Yes.'

'In the end he used to come too often, and nearly always at night. To tell the truth, I didn't like the idea of his calling at such late hours. He used to come in the taxi. You remember, the one that was always parked outside the town hall. That beautiful black car, with that ridiculous engine contraption that ran on gas?'

'Yes.'

The woman shook her head. 'I never heard those two talking. I used to eavesdrop on them, I'm not ashamed to admit it, because it was my duty. But there was always silence, almost as if there was no one there at all. I wasn't at all happy about it. But promise you won't repeat any of this to your friend. They began to stay up late, each time later than the last. If they'd always stayed just outside here, under the cherry trees, I wouldn't have been so worried. But they started going for walks. They used to make for the top of the hill.'

'Which way? Which way did they go?'

'What? Sometimes this way, sometimes that way, but mostly they used to make for the river. You know, where the river skirts the hill.'

'I see.'

'Of course I used to wait up for her, but they came back later each time.'

'What time would they get back?'

'As late as midnight. I should have spoken to Fulvia about it.'

Milton shook his head violently.

'Yes, I should have,' said the woman, 'but I never mustered enough courage. I stood a bit in awe of her, even if she was young enough to be my daughter. Until one evening, at least one night, she came back alone. I never did find out why Giorgio hadn't brought her home. It was very late, after midnight. I remember even the crickets had stopped singing on the hill.'

'Milton.' Outside Ivan whistled.

He didn't even turn round, only a muscle twitched at the top of his cheeks.

'And then?'

'And then what?' said the caretaker.

'Fulvia and ... him?'

'Giorgio never showed up again at the villa. But she used to go out. They used to arrange to meet. He would wait for her fifty yards off, huddled against the hedge to hide from view. But I was on the alert, and I would spot him, his fair hair gave him away. On those nights the moonlight was penetrating.'

'And how long did this go on?'

'Oh, till early last September. Then came all the rumpus of the armistice and the Germans. Then Fulvia left here with her father. And though I was very fond of her, I was glad to see her go. She gave me too much anxiety. I don't mean that they actually did anything wrong ...'

He was rooted to the spot, shaking like a leaf in his sodden khaki uniform, his rifle trembling on his shoulder, his face ashen, his mouth half open, his tongue thick and dry. He feigned an attack of coughing, to give himself time to recover his voice.

'Tell me, when was it exactly that Fulvia left?'

'The twelfth of September exactly. Her father had already realized that it was going to be much more dangerous in the country than in the big city.'

'The twelfth of September,' echoed Milton. And he, where had he been on the twelfth of September 1943? With a tremendous effort he remembered. At Livorno, barricaded in the station lavatory, having eaten nothing for three days, wretchedly dressed in cast-off clothing. On the verge of fainting from starvation and from the stench of the latrine, he had come out into the corridor and collided with that engine driver who was buttoning his flies. 'Where have you come from, soldier?' he whispered. 'Rome.' 'And where's your home?' 'Piedmont.' 'Turin?' 'Thereabouts.' 'O.K. I can take you as far as Genoa. We're leaving in half an hour, but I'd rather hide you in the coal tender straight away. You won't give a damn if you look like a chimney sweep?'

'Milton!' Ivan called once more, but with less urgency than before, though the caretaker gave a start of fear.

'You'd better be going you know. I'm getting frightened too.'

Automatically Milton turned and went towards the door. The necessity of bidding the woman a decent farewell weighed on him like some crushing enterprise. He screwed up his eyes and said: 'You have been very kind. And brave too. Thank you for everything.'

'It was nothing. It's been a pleasure to see you here again, even wearing all those weapons.'

Milton gave a last look at Fulvia's room; he had entered it hoping to find inspiration and strength, and he was leaving it stripped and destroyed.

'Thank you again. For everything. And close the door after me.'

'Things are very dangerous for you, aren't they?' she was still asking.

'No, not very,' he answered, hitching his rifle on his shoulder. 'So far we've been lucky, very lucky.'

'Let's hope your luck lasts till it's all over. And . . . you're sure to win in the end, aren't you?'

'Sure to,' he replied listlessly, and he rushed suddenly away along the little path through the cherry trees, leaving Ivan standing.

Translated by Pamela Swinglehurst

Pier Paolo Pasolini

PART OF A LETTER TO THE
CODIGNOLA BOY

Dear boy, yes, certainly let us meet,
but not expecting anything from this meeting.
If anything – a new delusion, a new emptiness :
of those to whom narcissistic dignity does good, like a sorrow.
At forty I am as I was at seventeen.
Frustrated, the 40- and the 17-year old
can certainly meet, stuttering
ideas that converge, on problems
– among them those
on which two decades open, an entire life,
and which only apparently are the same.
Until one word, from uncertain throats,
a word dry from weeping and wish to be alone –
reveals their incurable disparity.
And, altogether, I shall have to be 'the older poet'
and then I shall fall back on irony
– which will embarrass you : being the 40-year old,
gayer and younger than the 17-year old,
himself now master of his fate.
Beside this appearance, this certain air,
I have nothing else to say to you.
I am a miser, what little I possess
I hold tight pressed against my devilish heart.
And the few inches between cheekbone and chin,
under the mouth distorted by dint of smiles
of timidity, and the eye that's lost
its sweetness, like a fig gone sour,
you will have seen; the true portrait of that maturity

that wounds you, a maturity not fraternal.
What good can a man of the same age be to you?
Simply saddened in the leanness that devours his flesh?
That which he has given, he has given, the rest
is arid piety.

SOMETHING'S ALWAYS MISSING

Something's always missing, there's a void
in all my intuitions. And it's vulgar,
this not being complete is vulgar,
I was never so vulgar as in this *angst*,
this 'not having Christ' – a face
that might be instrument of a work not all
lost in pure intuition in solitude,
self-absorbed love with no other interest
than love, style, that which confounds
the sun, the real sun, the sun ferociously ancient,
   on the elephant backs of barbaric castles,
on the hovels of the South – with the sun
of a film, mellow, grainy, grey,
pounded white, and negative, negative,
   the sublime sun that remains in the memory,
with as much physical presence as at the hour
when it is high, and sails in heaven towards
the unending sunsets of the poorer countries ...

                          Translated by Gavin Ewart

Edoardo Sanguineti

This extract is taken from *Capriccio italiano*, an outstanding and original form of the anti-novel. Each section is complete in itself and is written in one mood like a single poem. There is no real story, merely a situation : that the narrator's wife is expecting a third child and that her pregnancy is causing acute nervous tension in her husband. Memories slip into dreams and into memories of dreams, often erotic.

AN ITALIAN CAPRICE

1

We moved the chairs towards the walls, while the four, gloomily, struck up *When I stop*. The deformed boy rushed again to the tape-recorder. My wife was now with E., in that corner. They had come upstairs to drink orangeade at the bar. Then they had slipped into the manager's room. My wife, now, was looking at me. She had taken off a stocking, and she was bandaging her wrist with it, maybe. She made a sign of greeting to me, also. The manager was hanging a picture on the wall, when they came in. When the lights went out, my wife had to drink her orangeade. Now she was in that corner, and was drinking coffee. Now E. was turning his back on me. There was thick smoke in the basement. 'What about the Sammartin affair, then?' asked black belt. I say black belt because he said he was black belt, and he said we could all get out without paying. But we had to pay him, of course, but we hadn't to pay him much. When the lights went out my wife must have started screaming so loudly that E. had to stop her mouth. Then he began to paw her all over, naturally. Also under her dress, naturally, he must have pawed her. Then she must have bitten his hand, however, afterwards there was nothing to show. Then he, too, maybe, had bitten her wrist. Then when he had begun to feel all over her with the other hand, too, who knows, perhaps she stopped

biting and also screaming. Then she felt herself being hit, I think.
I had gone upstairs, when it got dark. When the lights came on
again, on the other hand, I had slipped into the manager's room,
and he had gone back to busying himself with the picture. 'Damn
it all,' said G., 'we want to get out.' But now I didn't want to go.
I wanted to go before, perhaps, when I was in the manager's room,
for instance, holding up the picture for him. But now everyone
wanted to hear that story of the Martian. And when my wife
came, I told her at once to go downstairs again. Then I said nothing
more to her. Then, instead, I told her only to hold up the picture.
So I went downstairs, and sat there, in that same corner, and then
I called the waiter, and told him to bring me a coffee. I'd already
heard *When I stop* on the lake, that time when we had got lost in
the boat, G. and I, or the time before. Towards ten o'clock the lake
was deserted. 'The inscription is not decipherable, they say,' said
black belt. 'But it's a joke,' he said. 'This,' he said, 'is the first sign,
it's the one above, on the left.' And with his finger he drew two
lines on the table, with beer. Everyone leant over, to see. The deformed boy pressed the black key, because the piece was finished
now. The lake was dark and misty, which was why everyone had left
it. He made a short, curved stroke, and, under it, a short segment.
'Charon's boat,' he said, 'if we turn the inscription upside down.'
We had no oars, and the wind had dropped. 'But there's nothing
to turn upside down,' he said. We were rowing with the rudder,
and later, in the pavilion near the lake, C. had chosen the record.
'But it's an eye,' he said. 'It was November,' he said, 'and the stone
was deciphered by Campomanes.' When the lights came on again,
he was feeling all over her with both hands, and she was drinking
her orangeade. He stopped pawing her at once, naturally. My wife
had stopped bandaging herself, too, now.

2

C. was sitting behind, with my wife. We had got out first, and had
begun to yawn noisily. The two girls, sitting at the back, went on
talking in low voices, and didn't move. Then we began our usual

game. We came close to one another again. We spoke into each other's ears, like that, to make them understand they must stop. Then, at a certain moment, he recited Pythagoras' table, too. Then we left them in the car, putting on lipstick. They exchanged lipsticks, and got them mixed up. They tried them on the backs of their hands, however, because that's what's done. We arrived at the little quay, and looked about us. There were a lot of people there, and on the grass slopes, and at the tables of the cafés. There was a gentle but steady breeze, on the lake, making little waves and hardly stirring the reeds on the right-hand shore. Then there was a bed of canes, on this side, and there the shore was all deserted, sandy, with big patches of scrub on the slope. We noticed that later, too, when night came on and we were caught in a patch of some sort of sargasso, as we said, and we really did say some sort of sargasso, and we couldn't make the shore, and it was no good shouting, and it was pouring with rain. There was a mist, but we could see those bushes, because they were really still, and there were clouds of mosquitoes round us. And so we had supper when it was nearly midnight, we four, and G. and I went on laughing, just as when we were whispering to one another, and we weren't whispering any more, now, but we had only to look at one another, now, to laugh. And the two girls, naturally, didn't understand. But C. was serious, indifferent, as she always is, when eating. But my wife was sad, now, with that big pregnant belly of hers, and that odd lipstick she had put on which in the odd light made her face look twisted, unpleasant. So we laughed, and they were silent, which made it really an odd sort of supper. When C. put on the record in the pavilion, and I made my wife dance, although she was so pregnant, C. told our friend that I was playing with my wife, that I was losing her, what with her being so pregnant, and if I didn't lose her at once, because, of course, it wasn't the right moment, I'd lose her later, but at once, after her confinement which would be soon, and was already her second. There is something odd about the way that pavilion is made, evidently, because, if there aren't too many people in it, it makes a kind of echo, and then you hear everything. So I heard, and my wife heard, but we said nothing at all. It had eight windows, the pavilion. There were vases of flowers in all the windows, but one. Then G.'s voice was heard, but not too loud. 'I'm damned if I care,' he said, because that's, anyway, what he always says.

3

Now E. must have been talking a lot, because he was gesticulating so. Then they got up to dance. Black belt went on with his story, but only a few stayed to listen to it. And even I didn't really listen any more, there was so much noise, all around. Then C. said I must dance with her, and she said something to me that made us laugh a lot. So we clasped one another tightly, but only because we were laughing, and it almost hurt, we were laughing so much, and we nearly lost our balance, and certainly we weren't talking any more. I bumped against my wife, too, she was now dancing in a stiff, cold manner, and then she opened her mouth to say something to me. But E. pulled her away. The music then stopped unexpectedly, and there we were, standing still, hugging each other, C. and I, but almost inert now, and not laughing, so that one can't explain it. I wanted to say something to C., too, and we stopped there, not knowing what to do, and she had that look of hers, as though she were really ill. Then E. seized me by the arm and wanted to take me away. Then he didn't know where to take me, and stopped midway. He was speaking, but I didn't hear him. He was the same as before, making a lot of gestures. 'Why are you telling me this?' I asked, almost ready to cry, now, but I hadn't heard anything, only seen his gestures. Then I looked round me. I was looking for my wife, perhaps. 'That girl's gone,' I said to him. But he said nothing, now, didn't gesticulate any more, didn't do anything.

4

At the hotel I found my wife, asleep. I had a great urge to make love to her, because I wasn't sleepy any more, now, and those are just the best times, when you take your wife even if it's only to go to sleep, and you take her like that, while she's asleep, and she kicks you. However, I wanted to shave first, and she, hardly opening one eye, said she was wide awake and waiting for me, because it was clear she didn't want it, but then she immediately went to sleep again, so I didn't really know what to do. Then I started to smoke there on the bed, dressed, because I wanted her to get well asleep, first, and I went to the bathroom, two or three times. Then G. telephoned, from his hotel, all breathless, because he couldn't find anyone any more, anywhere. Then he began a long rigmarole and said perhaps my wife had really woken up, meanwhile, and I listened to him for a time, but couldn't understand at all well what he wanted. Then I said that it seemed to me rather complicated. I said we could meet in a bar, and said which bar. Then I cut him off. Afterwards I decided to have a hot shower, and make him wait. The hot shower immediately made me want to make love again. So, without drying myself, all dripping still, and warm, I climbed carefully on to the bed, and I'd never seen a bed like that before, a bed with all those mattresses, almost reaching up to the canopy. Because there was a big canopy, too, and everything in the room was thick, heavy. While I was quietly climbing up, I got a lot of kicks. Then, after a bit of a struggle, I decided that it was much better to stop it, and to dry myself, tired as I was, and to dress again in the bathroom. Then, in the bathroom, I decided to have a cold shower because I went on sweating, meanwhile, and so I undressed all over again and had the shower. At the same time I was bleeding because I had cut my face all over with the razor, and I had already spoiled everything in the bathroom, with blood. Then I decided that I would go to sleep. So I lay down naked on top of the bed-clothes, and my wife remained still and quiet, and I didn't do anything. When I woke up, it was dark. My whole face was still covered with blood, naturally, and my watch had stopped, too, full of water. On the table, however, there was a note from my wife written with red nail-varnish, I think: '*It is 5 p.m., and I am going to pick up C. at her hotel.*' So I decided to have another cold shower and go to sleep until something happened.

5

My wife had a look from the terrace, but she couldn't see anything, however far she leaned over. Perhaps they hadn't rung the
bell. But there was a lot of noise from the stairs, and one could
tell that a lot of people were arriving. Then they all came into the
sitting-room, and perhaps they were thieves, and my wife said
that they mustn't wake the children. But they continued to make
a noise, but the children, it seemed, didn't really wake up. I must
have been in bed, and I got up, and I came in all naked. My wife
made energetic signs to me that meant I ought to telephone to the
police. And, it seemed, I didn't understand. Perhaps my wife, however, hadn't looked from the terrace, but was in bed, too, when she
saw a big man with a big bottle in his hand at the door of our
room, and she got up, and woke me, and said to me: 'I'm going to
the next room, with him.' The thieves hadn't come up by the staircase, however. They had come up by a hole that they had made
near the front door, or perhaps by the window on the stairs. Then
a big man with a big bottle in his hand said to my wife: 'Look in
the kitchen.' Then my wife went into the kitchen, and I was there,
naked, with a woman, and we were doing something, and the
woman, my wife thought, seemed to be a servant, however, she
didn't say anything. I looked calmly at my wife, and didn't speak.
In fact, she didn't speak, either. She went back to that man, and
said nothing. Then she said: 'I saw.' Then everything turned out
to be like the other dream, because big patches appeared in the
ceiling, as though it were raining and there were a lot of holes in
the roof, and the water began to come into the house. Everyone
was then looking at the ceiling, and it seemed to my wife that part
of the floor, too, had given way. Then they rang the street bell,
and my wife looked out from the terrace, and leant out, but saw
nothing. Then I came out of the kitchen, or perhaps I got out of
bed again, and I was quite naked, and I said to my wife: 'Now I'm
going to telephone to the police.' But now my wife said: 'It's too
late, now.' The thieves, however, were now going away, and the

big man with the big bottle said: 'Look in the kitchen.' In the kitchen my wife and I were naked, and my wife had a big bottle in her hand, and drank from it. Then we went together on to the terrace, and maybe we looked over at the deserted street, in the silent, gloomy night.

6

Towards midnight, I think, B. telephoned to me, with a voice that wasn't his. Then I told him I didn't understand whether he was laughing or crying. Meanwhile my wife wasn't there. Her note was still there, written with red nail-varnish. Then I lit a cigarette, holding the telephone receiver between my face and my shoulder, so that I spoke with my mouth all crooked and a queer voice, and I took the note and put it in the ash-tray and burnt it, and looked at it burning, and smelt the burnt paper and another smell, which must have been the smell of burnt nail-varnish, I think. Then B. said that he was coming to fetch me at once, in his car. Then, I explained, it was I who didn't know whether to laugh or cry. Because, I explained, I was still asleep, and I wanted to go on sleeping, and then I didn't know where my wife had got to. 'Look for C.,' I said to him. 'She's posed for me,' he said. 'Who?' I said. 'C.,' he replied. 'But where do you want to take me to?' I asked. 'Hell,' he said, and he really seemed now to be crying. 'Why hasn't G. telephoned again?' I asked. Then he said, coldly: 'And who is G.?' And I said: 'It doesn't matter.' He was someone who didn't matter, I explained, to make him understand, now, that I really was asleep. And he said: 'What about your wife, then?' But I said: 'She's not sleepy, obviously, my wife.' 'Then I'll come,' he said. 'Find C.,' I said. 'She's here,' he said. 'No,' I said, 'it's my wife who wants to find her.' 'You must tell her,' he said, 'that she's here.' 'No,' I said, 'I can't tell her now.' 'I'll come, then,' he said. 'Why, then?' I said. But he had already rung off. Then I decided to have a cold shower. Then I said: 'Now I'll ring him up and explain everything all over again.' But when I was under the shower, which was very noisy, I went on saying: 'Everything, all over again.' But then I started to sing that song, which had really got stuck in my head, obviously. Because when we went on to the lake, and he hoisted the boat's sails, there was a faint breeze, and all round the lake there were a lot of people, sitting on the grass, in the shade, under the trees, and near the pavilion, and at the tables outside the inns, because there were at least two inns near the landing-stage, and there was all that colour and all that light. It seemed about to rain, but he hoisted sail and said that anyway we wouldn't be long. But my wife, who was pregnant then, and very big, climbed into the rowing-boat, and there was C., too, who rowed. Then we lost sight of the rowing-boat too. Then the mist began to come up. Then it began to rain, and the rain made a lot of noise, and there was C. on the shore shouting to us, and my wife was shouting, too, and they had been back a long time, but with all that noise one couldn't hear what they were shouting, and their voices seemed lost, with all that mist, too, and it was night now, and I didn't notice that B. had come in, but I saw him in the mirror, which was still splashed with blood, and I was now singing frantically, with my mouth open under the water, and drinking in all that noise. And then immediately I began to spit at the mirror, and then my face began to get all smeared, and I couldn't see my navel, only a sort of frothy patch, and one of my knees began to come to bits, and then one ear became nearly obliterated and then the testicles, and all just like that, in a haphazard sort of way. And B.'s head was just behind mine, and he was laughing. Then he took my pants and put them on his head. And seeing him like that in the mirror, with his face, too, all smudged with spittle, it seemed just as though he were crying.

7

When the roller shutter went right up, I saw my wife on a divan, stretched out, almost naked, and all spattered with blood. E. was still there feeling her, but now he did it more like a doctor. And everything was just as B. had explained in the car. We were driving in the mist, when B. stopped the car suddenly. He was speaking of his last paintings. I was behind, all dull now, curled up. 'You know,' he said, 'I've really got to tell you now.' I said nothing. He waited a moment, then he said: 'She's at the studio.' Of course I knew what he meant, but naturally I said: 'Why?' And he, naturally, didn't answer. The studio was a kind of shop, which he was renting then. He started talking again of his last pictures, but I said: 'You really needn't tell me all this.' He said something else again about the pictures, and I began once more: 'Don't tell me about this,' and I was almost laughing, 'all this stupid stuff.' He accelerated the engine, but didn't start the car. Then he told me everything, quite suddenly. He said that she was bleeding, my wife, that blood was issuing from her everywhere, firstly he said from her mouth and her nose, and then he said: 'Also from her ears.' And then he spoke about his pictures. And then: 'Also from the navel.' Then the car started, and he said: 'From the belly, the buttocks,' and stopped the car again, and waited a bit, and so there we were in the mist, without moving, and I was crouching down, and couldn't think, and he opened one of the windows, and then lit a cigarette, and then he shut the window. Then I had to say something. So then I said: 'Why?' and I said it just because I knew that he wouldn't make any reply. But he had been speaking all the time without turning round, I think, and then, naturally, he did turn round, with a great effort, I think. He said: 'You know that affair of the Sammartin stone?'

8

But then, outside, there wasn't any more mist. So that, on leaving the pavilion, I was able immediately to see R., in that queer moon-light, and she wasn't looking any older, that is, the daughter of the door-keeper, and she was washing clothes at a fountain, close by. I hadn't recognized her at once, but then I lit a cigarette, naturally, and was already starting to walk along the lake, by the path, and I got glimpses of her over my shoulder, sideways, and so I said, to make sure, because she turned away: 'Oi, the pretty laundress.' And she turned, and there was really no more doubt, none, because it was really her, that is, the daughter of the door-keeper. Then someone put on the same record again, in the pavilion, and the music reached us, but rather muted, and it so excited me that I said at once: 'Oi, oi, when did we stop making love, then?' When R. turned round, she didn't stop washing the clothes at once, no. First, she smiled a little, not at all surprised, and then, very slowly, she dried her hands on her dress, which was very short and tight, and I went on walking, but very slowly, with her behind me, silent, but smiling. I handed her a cigarette, naturally, which she gave me back all tasting sweet with lipstick, and then I handed it to her again, and it came back to me sweeter than ever, and wet, so that I began to chew the tobacco, which was all disintegrating. Then she began to walk ahead of me, though I hardly noticed, and we were leaving the lake and the path. The moon was high overhead, and R., who was little and plump, had her own little shadow, almost circular, beneath her, so that it seemed she was walking on it, on purpose, and heavily, as though she wanted to crush it. I could hardly hear the water of the fountain now, or that song. It seemed to me I could only hear her footsteps on the grass, where she was walking, bent slightly forward, silent, her legs bare.

9

Then, opening one eye, I saw the whole floor splashed with blood, and B. was there, not laughing any more, but I saw him in the mirror, kneeling on the bed, with his head up in the canopy, where there was a cloud of dust, and he was sneezing in it, and coughing in it. Then he began to jump on the springs, chuff chuff, and to bang his head on the tester, bump bump. 'If you spit on to a piece of soap,' he was saying, 'you're a bloody fool.' But I, in the mean-time, was feeling all shattered inside, pains everywhere, and I actually had soap in my eye, which I was trying to keep shut, it was smarting so, and instead, it kept trying to open. Then B. made a sort of terrific jump, and came down right in the middle of the room, and then he jumped up there again. 'What a place!' he said, throwing open the window. And I said, dully: 'Well, I'll be damned . . .' And he said immediately: 'All right, you are, all right, you are . . .' And went on and on, dancing about the room like a monkey, and always with my pants on his head, shouting at me: 'Cuckold, cuckold!' And he made me the sign of the horns. I said to him under my breath: 'Get it off your chest.' And meanwhile I was trying to get up, but my hands slipped on the wet floor-tiles, and my eye was smarting so much that my whole head felt swollen. 'Oh,' said B., dancing about the room, 'now I'm going to put the books into the pictures, and splosh, I'll smash them for you there, and splosh, curse you all I'll smudge them all properly for you, you cuckold, and I'll put horns on the portraits, it will make the pages stick together rather, but with some of them, you'll be able to turn the pages, if you want.' Then he said: 'Oh, but all beautiful art books, they cost me the earth, to paint.' And then again: 'Oh, I economize in the colours, anyway.' But now he was sitting in the armchair, that is, sitting more or less, but with his head down and he was scratching it desperately. And then he said: 'What a place this is!' I began then, shyly, and still lying on my stomach: 'What's all this about C., what is it?' And he said: 'What a place!' And in fact one couldn't get anything out of him. And then he said: 'Stand up, get on with you.' And I said, dully: 'And just look at yourself.' And he said: 'And you, you look at yourself.' And so on. And then he said: 'I've given Charles V horns, too.' And he scratched himself, below. 'Oh,' he said, after a pause, 'also to the Judith, get on with you.' And then: 'Oh, a pair like this.'

10

'Get up, now,' she said, 'that's enough, get up.' And I dragged myself up, with my head bursting. 'Curse,' I said, 'I can't get my balance.' And meanwhile I was glad that she had spoken, and meanwhile I was feeling around with my hands, in the dark, and I couldn't find anything at all. Then I heard her up, and I thought that she must be all covered with dirt. Then I bumped into the

wall. With my head, of course. Then with one hand I helped her
a bit to pull herself right up, and with the other I was feeling the
brickwork of the wall: 'I've no more matches,' I said, 'anyway.'
And really I hadn't any, of course, and the last ones I had used up
on the stairs, and there in the basement; and then, I thought, just
when they're needed, they're no use to me any more, naturally.
'Oh,' I said, with my head raised, and it was bursting more than
ever, held up like that, 'here we are two floors down, at least.' But
she said: 'No, no, the people in hell are lower down still.' 'No, no,'
I said, 'I counted the flights myself, and the landings.' But she
began to walk on, then, silently as before, tranquilly, as though
she could see. Because in going up and down the green slopes we
had come to a strange house, from where the lake was no longer
to be seen, almost, but there, in the strange moonlight, it might
even seem to you an old villa. And she slipped into it. And I, behind her. And so she at once went down the stairs, and I close
behind, with the matches, counting the steps, meanwhile, and the
turnings, of which there were so many that I would have said
three, even, not two storeys, down, and all in the dark, too, with
my hands against the walls watching her steps, meanwhile, so
that I didn't even touch her, meanwhile, and then suddenly, after
we had walked for a bit on the level, close to each other, and it
still seemed to me that she was smiling, as before, on the grass,
with that round shadow so that you seemed to throw yourself
right on to the shadow, and she went down suddenly and you felt
her all satisfied and fat, and didn't stop even to turn her round, and
instead stayed for a time grunting over her, and almost nothing
else, almost: 'Uh, uh.' But afterwards, when we were sitting together, and the moonlight came back again through a strange sort
of small window, low down, at a turning of the corridor below, and
we could just distinguish the bricks round about and the white-
wash in the moonlight, and the ground, in the dark, below: 'Oi,'
I said, 'would you like me to explain the theorem to you, then?'
And she, who still remembered everything, one could see that,
lifted up her dress, which really was all dirty with earth but
hurriedly, now, as though we were really still in the kitchen, and

stretched herself out, there, in her drawers and brassière, and they were all white, too, in the moonlight, and it seemed she wanted the moonlight all over her, and she was quite different now, and really as though in a hurry, so that she burst out laughing like a mad thing. 'Oh, go on!' she shouted, and she really seemed mad, so that I almost felt a bit frightened. 'Oh, talk, go on!' And I stayed there, naturally, partly pleased and partly frightened, too, now. And she kept saying: 'Oh, go on,' and laughed so that she seemed hardly recognizable any more, 'Oh, go on,' still laughing, and it seemed now that she was laughing at me, but she seemed almost mad, now, but almost affectionate, and she was punching me in the face, now, with her fists, and she took me, now, with her tongue out while I got below, to make her shut up a little, now, to make her stay quiet for a while, 'Oh, go on,' she said, all fat and foul, 'Oh, go on.'

Translated by I. M. Rawson

Anna Maria Ortese

THE LIGHTS OF GENOA

Two years ago, I was preparing to leave for Genoa, where I planned
to stay for a number of years at least. It had been described to me
(and, having passed through it several times, I remembered it as
being so, a little) as a magnificent Mediterranean city, very blue
and attractive, its harbour full of boats beflagged and, close by,
the mountain veined with streams and even a few rivers. Masts,
funnels and sailors everywhere. Now, I don't mean to say I disliked this image of it, but just that I wasn't prepared for what I
found, and so that I was very much surprised.

The journey – I left in the morning at ten – lasted till sunset,
and at sunset, after La Spezia, came a row of very beautiful little
towns, all in bloom, with the wheels running among flower-
beds and the train tinkling like a toy. Bell towers, small houses,
flowers, were all within reach. It was supper time, and through
the open windows we saw the soup being brought to the table
as the train flashed by. Then the clouds in that cheerful sky began
losing their colour, it grew dark, and as night fell we were in
Genoa.

Here I got off right in Piazza Principe, which is rather like
Piazza Missori in Milan, with those large grey buildings, and a
grey fog, at least that's how I remember it; but here there was a
strange beauty too, like that of an aquarium: the night was very
clear, and you could see everything, I mean really everything, the
smallest details that you sometimes miss, the pattern of the stones,
which I could have counted, the bottles of liqueurs in the café
windows, the pipes, necklaces, and varied knick-knacks in tobacco
shops, the red counters of the bars, what was happening inside
them, and outside the cars passing slowly, the sailor lighting a
cigarette in the light of a street lamp, and you could see the high

neck of his tunic, the collar with its blue bands and the black ribbon dangling from his cap. As clear as on a cinema screen. And clearer still because of a kind of silence that was not complete silence, in which you could make out the voices at the bar and on the pavement, but like a dark background, against which the softest word stood out.

I had a meal at a restaurant in the station itself. It goes without saying that these are sad places; they are also, and for this very reason perhaps, one of the truest things on earth. I ate little and poorly, gazing at an odd window which as far as I remember was made up entirely of small pieces of glass, such as I hadn't yet seen in Milan. Then the waiter warned me that it was hard to find a hotel room, because the fleet was in for three days, and everywhere was full.

He was right! I had to trail about a long time before finding a room free, but then my search was rewarded because I found one in the most remote and mysterious hotel of the whole town, embedded in the mountain itself, or if not in the real mountain, at least in the mountain of buildings. At any rate in order to get there I took so long that I thought I had left Genoa, whereas I was still there! Through doors, up in lifts, across courtyards and cellars, we went into a kind of church, and then it started all over again. In the end the waiter told me that we had arrived, or at least that there was only one long staircase to go, and no lifts there. I then had a feeling of being in Russia, at the National Hotel in Moscow, with those wide plain staircases, and a small table on every floor with a sleepy chambermaid at it. But when we got up, I was right back in that wretched hotel in Palermo, ten or twelve years ago: the room sad and poor enough to wring your heart, with the bed in the corner, just by the door, so that you could hear everything in the passage.

When I was alone I ran to the window and here was another surprise: a real Arabic *zenghet*, a dark, white alleyway, and two or three men – old, their gait suggested – seen from behind, whose black hats and sticks would have touched the window-sill, if they had raised them. This I really enjoyed, and almost laughed at it.

The first hours in an hotel room in a strange or at least unknown town aren't gay, as they were when I was a child, but they can always be interesting. Once over the first uneasy moments, you look round at everything: open drawers, search the wardrobes, examine the old torn prints, sniff at the ancient smell of newspapers, and sometimes read there the remarkable news of other days. I did all this, and after two or three hours it was the middle of the night, and there was nothing else I could do: neither sleep, because I wasn't sleepy, nor read because I hadn't thought of getting newspapers. So very quietly I dressed again and went to see what there was in the passage.

Because it was late, or there had been a breakdown, or someone had forgotten, there were no lights, except a tiny lamp rather high up, that looked like a phosphorescent insect. I went to the end of the passage, where a balcony was open, that I hadn't seen when I arrived, and from there I realized we were at an immense height. I think that on one side, judging by the *zenghet*, we were leaning against the mountain, while on the other we were jutting out of it. In any case, it was an impressive sight, and rather ghostly, I must say: the arch of light from the port, the glowing ships, the city streets, with the sailors passing one another in front of the neon lights, and an absolute splendour and silence.

I stayed there some time, smoking one cigarette after another, eyes wide open, yet not, I think, wholly awake. I was dropping with sleep and at the same time heard a voice saying: 'But who cares about sleep? Stay there. Come on, try and remember!'

It was the easiest and at the same time the most sinister thing possible that was happening to me: when one thing recalls another, and so on, till your present vanishes, and everything before you is purely past, the echo of a life that was more real than this one. I remembered myself as a schoolgirl at a school in this town – or one like it – in the mountains; or else I was one of those brisk youngsters reeling past down below on their way to the harbour. All sorts of gay things filled my mind, but above all a country. Soon we'd be going on board. And setting sail. For what country, or what past?

Next morning I changed my hotel, because in any case the room was already booked, and stayed for ten days in a smaller, more ordinary one. It was just by the harbour and the marvellous porticoes of Sottoripa opposite it. How many mornings I spent there! It was like watching the Tribunali, in Naples: an ant-heap of sun and dust, of shadows, gold, colours; an eternal crowd and an eternal solitude, with something that Naples hasn't got, besides: a feeling of space (although not very visible) and a seriousness and sweetness, a well-controlled madness, that belongs to great cities of the past, a past by the sea. Everything came to these tables: the spray of the open sea became man, woman, boy; there was the foreigner with eyes that were almost white, and the careful docker, whose life might be over, and who sat bravely in a corner. I had little to do, some mornings, and would quietly watch Genoa, brooding on what it was like and what it wasn't like. And it seemed to me more and more that it had no connexion, strictly speaking, with the rest of Italy.

Here the irrepressible appearance of Italy, or the inner stillness, characteristic of seaside or mountain peoples, didn't exist, and instead there was something different, something more, which I don't say I liked or disliked: it was something I hadn't experienced, and it interested me.

First of all, the sky of Genoa – and the whole business may start off from this – isn't very Italian, isn't blazing the way it is in picture postcards, or empty the way the sky is in the Paduan lowlands. It is silver and steel fused together, with clouds running across it, sometimes gaily, sometimes with animal violence. As for the sea, the famous blue beflagged sea, it isn't there: all I saw in its place was something grey, pushed back on every side, as in an undeclared but no less real war, by concrete buildings. But although the sky was metallic and the sea remote, you could feel their greatness and freedom and their breath, and the Genoese seemed to me to have come from that noble air. Here's what a Genoese is, I thought, someone very calm and swift, clean and laughing. History is something that, like the rest of Italy, it no longer has: but what it has is the present.

I discovered another thing, together with this remarkable purity of spirit: a chance of being brotherly without knowing it, brotherly and concerned with any passer-by who happens to be weary, a spontaneous and almost miraculous capacity for supporting the weary.

I can see myself on one of those everlasting days of bustle, weariness, worry and even trouble (I was trying to find other accommodation, and couldn't) crossing the harbour district. I was searching for a piece of luggage that seemed to have been mislaid, as my own life had for some time seemed slightly mislaid; and what I saw – wharves, trains, dust, ships, sheds, implements, stores, lanterns, offices, ropes, packing-cases, dockers – and what I heard – whistles, motors, ships' sirens, hammer blows, an immense dull throbbing under that sky of white dust, behind which was a hint of even whiter sea – wasn't exactly reassuring. At one point I lost my way, and had no idea where I was in that enormous sea-station, and I must confess that I felt most desolate at the thought of the inevitable rudeness or raucousness that, in Rome or to some extent anywhere else, greets anyone who is lost and stops someone to ask the way.

A docker meantime was coming towards me, a porter, one of those men who by force of circumstances end up looking like motor vehicles. Half buried as he was under a terrifying load, a trunk or crate or something, from which a half-golden, half-white head just peeped out, and a face turned scarlet with effort, there was nothing very cordial about him just then.

I took a step towards him, and, hoping that at the worst he'd look at me without answering, stammered out something: where was such and such an office, if he knew. As I said this, I stopped, waiting for the glare or curse that was the least I could expect.

Instead, to my amazement, the man stopped, and first of all, as there was a low wall there, he put his load down on it. So my amazement at his agility was mixed with a thoroughly human surprise I hadn't felt for some time, and which was very sweet to feel.

So the life he led hadn't defeated this poor man: at least he had a pair of blue, kindly, even if slightly bloodshot eyes. And he laughed with his eyes; and as he took off his cap to air his sweating head with one hand, he laid the other, a sort of red stick, on my shoulder, and pointed out the office I was looking for, not far away. And as he talked, with the kindness of an uncle or a brother who hasn't seen you for some time, and is glad to see you, his heavy hand on my shoulder was something that wrung my heart with joy: like an assurance, rapid but no less grave and authoritative for that, of the place even I had in the human world, and which, with this gesture, he guaranteed. He gave me further instructions about getting back to Piazza Di Negro, which seemed to me immensely far, and wasn't; but I might go wrong. I should go here, turn there, etc. At the end of it I was so happy I gave him my hand, and he gave me his, and as I moved away I turned to look at him, and saw that he was standing by his load and watching me, as if to make sure I wasn't going wrong, or for some reason I can't explain, that expressed a sense of our common difficulty in living, a sudden sorrow that was like a light for lost, ever-weary humanity.

Because of that man, among other things, I thought for a long time that there was something superhuman about Genoa. I still think so today, and when I feel depressed and nothing seems worthwhile, to help myself I still think of that old Ligurian docker.

The house I went to live at some time afterwards was not beautiful, in fact it was rather sad; it was at the point where Genoa, scowling among the buildings of Sampierdarena, seems to be trying to escape into the mountains. The mountains and the rough countryside were close at hand, like an enormous shadow, and below, a crowd of steps, houses, and courtyards, like walls or wells or caverns from which the sea had withdrawn, made the blue distance seem to melt away. There was in fact no blueness, only sad buildings, among them a church, a nursing home, a public hospital, and some small shops. Outside the church there was always a hearse, and at night, on the pilasters of the gate, they lit nightlights. All this, in that half light, under that ever silver sky, with that street lamp lit rhythmically at night, as if to say 'here was the sea', wrung the heart, yet I must say there was something human about it, something that gradually grew dear to me.

I wasn't well at the time, I had lost touch with everyone, I hadn't even any money and, from what I read in the newspapers, around me was a heavy summer full of violence and sunshine and earthquakes and drought. But in that sad neighbourhood there was no echo of all this, nor of man's increasing harshness and dryness, and of the indifference that had become a habit and, I would say, a matter of intellectual pride.

Here poverty and humble work went with great simplicity and friendliness.

People were alone, and at the same time never alone, at least not in the terrible way you are in Milan and in Rome, where, if you aren't socially eminent or rich or important, others simply don't notice you, and if you're ill you could be thrown out with the rubbish; here in Genoa other people, strangers, are dear friends, as they are among children, and nobody cares about money or prestige. At least not among the poor.

One day I was alone at home: I went out on to the landing for a moment, and the wind slammed the door behind me. I had no other key, in fact the one key was on the inside, in the lock, and I still knew no one in the building; I felt lost.

I went to the porter (but with little hope of help), and hadn't even finished speaking when he called a workman in the same street, who was busy on some work of his, polishing. The man ran out of his shop and upstairs. Behind him came another. Doors opened, and up came a very old man, and then some young men, some women, and a big dog as well. They all stood outside my door, discussing what had happened, and what was the best way of getting inside without breaking down the door and doing further damage. I was partly cheered by all this interest, and partly worried at the thought of how I could pay back so much kindness. Finally the old gentleman decided that the easiest way was to get inside from the front by going through a room next

door. But there was a high strip jutting out to divide the stone
balcony between the rooms, so the only way to get over it was to
climb down on to the rather narrow cornice, and this at a fearsome
height. I didn't like the idea, and got worked up about it, but no
one took any notice of my protests, and in the end there were a
dozen people on the next-door balcony, quarrelling for the privilege of undertaking the feat. The man who won it was elderly,
with peppery hair and a blue overall. He climbed down, and reappeared. Two minutes later I was home again, and offering all
I had: coffee, a little wine, a few thousand lire. Others came, from
the floor below and from round the landing, the big dog wagged
its tail, meaning no, like the others, he wanted nothing, neither
coffee nor wine, and I must keep my two or three thousand-lire
notes. This was a way (not that they knew how to say it, the
Genoese can't express themselves), a way like any other of being
neighbourly.

I cannot say that in those three months I got to know Genoa,
which is enormous, and mostly stuck up on the hills, or to
love it, because in order to feel anything you need strength, and
I had none. I know just this: that it gave me confidence, and an
underground feeling, the sort you feel, though you can never pin
it down, on crossing somewhere that is already familiar.

Going into town, when I could take the bus, was a happy business. I knew I should never meet strangers. On public transport,
in the shops, walking about the port, everywhere people looked
kindly at me, and familiar voices spoke words as familiar as those
heard at home. Nowhere was there any fear. No one jostled or
judged one: but there was always a hand ready to show the way,
a frank smile, a loving simplicity, and the impossibility of dis-
tinguishing between rich and poor. If I had stayed there longer I
might have been able to recognize the various classes, from their
manners if not from their clothes: but in that short time I
couldn't.

Translated by Isabel Quigly

Carlo Emilio Gadda

This extract is taken from the unfinished novel *La cognizione del dolore*, published in 1963 and awarded a Formentor Prize. The story is set in an imaginary South American country, but the background is clearly that of the author's native Brianza, the region of Lombardy that lies between Milan and the Alps. Written partly on a realistic and partly on a symbolical plane, the literary style is condensed, often obscure, and essentially poetic. The author uses words derived from many sources, susceptible to various shades of meaning : here, there is a strong classical element, with echoes of Horace and an ending on a Virgilian note. An underlying theme in the book is the author's detestation of Fascism, and of the suffering that it inflicted.

THE COGNIZANCE OF SORROW

She wandered, alone, about the house. And were those walls, those copper pans, all that remained to her? Of a whole life. She had been duly informed of the name, the dark, cruel name, of the hillside where he had fallen in battle : and of that other place, serene in its desolation, where he had been taken and laid in the earth, his face restored once more to peace and forgetfulness, to silence, for ever. The son who had smiled at her, in so brief a springtime, who so sweetly, passionately, had caressed her, kissed her. After a year, a non-commissioned officer had called on her at Pastrufazio with a document, and handing over a tattered notebook had asked her to put her signature to another : saying which, he offered her an indelible pencil. First of all he had asked : 'Are you the signora Elisabetta François?' Turning pale at the sound of her name, which to her meant torment, she had replied : 'Yes, I am.' And trembled, as though at a cruel exacerbation of the suffering already inflicted on her. To which, after the first horrible cry, she would continue to be doomed by the sombre voice of eternity.

Before he left, and after signing the register, when, with a clink of its chain, she had taken the polished sword in her arms, she had said, as though to detain him: 'May I offer you a glass of Nevada?', clasping her thin hands together. But the man would not accept. To her he had seemed to bear a strange resemblance to the one who had lived his bright moment of time: of time consumed. The beating of her heart told her so: and, her lips trembling, she felt an impulse of love for the presence that had reappeared to her: but she knew that no one, no one, ever comes back.

She wandered about the house: sometimes opening the shutters of a window in the big living-room, to let the sun in. Then the light fell on her shabby, almost poverty-stricken clothes: the small repairs she had had to make, restraining her tears, in the humbled dress of old age. But what was the sun? What light did it shed? On the howling realms of darkness. She knew its dimensions and its intrinsic nature, its distances from the earth and from all the remaining planets: and their orbits and revolutions; many things had she learned, and taught: Kepler's principles and calculations, too, which pursue into the vacuity of impassive space the ellipse of our desperate plight.

She wandered about, in the house, as though in search of the mysterious way that would lead her to a meeting with someone: or perhaps only to a solitude, empty of all pity, of every memory. From the kitchen, where the fire was out, to the upper rooms, where voices were no longer to be heard; occupied by a few flies. And surrounding the house she could still see the countryside, and the sunlight.

The heavens, so vast above the world of time in dissolution, would become gloomy, now and again, with heavy clouds: which, white and rounded, gathered about the mountain-tops and then, grown suddenly black, seemed dreadfully threatening to a woman left alone in the house, her sons far from her. This happened, too, towards the end of that summer, on an afternoon in early September, after the long period of heat which everyone had said would never end: ten days after she had summoned the custodian, with her keys: and gone down with her to the cemetery. The threat was deeply wounding to her. It was the sudden shock, the animosity, of forces or beings not known, yet inexorable in persecution: the evil that rises again, again and always, after bright mornings of hope. What dismayed her most had always been the unforeseen malevolence of those who had no reason whatever to hate her, or to injure her: of those to whom her own unquestioning trust had been given whole-heartedly, as to equals, and to brothers, who, all of them, belonged to the same high-minded society. Then, every reassuring experience and the memory of her own courage and achievements, of help from other people and the city, would be blotted out instantly by a desolating sense of mortification, and she became bewildered: like a child pushed here and there, overwhelmed, by a crowd. The barbarized crowd of ages lost to time, the obscure evil in things and in people's minds, were to her a dark enigma before which, unknowing as a child that has lost its way, she asked herself in anguish, 'Why? . . . Why . . . ?'

The hurricane, that day, too, came, as was its wont, whistling through the fearful mountain gorges, to discharge itself in the open against the places where men lived and worked. Every time that its grim, mounting rancour was unleashed the whole sky was given over to flashes of lightning, as though the brutal leader of a marauding band of mercenaries were indulging in revelry amid devastation and gunfire. The wind, which had carried her son away from her towards unremembering cypresses, seemed, at every window, to be seeking her, her too, throughout the house. From the narrow one on the stairs a violent gust had caught her by the hair: the boards and beams of the wooden floor creaked as though about to give way, like planks on the deck of a storm-tossed ship: and the window-frames, closed and barred, were bent by the fury from without. She, like a hunted animal, already wounded, was conscious of the savage blasts from the horns of the chase, sounding, again and again, above her, and braced herself as best she might in her exhausted state to find a refuge below, at the bottom of the stairs: and so went down, down: to a corner. Overcoming, in fear and trembling, the void of each step, feeling for them one by one with her foot, clinging to the handrail with hands that no longer had the power to grip: going down, down, lower, lower, into the darkness and damp of the basement. Where there was a small shelf.

And on this, at least, she was able to find, by groping for them, a limp candle and a plate with some matches, put out for use at night by whoever came home late. But no one came. She tried, repeatedly, to strike a match, then took another: and when at last its uncertain, yellow light fell on the brick floor, there, there she saw a horrifying, fugitive splinter of darkness: which then instantly checked itself into immobility, as though lying in wait for her: the black shape of a scorpion. She drew back then, her eyes closed, in her ultimate solitude: raising her head, as one who knows any plea for mercy to be vain. And shrank into herself, a woeful flicker of life's flame, near to extinction: yet in her lifetime she had been woman, wife, and mother. She stiffened now in terror at the dastardly weapon to ward off which she, too, had to avail herself of the shadows. And even there, in her descent, down into the dark depths of memory, the thunder-claps pursued her, ruthlessly, and the vandalistic pride of the tempest. The revolting snare in the darkness: a blot that was blacker still, born of humidity and evil.

Her mind no longer asked why, why! forgetful, in her sense of extreme injury, that an appeal to the love, the charity, of others is possible: she no longer remembered anything: any former help from her own people was lost, far distant. In vain had she borne her children, had given them of her milk: no one would allow her credit for that, amid the sulphurous splendour, the chaos, of the great storms, no one gave it a thought any more: other things had come to obliterate the physical life of long ago, the agony and the sweetness: and then the blaring trumpets of victory, the speech-making and pomp of victory: and for her, old age: this final solitude, shutting out the light of heaven from the spirit.

Drops of hot wax from the guttering candle fell on her shaking hand, scorching her; from the small window on the stairs the gale's icy breath flattened the feeble flame above its puddle of coagulated wax, as the wick, in its last throes, blinked a final farewell.

She could no longer see. All was horror, hatred. The thunder weighed on everything and the grill-like reflection of the lightning through the slats of the closed shutters above flashed incessantly, joining in the elemental wrath. And now the scorpion, re-aroused, had moved on sideways, as though to circumvent her, and she, trembling, had withdrawn into herself, extending a tired, chilled hand, as though to stop it. Her hair hung over her forehead, from her dry, bloodless lips no word dared come: no one, no one could have heard her, in all that din. And to whom could she turn, in these changed times, when, after the passing of the years, she was held, today, in such hatred? When her very children had come, in time, to mean suffering in vain, a glory only to the cemeteries: lost! ... in the futile emptiness of the earth ...

Why? Why?

From the darkness at the foot of the stairs she raised her face now and again, as she had before, to note, above, some quiet interludes in the gale, the blank nullity of empty space: and to listen, as evening fell, to the drip, like tears, from the eaves: or the merciful stillness. She imagined that the cutting gusts of wind, having streaked through every room, had left like a belated gang of thieves, hastening to catch up with their migrant main troop, out in the plain and the night. A loose shutter was banging against the wall of the house, dealing it blow after blow. As night came on she could hear the trees, outside, let fall an occasional drop, cleansed as though from weeping.

No one saw her down there, alone, plunged into these depths of fear, while, on the shelf, the yellow flame of the candle, all but spent in its melted wax, glimmered and grew pale in the shadows. But had someone chanced to catch sight of her, oh, even a marauder, he would have felt within him that that stony, upraised visage showed no desire, even, to implore help from what was long-past, long-vanished. Her loose, damp locks stood up as though in horror from her forehead. Her face scarcely emerged from their shadowy frame, her sunken cheeks were scored by tears that would not come. The claw-like fingers of old age seemed to press the features of one inured to solitude down, down, into the mould of darkness. That face, like a spectre, was turning from the obscurity below ground to the society of living people above, perhaps imagining, without hoping for it, the succour, the voice of a man, of a son.

This word lay lightly on her mind: it called up an image dear to her, a suggestion almost of morning and of dreams, a passing wing from on high, a light in the darkness. Yes: there was her son, in the world of the present, in the certain knowledge, the cognizance, of living beings: even after the transmutations, after the precipitate passing, of the years. He walked among the living. He trod the ways of men. Her first-born. In whose little body she had wanted to see, oh, in those days, the proof of a defect in nature, the failure of her womb to overcome the deception transmitted by the seed: reluctant to have borne, to have generated, what was not her own: in a long and irremediable darkening of her whole being, in weariness of mind and body, exposed to the slow indignity of childbirth, to the insolence of shrewd intermediaries and dealers, enforcing her fulfilment of duties so nobly presented as for the good of all, but which were pain and distress to honest people. And now he was her son: the only one. He went about the parched roads beneath the elms, in the evening, after the dust and the trains. Her eldest son. Oh, only the cloudburst – whipped by the sibilant skies above the engendering hills – only terror could have detached her in such a way from the truth, the security, of that memory. Her son: Gonzalo. To Gonzalo, no, no! the burial honours of the shades had not been rendered: she shuddered at the remembrance: away, away, from the meaningless funeral, the dirges, the obscene wailing, the lamentations: no candles, for him, had burnt low amid the pillars of the cold nave and the tombs of the tenebrous centuries:[1] when, amid the candles, the chant of the

1. *Secoli-tenebra*: a typically Gaddaesque word. It conveys, presumably, not only the gloom of the church and the dimness of past centuries, but also, possibly, a reference to the Catholic 'Office of the Tenebrae', in which the candles are put out one by one.

abyss summons the sacrificed, that they may go down, down, into the verminous grandeur of eternity.

The sound of a motor-horn, from the high road: and the emptiness of present reality. All was silent at last. The cats, at their usual time, had penetrated into the house, by ways that were theirs only: velvety presences stared at her from halfway up the stairs, with eyes, in the dark, like cleft topazes, eyes that delineated hunger: directing towards her, mewing, a timid salutation, an appeal: 'It's time.' Domestic good order and kindliness were recalling her to the floor above. And she, forgetful of her own distress, and, as ever, quickly alive to that of others, climbed up the stairs again. The heavy footsteps of the peasant, in his clogs, sounded on the paving above: returning with his purchases of tobacco, and perhaps, she hoped, of salt: he called to her in the gloom, spoke of the provisions and the fire, told her the time, and of the damaged crops: began, still intermittently shouting to her, to throw open the windows and the shutters. Taking heart once more, she saw again soft, distant lights in the countryside, and Leopardi's words, timeless, familiar, on the opening-up of each household as the storm passed[1] came freshly back to her, a tender memory: it was almost as though the society of men, formed anew, were re-appearing before her eyes after a long night-time. And here was the peasant, with the cats at his heels, going about the house: bringing lighted tinder: from his own hearth to hers, so large and cold: and then on, up the stairs; behind the four-footed scuffle around his clogs, doors slammed. And twigs and firewood were strewn, with masculine heedlessness, wherever he went. And the wind had lost its way in the plain, over towards the Pequeño.

On summer evenings, from the terrace, she could see on the far horizon smoke rising from the farmsteads, in each of which she pictured to herself the housewife, with her husband in the byre, and sons and daughters. The girls would be returning in flocks from the workshops, from the looms, or winding-machines, or

1. 'Apre i balconi – apre terrazzi e logge la famiglia' (From *La quiete dopo la tempesta*).

vessels where the silk was washed: bicycles brought the young men back from the anvil: or they followed the swaying oxen from the fields, with their fathers guiding and braking the low, open carts with sloping sides and small wheels, the axles well-oiled and silent: carts piled high with produce and the work of their hands, with casks and fodder: on which lay, as though forgotten, the weary scythes, in the evening shadows.

Offspring of the countryside, returning in countless numbers from their labours to their firesides: to the rough spoon and pitiful bowl of soup that was their due after the day's work.

Distant gleams of light, and the sound of singing, reached her from outside. As though some housewife had put her copper pans out to dry on the threshing-floor before her house, to reflect, in their polished splendour, the sunset. Perhaps as a greeting to her, the lady, who in her time had been, like them, woman, wife, and mother. She envied none of them. She hoped the women, every one, would find happiness, and quiet strength in their sons, and that these might enjoy health, work, peace: good service in the morning of their lives, under their officers: and, after leaving their regiments, that they would soon find their brides, amid the fragrant grove of girls.

Thus, every day, she found a reason or pretext for summoning to her the washerwoman, the baker's daughter, the woman who sold lemons or at times some rare oranges from Tierra Caliente, the eighty-six-year-old mother of the peasant-worker, the fishmonger's wife. (There was reason to suppose that certain obligatory items of clothing were missing from the latter's person.) They were poor fish, pike, dark in hue, with the dismal, pinched snout of the needy, who had swum their best in the green dearth of the waters before encountering the flash of the harpoon: or big, yellow tench from the lakes, of a greasy and savourless viscidity that even amid carrots and celery still retained the taste of mud: hooked after sunset with rod and line from the Seegrün or that other valley, so fair in autumn, of the abbé-poet,[1] or, still a little further off, from

---

1. A reference, it would seem, to the eighteenth-century poet G. Parini.

that of the disciple-painter,[1] when, beneath melting clouds, the jagged lines of the mountains are mirrored upside-down in the waters.

With carrots and celery, in the long casserole for pike, on a slow fire; she would stir the concoction with a big wooden spoon: it would turn out to be full of fish-bones and celery-fibres, but not unpalatable. In the end she would hardly taste it, but she was content: and gave it all to the women. They praised her skill in cooking and told her gratefully how good it was.

She envied nobody. Perhaps, after so much fortitude, and study, after having laboured and suffered, and having given, without tears, the fruit of her womb, the best of her blood, to the military leaders of the Republic, to dispose of according to their own judgement: perhaps, after the tempestuous passing of each day, and of the weary ellipses of the years, perhaps the judgement of time was right: time, which gently leads us from renunciation to renunciation: oh, it would lead her to where one forgets and one is forgotten, beyond the houses and the enclosing walls, to the long-awaited path of the cypresses.

Offspring of the countryside: yeast of the daily bread of life: let them grow, let them love. She felt herself at the end of her vicissitudes. The sacrifice had been consummated. In purity: of which God alone is knowledge. She was glad that other men and other women would be able to gather up the vital significance of the tale, though still, in the warmth of their blood, under the illusion that they accepted its necessary truth. On the far horizon smoke was rising from the homesteads. Of herself, of her spirit, or her blood, no one would remain, in the empty days to come.

Translated by I. M. Rawson

1. Presumably Luini, a pupil of Leonardo da Vinci. Like Parini, he came from the Brianza.

Camillo Pennati

WALL

Like a poetry that moves horizontally
in its lines and vertically in time,
if it were turned upside down to develop, if
the mortared union corresponds to one of the two halves
above its centre and underneath cemented,
it is a wall of bricks
insofaras with tensions and resistances
the geometry of building raises it high in its layers.
Now it has a colour that's opaque and inward
absorbed by the surface. Now suddenly
a branch projects its shape upon the wall,
even its movement, and acknowledges
a shadow that is not a substance,
as the most ancient mirrors where
likeness is in the outline of the light
not in the dark coloration of the inside —
it can last a day. It can
disappear, now, as when one weeps
the outlines blur. If shipwrecked
the sun floats among the clouds.

WOOD

Ferns, like a wet green Egypt
grow in tiers, hanging pyramids, and
every leaf takes them for its model, low
where only the sun penetrates and stains
beneath the wind, fresh fans in arabesque.

Birds quarrel, hide themselves, listening
for threats, for mating calls, and couple
instinctively. Under the first crackling quilt
putrefaction reigns, bleached wood
that weighs nothing, mast of rotting leaves
where the rain is transformed without evaporating
into various colonies of insects and softens
the seeds that are next to explode in cotyledons.
Now the white eggs of ants, the mouths
of dens, a mushroom, above the leafage
scraps of newspaper. We only stay one day's
most luminous hours, but we continue to measure
the secret that oppresses the mind
more and more as that alien rhythm of fulfilment
infiltrates it. There everything happens.
The moment ripens the moment and the world
that belongs to it, complete, without
perplexity or delusion, where it achieves
in its fourth season every duration.

Translated by Gavin Ewart

Luigi Meneghello

These are extracts from *Libera nos a malo* – a pun ('Deliver us from evil'), for Malo is a real *paese*, the author's home. In some ways the book is a sociological essay based on Meneghello's childhood, in others it is a novel, in others it could even occasionally be a prose poem. At the end of *Libera nos a malo* there are pages of notes on dialect words.

DELIVER US FROM EVIL

'I'll take Norma, you take Carla.'

So I took Carla, but secretly I admired Norma. Oh the paleness of Norma! that white skin on the inside of her thighs. Carla was a lovely little lass, curly-headed and well made, dark-skinned and jolly; but Norma was a downy trap into which I longed to fall.

However I took Carla: the idea of contradicting Piareto never so much as flickered across my mind. I was the youngest (and Norma, who was perhaps six years older, the eldest) and it was not up to me to choose. Then I wouldn't have liked to offend Carla, she was so nice and willing.

And so, in the depths of the undergrowth, half-way down the kitchen garden, in a green subaqueous twilight, and under the vines' wooden supports, we did sinful things to our women as they lay stretched out on the ground.

But I did have one hour of sublime ecstasy with Norma in the big room above the cellar, behind an object which I remember in its essential details – a nest, a screen, a roof all in one – probably it was part of the body of a motor-car. There were leather-covered seats and little silk curtains, worked by springs and with tassels so that they could be lowered over the glassless windows. It was one of many curious pieces of junk up there: we had hoisted it on to some tins and trestle tables, high up on a level with the window that looked over the fields. We felt as if we were in a little drawing-room without a back wall, but well shielded all the same from the outside world.

Norma and I climbed up there to play, and without any pre-liminaries, without words, I was admitted for a brief hour into that communion of surfaces, into that sweet knot where we both expired.

Atinpúri![1] For first communion, which one made in church at the age of seven, they dressed us in sailor-suits; and the girls in white. When my turn came and I had to go to confession for the first time, it became clear to me that I would have to confess some sinful things, years and years of them, a whole lifetime of sinful things; but how, and what would I say? I consulted Norma. She had been to first communion some years before, and for a little while she had kept away from the forbidden games, to which she returned in due course, albeit infrequently and with reluctance.

One day, whilst I was peeing on the side of the compost heap, Norma passed with a wire basket on her way to the kitchen garden to pick lettuces. I turned towards her, and by way of invitation gaily waggled up and down what I held in my hand. But Norma was annoyed.

'Go away, man!' she said. 'Remember that soon you've got your first communion!'

Later we met in the courtyard (evening had fallen) and as she walked up and down Norma confided in me that formula she used for her confession. I learnt it by heart and in due course repeated it to the priest: '*Atinpúri*'.

The game that I thought so secret was already well known to priests and grownups, she said; and that was what they called it.

We realized that the time had come to confess our worst sins. It was like a farmer making a hole through a thorny hedge, first by sending through a chicken, then the mother hen, next the dog, then the goat, then the pig, and finally the cow; if one starts with

1. A childish version of *atti impuri*, the technical term for 'sins of impurity, unchastity'; from the Italian traditional text of the Seventh Commandment: *Non commettere atti impuri.*

the smallest, the effort and the scratches are just as bad on each occasion. But if one sends the cow through first, thereby producing a nice big hole in the hedge, all the others are unscathed.

For us the cow was usually the same: the one we called Binda, the one connected with those sinful things. We never, however, had the courage to send her through first. Sometimes we arrived in church with another cow. Mino, one Saturday, had an enormous one; this was 'Bisa', and he dragged her in behind him, with supreme embarrassment and reluctance; red in face he forced her up to the confessional. It was out of the question to send her in first though. So he confessed all his other sins, one by one; he even went back to his most remote past, accused himself of totally hypothetical crimes, punctiliously produced the most marginal of cases. He was praised for his zeal and exhorted not to fall into temptation: now there remained Bisa.

For some time the priest had stopped saying 'And then?' and when Mino fell silent he began to pronounce the preliminary words of absolution. In a panic Mino brought up Bisa.

'I've got another sin, a terrible sin. I've spoken evilly of priests.'

His tone of anguish alarmed the confessor who wanted to know exactly what he had said about priests; but Mino held back. 'Well . . . you know . . . really evil. . . .' Finally he forced himself to bring out the actual words. He had said that priests are *bài da tabacco* [literally: worms for tobacco].

Instead of being annoyed at the sight of Bisa, the priest was convulsed with violent laughter. Mino, taken aback and somewhat disappointed, had to wait a minute or two before he had his absolution.

There are two layers in the personality of a man;[1] the top ones are like superficial wounds – the Italian, French and Latin words: underneath are the ancient wounds which on being healed have formed scars – words in dialect. On being touched the scars set off

1. This passage follows a section mostly written in dialect and representing the babblings of a Venetian child who applies his linguistic equipment to descriptions of nature.

a perceptible chain reaction, difficult to explain to those who have no dialect. There is an indestructible kernel of *apprehended*[1] matter, attached to the tendrils of the senses; the dialect word is *always* pegged to reality, because they are one and the same thing, perceived before we learnt to reason, and never to disappear even when we have been taught reason in another language. This holds good, above all, with names of objects.

But the kernel of primitive matter (whether in connexion with names or any other word) contains uncontrollable forces because it exists in a pre-logical sphere where the associations are free and fundamentally unstable. Dialect therefore is in certain respects reality and in others instability.

I feel an almost physical pain in the nerves, deep down inside me, which produce words like *basavéjo* (sting of a bee) and *barbastrìjo* (bat), *anda* (snake) and *ava* (bee), even *rìa* (wheel) and *pùa* (doll). It comes shooting up through me like a *lampo-sgiantìzo* (flash of lightning), I feel conscious of that ultimate fusion of what we call life, that indestructible core, the very bedrock.

I do not say that this is dialect, but dialect is in this. I know well too that the business of dialect has much more to it than this. There are also different kinds of dialect, those connected with the eyes and other organs of the senses, which are set off when circumstances or certain emotive factors produce a displacement between the world of words and the world of things.

Translated by Raleigh Trevelyan

1. This word in English in the original.

Paolo Milano

Paolo Milano is literary editor of *L'Espresso*, the Roman weekly paper, for which the following review of Landolfi's translation of Dostoyevsky's *Letters from Underground* was originally written.

CENTENARY OF THE INVERTEBRATE MAN

Faith in human reason reached its peak about 1860, wrote Bertrand Russell in one of his essays. The remark may or may not be true, but it is worth reminding ourselves that it was at the same moment that a major attack was launched on the idea that Mankind aspires to reason and order – and not by a philosopher, but by a novelist, in an 'anecdote' of a hundred-and-fifty convulsing pages, the *Letters from Underground*, a masterpiece a hundred years old this year (1964).

Dostoyevsky wrote *Letters from Underground* in a mingled mood of feverish inspiration and anguished hesitancy, during one of the most distracted periods of his life. His first wife, Marija Dmitrievna Isaeva, lay dying; but the novelist, possessed as he was by his subject, already assumed with agonizing certainty that her death was a *fait accompli* – so at least it would seem from a letter to his brother Michail : 'I am frightened my wife's death may take place soon, which will mean I have to interrupt my work.' His constant terror of an epileptic attack, his chronic and desperate need for money, were forgotten, after a daily battle with himself, in the flood of his inspiration and his conviction of his own genius. 'I don't know how what I am writing will turn out. It may be a fiasco, of course. But I am pinning great hopes on it myself. It will be something strong and sincere. It will be the truth.'

In an excellent Introduction to the Italian translation of *The Naked Lunch*, the most notorious work of William Burroughs (the Pope of the Beatniks), Oreste del Buono argues brilliantly for the view that *Letters from Underground* was 'the beginning of modern fiction', the work that 'gave the cue to the strongest and most authentic talents of our own century, from Kafka to Beckett and Burroughs'. He argues indeed that it was not only their starting-point but their finishing-point, for the themes of those three contemporaries of ours are all there, implicitly, in the pages of their great model. 'I couldn't even learn to be an insect,' sneers the hero of *Letters from Underground* at himself – whilst Gregor Samsa in Kafka's *Metamorphosis* is physically transformed into an insect. Similarly the droning 'underground' voice soliloquizing in the novels of Beckett, like the wild drug-addict visions in those of Burroughs, might be considered merely a reflection of the livid Dostoyevskyan light. However, I must confess that re-reading *Letters from Underground*, as I have recently done, in the new Vallechi edition, led me to different conclusions from those of del Buono. I must try to explain why.

Letters from Underground consists of two parts, one mainly reflective and the other mainly narrative. 'In the first fragment, entitled "Life Underground",' Dostoyevsky tells us, 'the hero introduces himself and his ideas and seems to be trying to explain how such a human phenomenon as himself not only exists, but inevitably had to exist, in the midst of our society.' In the second part, significantly entitled 'Apropos of the Falling Sleet', the same protagonist describes episodes from his early youth, his relations with a group of young friends, and his encounters with a prostitute called Lisa. The story of the hero as a twenty-four-year-old is the prolegomenon (morally as well as psychologically, be it noted) to the present situation of the forty-year-old narrator.

Thus the two parts of the story are indissolubly united. It is strange, therefore, that most critics of *Letters from Underground* have concentrated on one of the two panels of the diptych at the expense of the other, stressing the existential theme in the work, or on the other hand the psychological one – sometimes, indeed, taking this to extremes, like Oreste del Buono in the article I have quoted, which makes no mention of the second part at all. But let us look closer at the work itself.

What is the 'Underground'? It is not the Unconscious, as we are in a hurry to assume nowadays. It is, certainly, the irrational mind of contemporary man, but as it is revealed in his conduct, that is to say in his relations with society. The 'underground man' is a human archetype, and it is not an accident that he lives in St Petersburg, 'the most abstract and premeditated city in the whole world'. All the first part of the *Letters* is a marvellous polemic against the vaunted Progress, Utilitarianism and Fourier-type Utopian Socialism of the mid nineteenth century.

'To begin with, when, in all the thousands of years of human history, has man ever acted purely for his own advantage?' Through the mouth of his protagonist Dostoyevsky asserts that the human spirit escapes the narrow confines of rationalism, 'the greatest good of the greatest number' and enlightened egotism. It is not so much that at times 'man can, and should, seek evil for himself rather than good'; it is that 'this inalienable, free and independent will, this ingrained – perhaps even insane – cult of private judgement, this capriciousness amounting at times to mania, represents that indefinable and constantly-forgotten "interest beyond self-interest" which falls into no set categories and thumbs its nose at all systems and theories'.

The subtle and profound irony of the *Letters* consists in the fact that these penetrating insights are expressed, amid all sorts of contradictions, by a grovelling and cowardly individual, a seething mass of rancour such as Nietzsche and later Max Weber were to call the 'resentful man'. The psychological portrait of this invertebrate type, the man-in-the-street of our own age, is drawn with astonishing precision and prophetic insight in these pages.

He takes pleasure in denigrating himself ('I am malevolent, I am hateful'); he regards conscience 'as a disease'; he despises the 'stupid' man of action at the same time that he envies him; he has a secret itch for humiliation ('I experienced a sort of base delight in creeping back into my corner'); in sum, being 'neither hero nor insect', he enjoys taking himself to pieces, he enjoys deflating his own grotesque tirade at the very moment he is most playing to the gallery; he enjoys being 'one who idly gratifies a taste for playing the scarecrow'; he enjoys, in fact, producing literature, while complaining of it as a 'penal servitude'.

But this analysis, miraculous as it is, is by no means the essential theme of the *Letters*; for psychology is never central in Dostoyevsky, as may be seen even from the mistakes of his disciples, who traditionally have only been aware of this one aspect of his work. The central theme of the *Letters* is moral, that of love for another human being; the second part of the story reveals this unmistakably.

Lisa, the girl from the brothel, whose bizarre client, having painted her a soul-freezing picture of her life as a whore, has given her a glimpse of salvation, and then, finding a convert on his hands, turns round and tells her he has been fooling her, and woundingly offers her money – Lisa remains, in her humble way, the victor; for she has guessed the motive for so much insane spite : 'She guessed at once, in the whole affair, what a woman always guesses, if she really loves someone – that is, that I was unhappy.'

So, against the nadir of nihilism in *Letters from Underground* ('We are born dead; indeed for some time now our fathers have been dead when they conceived us; we have come to find pleasure in this, and pretty soon we shall invent a way of being born of the Idea alone') we see another truth dawning and shining : 'Every kind of resurrection, every kind of restoration of what has been lost, every regeneration, is contained in Love.' It is a truth which, though it can do no more than glimmer among the grotesque ironies of this book, was to shine out in full splendour in *Crime and Punishment* two years later. The *Letters*, therefore, are the turning-point in Dostoyevsky's work, though they must be read in the light of everything that follows, right up to *The Brothers Karamazov*.

The translation of *Letters from Underground* reprinted here is by Tommaso Landolfi, and there is one obvious reason why it should be so good; the author of *Rien va* has drunk at Dostoyevsky's fount for a whole lifetime, and translating Dostoyevsky is for him, before anything else, the surest way of exploring himself.

Translated by P. N. Furbank

Leonardo Sciascia

The horrifying story reproduced here forms the core of Sciascia's book, *Morte dell' inquisitore*, an historical reconstruction of a notorious auto-da-fé under the Spanish Inquisition in seventeenth-century Sicily. Those put to death included Friar Diego la Matina and Monsignor Juan Lopez de Cisneros. Diego later came to be regarded by some as a saint-martyr and by others as a kind of Giuliano. Himself a Sicilian, and passionately proud of it, Sciascia meant his book to illustrate, in historical perspective, the mentality and attitudes – the obstinacy, the capacity for enormous suffering and sacrifice – of his people.

DEATH OF THE INQUISITOR

On the 2nd March 1658, Matteo Perino, the town-crier of the 'happy' city of Palermo, was at last able to announce to the Faithful in Christ that, 'at the order and command of the most illustrious and most reverend Signore Inquisitor the Archbishop of Monreale, on Sunday the 17th day of the present month of March, a General Spectacle of the Faith will be celebrated in the square in front of the Mother Church, and all who are present will receive the Indulgence accorded by the Supreme Pontiff'.

Preparations for this spectacle were soon in hand – at the cost, of course, of the Royal Treasury, 'as the religious liberality of the Catholic Kings disposes'. In the piazza before the cathedral, a huge wooden amphitheatre was erected, composed of nine tiers, with four large stands for spectators above, a small stand for the musicians, and an altar. The proscenium itself, the *infamous stage* for the accused, was equipped with eight rough wooden benches of equal size, placed against a background which had been painted black, *to correspond with the darkness of their souls*. Behind these stands five large rooms were constructed, where the Ministers of the Holy Office, the Captain of Justice and his attendants, the Senate and the ladies, could take refreshment during the lengthy ceremony; while *buvettes* were installed for the gentlemen. Purple or crimson velvet, silk and gold cloth, rich carpets, seats decked with damask or velvet, embroidered cushions, cypress and myrtle boughs, silver vases and candlesticks, were placed with *an art conformable to the architectural structure*. To the Dominican fathers was accorded the honour of decorating the altar; while the most thankless task was given to Monsignor de los Cameros, of establishing the order of precedence. For the theological Qualificators were in dispute with the legal Consultors. The first claimed that they should have precedence, because the theological error of the accused must be defined before the jurists could be consulted; the latter, for their part, considered that a public Act of Faith was a legal matter, which gave them precedence. The ecclesiastical Consultors argued with the lay Consultors, whose faction was, in turn, rent by internal squabbles between the robed *togati* or *ordinary* lawyers, and the 'secret' lawyers of the Inquisition. The nunzio of the 'secret' lawyers argued with the civil notary; while the various Commissioners and their followers who had come from other villages in Sicily – among them the parish priests of Sant' Antonia, San Giacomo alla Marina and San Nicolò alla Kalsa – were also continually bickering. Hell, one might say, had been let loose. But thanks to the *unexampled wisdom* of the Archbishop, and the *circumspection with which he is accustomed to judge*, he either promptly rejected their claims, settled them one way or the other, or reconciled the disputants. 'Promptly' is perhaps not quite the word, for the protest of the *Capitaniale* Court was not settled. They considered themselves affronted because they had been allotted seats covered with purple damask and not, as was of course correct, the more exalted ones of crimson velvet.

By God's good grace however everything was settled by the 16th of March, when this prodigy of construction was revealed to the people. Strong winds blew from the west that evening, accompanied by fast-moving clouds heavy with rain. But, as Matranga tells us himself, thanks to Divine intervention, no sooner had the hour of the procession arrived than the skies cleared. Between the palazzo of the Holy Office and the cathedral square a huge crowd had collected, through which German soldiers had cordoned off a lane for the procession. A long cortège of carriages containing the well-born ladies of the town added to the general excitement and confusion.

The standard of the Holy Office was borne by Don Giovanni Ventimiglia, Marchese di Geraci; and the crimson ribbons hanging on either side were held, on the right, by Don Domenico Graffeo, Prince of Partanna, on the left by Don Blasco Corbino, Prince of Mezzoiuso – all three men officers in the household of the Holy Office (as were most of the two hundred titled persons behind them). Then came a hundred noblemen belonging to the company of the Assumption, wearing white sackcloth, with hoods and blue cloaks, each bearing a lighted taper. Then came the musicians, followed by the two congregations of Orphans; then the Cappuccini, the reformed religious orders of Mercy and Sant' Agostino (the last clearly distressed by the disgrace their fellow-member had brought upon them), the Tertiaries, the Minims, the order of the Redemption of Sinners, the Carmelites, the Agostinians, the Observant Friars, the Dominicans. The Franciscans were not present, for the *unexampled wisdom and circumspection* of Monsignor the Archbishop had not yet succeeded in mitigating their dissensions with the Dominicans over the question of ceremonial.

It seemed a never-ending procession, whose head had already reached the cathedral square when the tail was just emerging from the doors of the Holy Office – a tail consisting of the green cross of the Tribunal veiled in black, carried by the Benedictine father Giovanni Martinez, in a violet cope, and the Archbishop Inquisitor, followed by the Principe della Trabia, the Alcaide or Spanish mayor of the secret prisons, and sundry other officials and gentlemen.

On reaching the amphitheatre, the green cross was placed on the altar, where it was to remain for the night, guarded by thirty monks. The rest of the procession broke up, while a small section continued to the piazza of Sant' Erasmo, where the wooden grid for the pyre had been erected. A cross was placed here too (a white one), with four candles in glass containers, to shield them from the wind. *Some of the more zealous members of the congregation remained on voluntary guard.* But it was already 3 a.m. and the remainder returned home *by the shortest route,* to the pleasures of food, rest and the bed. For Fra. Diego, however, the long night was only just beginning.

We may here now quote the words of Matranga himself :

The perfidious malefactor was taken into the basement of the secret prison, where he was dressed in the solemn vestments of the Venerable Religion, whose balm he had not merited. A heavy wooden chair had been constructed expressly, equipped with manacles and chains which girdled all parts of the body, so that he seemed more chained than seated (such was the apprehension of all before this untamed will that it might threaten again, at any moment, death and destruction). At 3 a.m., as was the custom, Don Giovanni di Retan conveyed the final sentence to the man who would in a short time be handed over to the secular arm. Appointed to be present with him were Monsignor Archbishop Inquisitor, the doctor Don Francesco Vetrano, parish priest of San Nicolò alla Kalsa and Consultor, Padre Angelo da Polizzi, the Observant Friars, and Qualificators, Padre Melchiore Balducci, of the company of Jesus Consultor and Qualificator. I likewise was among them. Which persons had on earlier occasions, on his behalf, struggles rather than discussions, in their striving, as now, at this limit of his life, to bring to him that conversion so despaired of by all. To these persons were present in addition Padre Bacilliero, Fra. Vincenzo Muta, prior of San Domenico of the Father Preachers, P. D. Giuseppe Cicala the Propositor of the Casa di S. Giuseppe Teatino and Consultor, P. Plachido Agitta, Consultor of the Camillian attendants of the sick, and two of the company of the Assumption. None would abandon him. All night, present before the person designate, they were to banish sleep from their eyes, so that, with the unified persuasion of the many, the soul of that person might be freed from its vile lethargy. And all this night, through the bountiful hospitality of the Alcaide, they were withdrawing to his rooms apart, where magnificent and exquisite foodstuffs had been prepared, that they might refresh themselves.

Here surely is one of the most hideous and degrading scenes in the history of human intolerance. These nine men, racking brains crammed with theology and morality as they stand around the condemned man – yet repairing from time to time to their 'exquisite foodstuffs' – will remain for ever in the annals of human indignity. By the same token, Diego la Matina will remain as an eternal symbol of man's dignity and honour, the greatness of human thought, the tenacity of man's will, and the victory of human liberty.

How he replied to their charitable exhortations, how he parried and retorted to the ingenious propositions and subtle arguments, we do not know. Certain it is that he did not succumb. Certain too that Father Matranga and his colleagues, even if refreshed by the 'exquisite foodstuffs' and the liberality of the Alcaide, must have passed a poor night. They could hardly have been fully awake the next day to enjoy the auto-da-fé in all its complicated detail.

When the Fathers realized that they could do nothing more with the man, and had abandoned him to his infernal fate, the morning of Sunday 17th of March 1658 was dawning. Because rain was falling, there was some discussion about postponing the *festa*. After such preparation and expense, it seemed a pity to allow the rain to spoil the elaborate decorations (as for the question of setting fire to the pile of wood in the middle of piazza Sant' Erasmo, no one gave a thought to such a domestic detail). It was finally agreed to wait a while, the time to be passed in the celebration of a number of masses.

By midday the sky had cleared, and the procession was able to assemble. This time the prominent places were occupied by the disciplinary authorities, inquisitorial and lay: Don Antonio Cabello, the Alcaide, accompanied by the nobles and officials of the Secret Office whom he had just entertained to a sumptuous meal in his rooms; and Don Francesco Cappero, Captain of Justice, who was also accompanied by many noblemen, with Don Otavio Lanza and the Principe della Trabia at his side. Between the lay justices and those of the Holy Office walked the accused men. To quote Matranga again:

There were thirty-two of these, each with his clothes undone, without belt and wearing a humble mitre, so that thus in visible form the gravity of their crimes might be proclaimed. Those without insignia on the head went with hair dishevelled. Those condemned to the Royal Galleys, or to the public whipping block, went with great ropes about their necks; the blasphemers went with muzzles on their mouths. Last of all, cynosure for every scornful eye in the realm, went that monster of our age, in desecrated garb, his mitre dyed black with pitch, like unto the flames of hell – carried by porters in the aforesaid chair and surrounded by armed men. And around him circulated the other religious persons; and the Brothers of the Assumption were at his side, seeking most ardently to reduce that obstinate knowledge in this man to the true, the Catholic faith.

Before the procession moved away from the palazzo of the Holy Office, the Marchese di Geraci and the Principe della Trabia approached Fra. Diego. 'With ineffable energy, truly moved by God's will,' says Matranga, 'what words of consolation did they now pronounce? What salvation did they promise? Of what sins did they rebuke him?' But Fra. Diego repulsed these new offers sharply – whereupon the compassion of the two gentlemen turned to indignation, and 'they would have plucked the sacrilegious tongue from his mouth with their own hands'. Had they done so, it would not have been the first occasion in Palermo when the nobles had usurped the office of executioner. Some ten years before, Don Alessandro Platamone, a member of the old Spanish aristocracy and the descendant of a viceroy, had the pleasure and honour of decapitating Giuseppe d'Alesi.

Held back by the German halberdiers and the Spanish musketeers, the people were now granted the spectacle of the *Holy Office mounted*, a ceremony reserved only for occasions when an Act of Faith was celebrated. The fearful significance of this is still expressed in a popular proverb – *Di fazzu vidiri lu sant' Ufficiu a cavaddu* ('You shall see the Holy Office mounted' – a sinister way of saying 'I'll give you such a shock that you'll see the stars'.)

All were mounted, from the Inquisitor in his ermine cape and pontifical cap down to the individual monks, on horses with elaborate saddles and saddle-cloths. According to Matranga, the spectacle of mounted monks was so unusual that it moved the populace to tears – owing to the contrast between the elaborate decoration of the horses and the coarseness of the monks' heavy sackcloth and grey wool garments. But this spectacle of monkish humility and poverty has, it is well known, little effect on the Sicilians who, on these occasions, are moved by quite other considerations. Nor if they cried this time, was it on account of the pitiable charivari they witnessed, the criminals with ropes around their necks, the wretched Fra. Diego la Matina about to be burnt alive. So far from showing compassion, the plebs of those days were ruled entirely by their brutal and superstitious instincts. If some isolated individual should feel pity for the accused (and unwisely show it), he risked being overheard by the police spies who, as all knew, were hovering about in the crowd like vultures.

The crowd therefore shouted accusations at Fra. Diego, calling on him to repent. To which he replied 'with even greater shamelessness and blasphemy than hitherto'. So blasphemous did he become that it was possible, following the tradition, to silence him by *applying the bit and the gag*. A grotesque spectacle it must have been – the minions waiting for the word or phrase which permitted them to thrust the gag and horse's bit in the mouth of the man of whom all were still afraid.

When the procession reached the amphitheatre in the cathedral square, Don Martinez Rubio, Archbishop of Palermo and President of the realm, appeared on the balcony of the Archbishop's Palace. The expression on his face was (we are assured by Matranga) one of radiant pleasure at surveying such beauty and orderliness in the procession. But as always on these occasions, more people had managed to find places on the platforms than the authorities had catered for (in Sicily, even today, there are always more guests at public or private entertainments than those invited); and often the platform collapses. When the Duke of Alba was installed as viceroy in Palermo, a bridge which had been constructed specially in his honour collapsed, only a few seconds before he set foot on it, killing a number of people and giving him thereafter the reputation of possessing the evil eye. Mindful no doubt of the misfortune which had befallen a fellow countryman, Monsignor de Los Cameros suddenly became most concerned with the stability and strength of the platform; he ordered more props and supports to be inserted. This took up some time, but at last word was given to the orator of the day, the Dominican Pietro Martire Lupo, to preach the sermon. Such was the hubbub in the *inquisitive multitude* that only those near him could hear his words.

The individual cases were now announced, the crimes being read out to the accused, each of whom came forward to receive his sentence (which none of them could hear). Meanwhile, the ladies in the boxes were served with *seemly refreshments*. We cannot tell if 'seemly' applied to the *liberality and magnanimity* of the Inquisitor who offered the refreshments, to the quality of the ladies, or to the hour, place and ceremony. As for the gentlemen spectators, the *buvettes* worked at full pressure, satisfying all their requirements. This too took time, and when Monsignor de los Cameros thought it was getting late, he ordered the cases of the lesser miscreants to be put aside, so that the main one could be dealt with.

Fra. Diego *as he was, bound in his chair*, was now brought forward by the *bastasi*, or porters, and the noise in the crowd subsided. 'Incredulously each gazed upon this villainous face, with stubborn impudence writ clear upon it, as he heard the full account of all his sacrilegious wickedness and heresy.' Matranga's words give us today a feeling of immense elation and pride that we, as free men, are in a sense Fra. Diego's belated contemporaries. Had he not been gagged, he would surely have poured forth his scorn before the public on the tribunal and its orator.

The statement of his case, as prescribed in the instructions laid down by the Supreme Council of the Spanish Inquisition, consisted only of a general enumeration of crimes. The need for this precaution is well explained in a Holy Office procedural document on the subject: 'We insist that the motives and explanations given by the accused, heretical pronouncements which might offend the ear of Catholics, must not be permitted; so that good Catholics should thus not be led into doubt or false learning – for in the past this has happened, so that many have learned heresy in the pronouncement of such sentences' (note 36).

So all that the public learned was that Diego was a heretic, an apostate and a blasphemer – a parricide too, for he had murdered Monsignor de Cisneros, his father in the hierarchy of the Order, as well as in Love and Charity.

When sentence had been pronounced, the condemned man was brought before the Archbishop Inquisitor; whereupon there was such a surge forward by the public anxious to savour the scene that the wooden floor nearly collapsed. Monsignor would have avoided the notorious reputation of his compatriot, the Duke of Alba, of possessing the evil eye, only by falling to death with the others on the platform. But order was gradually restored, and the ceremony of deconsecration began. The mitre was removed from Fra. Diego's head, and the *sambenito* from his neck; he was clothed in the habit of his order, and in the various vestments worn by a deacon (as he had been) when officiating – a somewhat involved process, for it is not easy to dress a man chained to a seat. These garments were then ceremoniously removed, one by one, with equal difficulty, Monsignor reciting a formula for each item as it was taken off. Between the removal of each garment and the next, the Holy Books, phials, chalice, towel and keys were brought forward to touch the bound hands, and then withdrawn. After which, Fra. Diego was again clad in his mitre and *sambenito*.

This process should, strictly, have been carried out with the victim lying prone or kneeling; but prudence counselled omission of this detail, 'so that there might be no question of the impious one, liberated from his irons, marking the infamous end of his life with a further atrocious crime'. Monsignor de Los Cameros had clearly no desire for martyrdom.

As far as the Holy Office was concerned, the dispute with Fra. Diego was now over. He was handed over to the Captain of Justice, and the 'final sentence was pronounced – to be burnt alive and his ashes thrown to the four winds'.

After the other thirty-one accused had abjured their sins, the procession formed up again, to pass before the palazzo of the Holy Office, where the thirty-one were taken back into custody. Fra. Diego was then placed on a cart drawn by oxen, and the procession continued to the Piazza Sant' Erasmo. Dusk had fallen and the scene was illuminated by candles and torches. The wine-vendors and sellers of fried foods and bric-à-brac, who had placed tables and benches near the palisades surrounding the pyre, regretted that rain had retarded the ceremony and affected business. For the ladies, too, the flickering artificial light hardly revealed the elaborate toilettes in all their splendour. But they could at least count on good illumination when the pyre was lit.

'When he saw the pyre before him, Fra. Diego did not alter countenance, nor show dismay, nor any sign of fear or horror.' Still bound to his chair, he was placed upon the wooden grid, and the chair was tied to a stake. The two learned priests who had tried to make him repent during the journey from the cathedral to the Piazza Sant' Erasmo now withdrew. A last attempt at obtaining repentance was made, by pretending to set fire unsuccessfully to the pyre, twice. Fra. Diego then said he wished to speak to one of the priests, the Theatine clerk Giuseppe Cicala. This man, perhaps because he had shown pity (which may also be why Fra. Diego called him back), or perhaps because he could not face the spectacle, had retreated into the crowd. They called for him, and he returned to the condemned man. 'Yes, I will abjure and submit myself to the doctrines of the Church,' said Fra. Diego, 'if I may be allowed to live.' The Theatine clerk replied that the sentence was irrevocable. Whereupon Fra. Diego said, 'To whom then did the prophet speak when he said "*Nolo mortem peccatoris, sed ut magis convertatur, et vivat?*" ' The Theatine clerk replied that the prophet had referred to spiritual, not to corporeal, life. 'Then God is unjust,' said Fra. Diego. And the fire was lit.

Translated by Anthony Rhodes

P. A. Quarantotti Gambini

This extract is taken from I giochi di Norma, the action of which takes place just before the First War, in Gambini's own country, the salt marshes of the Istrian coast, then the frontier between Austria and Italy. Paolo spends his holidays with his grandparents there, and more or less runs wild with the children of the place, including Norma whose mother has abandoned her and who is being looked after on the estate. Norma is an attractive little tomboy, often leading Paolo into trouble. After the war they play among the old trenches. An uncle, Marco, is the cause of some jealousy for Paolo, as he seems devoted to Norma – a mere peasant child. After the uncle's death, by which time Norma is fast turning into a beautiful girl, and after she has been packed off to boarding school, the reason becomes clear: she was his illegitimate daughter.

NORMA'S GAMES

After supper there was a long silence.

The grandparents were still at table in the dim lamp-light and they seemed lost in thought. Paolo had got up and had retired into the shadows to a corner armchair by the portrait of uncle Manlio in uniform, with a tricolour ribbon fastened to the frame.

The minutes passed and the two old folk still said nothing.

Finally the old man spoke up:

'We can't leave her like this.'

The grandmother did not answer at once. Then after a few moments came her quiet voice almost as if she were talking to herself:

'No,' she said, 'that's what I was thinking, too.'

No name had been mentioned but Paolo understood whom they were referring to.

Since the death of Uncle Marco and, more recently, of old Meneghina, there was no one left to look after Norma. The old people had had to take care of her for some time and it was obviously a responsibility that worried them.

Norma had grown – in the few months between winter and summer she had become almost another person. Lean, with long legs ever so skimpily covered by her skirt and knees still like a boy's, sturdy and rather knobbly, she had gone thinner in the face, too. Her cheeks were sunken, forming on her face, which was a little less bronzed than in previous years, two patches of shadow; her mouth, instead, prominent and round; and beneath her fair hair, two serious eyes.

And it was this, as well as Norma being taller, that surprised Paolo and in a way disconcerted him – those big, serious eyes, so different from the old days when they were always laughing.

Seeing her again that summer when he came back on holiday to Semedella, he hardly recognized her. A tall girl walking through the lane to the well with long, slowish strides – not at all like the Norma he remembered skipping gaily along as if her only desire was to run and play. Yet she it was.

(As for Paolo, he did not ask himself what Norma's impressions might be on seeing him once more. For he had grown much more than in former years. He was already taller than the old lady and Momi, taller than anyone at Semedella, and he was still growing. But he was very skinny and his face, too, was thin, almost painfully so. Soon – they said – he would be taller than his Papa.)

The first time that they came face to face (Paolo, spotting her from a distance, had thought of trying to avoid her) they could find nothing to say to each other.

Paolo looked into those luminous eyes of hers, now so fixed and wide with a kind of grave bewilderment. He gazed at her, remembered that Uncle Marco was dead and wondered if she had wept when they told her. But he did not, could not understand.

'What are you doing?' he asked her.

'I'm on my own,' she replied.

She lived alone in the old pigeon-loft – the turret as it was called. She was to be seen going in and coming out. And she stayed for hours inside. Paolo's grandparents sent her lunch and supper up to her there. She went to bed early, then Toni locked her in and opened the door for her the next morning. They said that she kept the place tidy, washed and did everything herself.

It was not really clear whether the death of Uncle Marco and old Meneghina had been a shock to her. There was about her just a curiously remote detachment together with that air of serious bewilderment. When she left the turret and wandered along the paths and lanes that she had always known so well, she seemed to move hesitatingly, as if mildly spellbound in a world strange and new to her. And she appeared to look at everyone in that same bewildered way, even Paolo.

Only once did he see her eyes crinkle smaller between the lids and light up with laughter as they used to, even before the laughter reached her mouth.

He waited, looking at her with eyebrows knit in perplexity. 'Did you see,' she said, and a crazy laugh broke from her lips and glistening teeth, 'did you see Livia yesterday?'

Livia was a girl from Trieste who had come to Semedella that summer for the bathing. She was beautiful, the most beautiful girl that summer, they said, and everyone was talking about her.

'Did you see the ribbon she put in her hair?'

'No, I didn't.'

'You ought to have seen her. She put a ribbon . . . a red ribbon in her hair. . . .' Norma kept on laughing and Paolo could not understand why, because a ribbon of any colour in her hair would be bound to suit Livia. But Norma went on laughing, tossing her head, and her small eyes shone, near to tears. And her face was all flushed.

'You ought to have seen her,' she repeated. 'What a silly thing!'

Paolo looked at her blonde head on the long, slender neck, made even prettier by laughter, and thought that a ribbon of one colour or another in her hair would have suited her, too.

'I didn't see her,' he replied.

All at once, while he was still watching her, Norma became

serious again and stared at him with something like suspicion. Then she abruptly turned on her heel.

' 'Bye,' she said and went off.

Now, in the dining-room, no one spoke. Paolo was still thinking of Norma and the feeling of uneasiness meeting her again had brought.

Later, in bed, he heard his grandparents talking at length in their room, even after they had retired for the night. And the next morning, he immediately realized from the thoughtful, determined expressions on their faces that something had been decided.

The months passed and with them the summer.

In September, the old man, who must have been more deeply shocked by Uncle Marco's death than was apparent at the time, and who now seemed to have taken over the uncle's task of looking after Norma, said one evening to Paolo:

'Norma's leaving tomorrow. She's going to boarding school. If you want to say goodbye to her. . . .'

Paolo ran to the turret but found that Toni had already locked the door and gone off somewhere or other.

He knocked and, looking up, called out. At last Norma appeared at one of the oval windows, with her hair in paper curlers.

'What are you doing, Paolo,' she cried, shaking her head, which, seen from a distance, seemed all the smaller on the slim, golden-brown neck. 'You'll break the door down !'

Then – Paolo was still panting and Norma certainly not laughing – they could find nothing to say to each other.

'I heard . . . you're going away to school?' asked Paolo eventually and sought, then evaded, her glance.

From high up in the turret, Norma nodded.

Another silence.

'You're leaving tomorrow?'

'Yes.'

'And . . . will you be away long?'

'I don't know. As long as your grandfather wants me to.'

'And . . . are you going to sleep so soon?'

'Yes. I'd gone to bed. I have to get up early.'

Their eyes met again (as if by mistake, unwillingly) and they both immediately looked away. – Why did I rush so madly here – Paolo wondered and felt slightly ashamed as a trembling started in his throat.

He had nothing to say to her, neither had she to him, apparently.

'Will you write to me?' he said, anyway, looking up at the window but avoiding her eyes.

'You write to me first.'

' 'Bye, Norma.'

' 'Bye.'

That night Paolo found it hard to get to sleep. Lying there in the dark, he felt a kind of dissatisfaction as well as remorse. He thought of the past months and the little time he had spent with her, those moments under the turret – she at the window with her hair in curlers, and both of them at a loss for words – and he felt a stab of regret. He thought of the old days in the country and at the sea-side, the games in the field in the war-trenches, and the anguish when he thought she was buried, and it made him more remorseful. His thoughts turned continually to Uncle Marco who had been with them both so often in the past and this made him even more remorseful. Yes, it seemed to him that with his uncle dead it was up to him to spend more time with Norma. Yet, that very summer. . . . The thought became intolerable. – If I had kept Norma company as in other years – he said to himself over and over again – if I hadn't left her on her own, perhaps Grandfather wouldn't have sent her away to school. . . .

He turned restlessly in bed and switched the light on and off. No, he could not let her go like this. He'd get up early in the morning. He must try to do something.

While the whole house was silent, instead of yielding to sleep he became more and more agitated. And he grew excited as he thought of what to do.

All at once he made to get out of bed. The idea had struck him to run down to see Norma and ask her opinion. He could get out of the house – through the window left half-open during the night, the one looking out on the grove – without the old people noticing. He wanted, at least, to wish her a better good-bye than the night before, really say something to her.

No, he'd do more than that. He had to arrange a plan with her, decide what to tell his grandfather. No, no – better for her to talk to the old man. But she must play on his emotions. Or else . . . she might hide, not be around when it was time to go. That would shake the old man, and Norma could speak to him later – and so would he.

He had swung his feet out of the bed, ready to slip on his sandals, and was just picturing himself outside the window in the September night among the dark shadows of the whispering pines, when he remembered that Norma's door was locked and Toni had the key. Should he go to the stable first and wake him up? He imagined the rumpus the dogs would raise – Eros leading the chorus – if he threw a stone at Toni's shutters or called out to him. Then again, Toni might have been drinking and be sleeping it off in Idran's stall between the horse's legs. What a hullabaloo there would be (with the house-dogs rousing all the others in the cottages on the hill – he could hear them now, one here, another up there, barking furiously) before he could hope to stir him from his drunken stupor. He'd only awaken the old people and the rest of Semedella.

No, that was no good.

Better wait until the morning. He'd have to wake early, catch his grandfather as soon as he got up and speak to him. . . .

He needed an alarm-clock. He slipped out of bed, went into the next room, which was deserted. He looked on the bedside tables and the chest of drawers. Nothing. The old people must have taken it. 'I'll wake up all right, I'll hear it,' he thought, gauging the distance across the passage to their room and imagining the clock on his grandmother's chest of drawers.

But he was still uneasy. Something seemed to be missing, something which might spoil his whole plan.

He tossed and turned in bed again. He felt discontented, almost angry with himself and found it hard to control his emotions.

Anger and agitation alternated and mingled, then eventually began to subside as his mind began to quieten.

He found himself at the foot of the turret, once, twice, three times. It always began in the same way. Each time they repeated what they had said before and gradually he added all the things he wanted to tell her. And he discovered that she, too, used new words and gestures.

Then – he was now completely still and his eyelids were heavy – he began to listen to himself talking to his grandfather. Yes, that's what he'd have to say. He'd have to play on his feelings. And show him that they could keep Norma there at Semedella. He must tell him that he would look after Norma; he could do it because that autumn he was not returning as usual to Trieste to stay with his parents and attend school there, but would remain in the country with his grandparents as they wished. He'd continue his studies at Capodistria in the grammar-school where his father, Uncle Marco and Uncle Manlio went – and his grandparents before them.

The nearer he drifted to sleep, the simpler everything seemed to become.

All he had to do was speak to the old man, a few words would be enough. Yes, yes, just a few words (he rehearsed what to say). That was it.

Finally, he fell asleep – and during the last glimmers of consciousness, he felt certain that Norma would not be leaving.

Translated by Gwyn Morris

Alfonso Gatto

THE SPIDER

With whom does he reason about himself in the dark
and with light and dusty lips
mark his mouth? the spider to his trickery
weaves the summer.

Since he has his wings curled in the brooch
of their quivering, the insect in delirium
swarms motionless and greedy in the eye
of his splendour.

From open eyes that do not see, man
slowly consumes himself in the track
of his past; vanishing from himself, lives.

A DAY WHERE THE HOUR

A day where the hour of death is
may not be the place, but the bier
goes down everywhere towards its doors
of darkness, the earth does not learn

the name which its living chose for it.
In the invisible boundaries that you touch,
from the sky to the mountains to the trees where you arrive
dying to look at it again with your eyes,

the earth is the distance and your journey.
But, once there, is earth all near to itself,
the perpetual eavesdropping of a mirage
that fixes on every eyelash its thorn.

Translated by Gavin Ewart

Umberto Eco

THE STRUCTURE OF BAD TASTE

If a message is read according to an inexact or incomplete code, its power of communication is not destroyed, but its meaning is necessarily reduced. At the same time one must admit that in many cases the exact opposite takes place: a message which in itself contains little information, if read in the light of an arbitrary code, may acquire a very much richer meaning than the author ever intended. A typical case is that of the Altamira bison when it is interpreted with reference to the acquisitions of contemporary painting – that is, in the light of a complex code referring to quite different criteria of taste, technique of the conscious representation of movement etc.: it acquires a richness of meaning which for the most part is *introduced by the receiver*. Most of the archaeological evidence of the classical age is interpreted by focusing on the object a whole series of references which were quite unknown to the author: missing arms and the erosion of centuries in a late Hellenic copy become expressions of an allusive incompleteness which refers to a vast store of meanings built up through centuries of later culture, and unknown to the late Greek craftsman. Nevertheless the object, being a complex of elements, was always, in fact, a complex of symbols and possible meanings. An educated man looking for light amusement in a popular musical entertainment may well find the show full of references to a Fescennine obscenity of which the wretched comedians have no inkling; nevertheless, by bringing together various coarse intuitions as to the tastes and expectations of a low-grade audience in a decidedly coarse programme, the comedians have in fact been building up a series of references to archetypal behaviour, which, in one way or another, still holds good.

And so the fate of a message that is interpreted with an overloaded code is the same as the fate of the *objet trouvé* which the artist takes from its natural context (or from a different artificial one) and sets up as a work of art. In this case the artist chooses certain aspects of the object as possible symbols of meanings which have been developed in cultural tradition. In the act of arbitrarily superimposing a code on a message that has no code (a natural object), or with a different code (e.g. a piece of industrial scrap), the artist is in fact inventing that message *ex novo*. But one must, at this point, ask whether he is arbitrarily focusing on to the object references that have been borrowed from an alien tradition, that of contemporary art (by which a stone may seem to be a sculpture by Moore or a mechanical device a Lipchitz), or whether contemporary art, in working out its own forms, has not already referred to natural or industrial forms, thus integrating elements from other codes with its own.

Thus it may happen, in ordinary life, that a bored intellectual listening to a symphony in a concert hall does not decode all that he hears, but simply receives it as fetish, whilst an ordinary man, who whistles at his work the notes of the same symphony heard over the radio, is really drawing on one aspect of it, and in this way corresponds to the composer's expectations better than the intellectual.

All these observations show us that *the informative power of the message is altered by the intention of the receiver*. The poetic message always remains a complex structure capable of stimulating a wide variety of decodifications. In the whirlpool of messages in which even the poetic message gets caught up and sold to its own public as consumer goods, the life of the work of art is far more varied and unpredictable than we could possibly imagine, even in our most pessimistic moments. In mastering ingenious or aberrant decodifications, in the indiscriminate use of codes, in developing specifically the various purposes of use demanded by various circumstances, we establish a dialectic between messages and receivers which cannot be reduced to any one plan, and which constitutes an unpredictable territory for inquiry. In this territory works of re-adaptation and orientation of taste and rescue operations all become possible, in spite of the thoughtless and full-blooded foolishness of a daily consumption which would seem to flatten out every message amidst the general 'noise' and standardize every act of receiving in the universal incurable carelessness.

Kitsch[1] seen as Boldinism

In the confused activity of this scene it is easy for the cultural industry to meet its clients half-way by taking the initiative of a partial decodification. If a poetic message is too complex, if (as usually happens) the inattentive beholder receives only one aspect of it, or accepts it whole and superimposes on it a previous decodification which has become a formula, then the cultural industry puts into operation a work of mediation, offering the public not the original messages but other, simpler messages, in which stylistic devices, drawn from old messages long famous for their poetic quality, are set like jewels and induce an immediate excitement.

Most of the operations of Midcult are of this sort. It is not a question of mass messages. There the desire to create an effect may be reasonable and it does not pretend to be a substitute for aesthetic experience; the use of formal methods taken over from art has an instrumental function : a stylistic device is used because in a given message it proved to have high communication value – if onomatopoeia provided the shock element in one of Poe's poems, why not use it to imprint a detergent advertisement on the memory? Nobody who avails himself of this advertisement imagines that he is enjoying a high-brow experience. No, the problem must be discussed at a different level : the relationship between art and Kitsch need not be brought to court.

But with Midcult there is a very different situation. If ever a stylistic element has at some time formed part of a prestige message, then it is in a strong position with a public that wants higher experience.

1. *Kitsch*. A German word which defines bad taste in terms of 'prefabrication and imposition of the effect'. The word has such a precise connotation and is so untranslatable that it has come to be used in other languages.

Thus the Midcult product tries to build up a new message (mostly aimed at producing effects), a message in which the old element is inserted so as to ennoble its new context. But, let us not forget, there is no reason why, in the hands of a clever craftsman, this insertion should not follow the norms of structural logic so as to make the new message acceptable and almost original. Was this not the case with those Renaissance architects who used Greek and Roman architectural elements because of their inherent nobility? The insertion may be done in such a way that it is always seen to be deliberate. The classical quotations in Stravinsky's music are an example of an element being drawn from another context and inserted in the new one: here the obvious deliberateness of the insertion gives it necessity and recalls the listener to a code of interpretation which recognizes this attitude. So it is with *collage*, with pictures made up of different materials, where the inserted materials preserve a deliberate reference to their origin. So it is with the fragment of the Serbian city wall which is inserted in the façade of Rome's railway station. There is no question here of trying to pass off a fragment of 'art' on the public so as to give the impression that the whole context is art, when it is in fact nothing but the craftsman's support to a stylistic quotation. The context is necessary for the insertion to be an explicit act of quotation. More rare is the situation in which the quotation, as such, disappears and is swallowed up in a complex of new relationships. One could mention several excellent examples in popular fiction – novels, that is, whose aim is pure entertainment – where, for instance, the stream-of-consciousness technique is used to depict a particular situation: it adapts well to the purpose and works like an original device; its real nature and its Joycean origin is forgotten.

But the *characteristic of true Midcult, that which denotes Kitsch, is the inability to fuse the quotation with the new context.* At the same time there is a lack of balance in which the culture-reference shows through in an irritating way, without being a deliberate quotation; it is passed off as an original invention but nevertheless stands out from the context, which is too weak to support it and too dissimilar to accept and integrate it. In such cases one could define Kitsch in structural terms as *a stylistic device torn from its proper context and inserted in another context, the general structure of which lacks the homogeneous and necessary qualities of the original structure, whilst – by means of this unlawful insertion – the message is presented as an original work, capable of stimulating novel experience.*

A typical example of this process is given by a painter, one who was rightly famous with the middle-brow public of the *belle époque*: Boldini.

Boldini was a well-known portrait painter, particularly of ladies, and his paintings represented for his clients both a source of prestige and a pleasing piece of consumer goods. Painting members of the aristocracy and well-to-do middle class of the society in which he lived, Boldini might well have been an ordinary salesman of products in high demand. When a beautiful woman asked him to paint her portrait, it was not first and foremost a work of art that she wanted, but a work proclaiming undeniably that she was a beautiful woman.

It was with this purpose in mind that Boldini built up his portraits, observing all the rules for producing an effect. If you examine his canvases carefully, particularly these portraits of women, you will see that the faces and the shoulders (the uncovered parts) obey all the canons of a refined naturalism. The women's lips are moist and fleshy, the flesh evokes sensations of touch, the expression in the eyes is sweet, provocative, mischievous or dreamy, but always direct, piercing, fixed on the viewer.

These women do not evoke an abstract idea of beauty, nor do they make feminine beauty a pretext for the painter to enjoy himself with shapes and colours: they represent *that* woman, to the point at which the viewer is moved to desire her. The nakedness of Cléo de Mérode aims precisely at rousing desire, the shoulders of Princess Bibesco are there to stimulate the viewer, and the coquetry of Marthe Regnier is meant as an invitation to look more closely.

But as soon as he starts painting the clothing, when he moves from the bodice to the folds of the skirt and then passes from the clothing to the background, Boldini abandons the 'gastronomic' technique: the outlines are no longer exact, the materials flake away in luminous brush-strokes, things become clots of colour and objects merge into explosions of light. . . . The lower half of a Boldini painting evokes an impressionistic culture. It is clear that Boldini, with his references to the high-brow painting of his time, is now being avant garde. In the top half he was doing gastronomy, here he is doing art. These busts and faces, which are there *to be desired*, stand out like the corolla in the middle of a painted flower, which, on the contrary, is only to be *looked at*. The client need no longer feel embarrassed at having been advertised 'in the flesh' like a harlot, for has not the rest of her body become a stimulus for spiritual tasting, for the experience of pure perception and for enjoyment of an altogether superior kind? The client and the viewer are now both at peace, for in Boldini they have experienced Art, but at the same time they have tasted the relish of sensation too, a thing which would have been much more difficult to achieve with Renoir's impalpable women or with the sexless silhouettes of Seurat. The middle-brow consumer swallows the lie.

But what he swallows is an ethical lie, a social and psychological lie, because basically the falsehood is *structural*. A Boldini painting is a typical case of inserting a stylistic device in a context that is incapable of integrating it. The disproportion between the upper and lower halves of these portraits is indisputably a formal question: these women are stylistic mermaids, whose consumer heads and shoulders are joined to clothing which is for contemplation. There is no formal reason why the painter should change his stylistic tune when he moves from the face to the feet; he may plead the justification that the face must satisfy the client while the clothes must satisfy the painter's own ambition, but this in itself condemns the work rather than justifying it, no less than the fact that the clothing too is treated with a view to satisfying the client and convincing him that even the face which emerges from such clothing must give rise to a respectable experience.

If the term Kitsch has any meaning it is not because it denotes an art which aims at producing effects, for very often art does set itself just such a purpose – or at least, this may be the purpose of some other perfectly worthy activity with no pretensions to be art; nor because it is the hallmark of a work lacking formal balance, for in that case one would simply have an ugly work; nor again is it the sign of a work which uses a device taken from another context, for this can be done without any error of taste: *but Kitsch is that work which, in order to justify its function of stimulating effects, struts about in the borrowed plumes of other experiences and sells itself unreservedly as art.*

Occasionally Kitsch can be inadvertent, a sin committed unintentionally, and so almost pardonable. In these cases it is worth pointing out only because these are the very instances in which the mechanism of Kitsch is particularly clear. For example, in the work of Edmondo De Amicis[1] we find a stylistic device taken from Manzoni's I *Promessi Sposi*, which is laughable in its effect. The device in Manzoni comes at the end of the first part of the account of the unfortunate Gertrude. The description has gone on for pages and pages, building up a series of pathetic and terrible details around the figure of the nun: the picture of this mistaken vocation, this repressed rebellion, this latent desperation, has been slowly drawn. Then, at the moment when the reader is about to believe that Gertrude has reached a pacified acceptance of her destiny, the wretched Egidio appears on the scene. Egidio tumbles into the situation at the end of this accumulation of miseries; he appears at once as the unforeseen intervention of fate, bringing the woman's position to the point of exasperation:

From a little window overlooking a small courtyard in that part, he had sometimes watched Gertrude passing by or strolling idly about; enticed rather than frightened by the danger and the impiety of such an enter-

1. Edmondo De Amicis: 1848–1908; wrote romantic novels with a strong educative purpose. *Cuore* (Heart) is his most celebrated work.

prise, one day he ventured to speak to her. The wretched [woman] replied.[1]

Innumerable pages of criticism have already been written commenting on the pithy effectiveness of the final sentence. Its construction is extremely simple: a subject and a predicate, with the subject consisting of an adjective. It informs us simultaneously of the decision of Gertrude and of its moral definition, as well as of the emotional commitment of the narrator. For the adjective 'wretched' pities while it condemns; by intervening to define the woman, putting itself in the place of a noun, it concentrates the whole essence of the character in that one attribute which sums up her situation, past, present and future. The verb is one of the least dramatic that one could imagine: 'replied' indicates the most general aspect of the reaction, neither the content nor the intensity of the reply. Yet it is precisely here that the sentence acquires its expressive power, giving a glimpse of the abyss of wickedness which is made possible by the first irreversible action, indeed, of the very wickedness implicit in the act, performed by a nun who, as we know, subconsciously awaits no more than the smallest spark before she will explode in revolt.

The sentence occurs at the exact point where it serves to resolve a piling up of detail. It resounds like a funeral chord. Its clarity is like an epigraph.

Subject, consisting of an adjective, and predicate: an awesome economy of means. Is it possible that Edmondo De Amicis had this discovery of Manzoni in mind when he wrote one of the most memorable pages of *Cuore*? Probably not; nevertheless, the analogy is there, and should be pointed out. Franti, the bad companion, has been sent away from school but returns to the classroom together with his mother. The Master does not dare to turn him out because the distraught woman, soaked in snow with her hair all awry, is a pitiful sight. But evidently these details are not

1. The Italian of Manzoni is '*la sventurata rispose*' – literally, 'the wretched replied': feminine subject formed by an adjective, and verb. The point of the author's following remarks is, of course, lost in the only possible English translation.

enough to produce the effect that the author wants, and he embarks on a long and rhetorical account by the wretched woman, who describes through her sobs a woeful situation which includes a violent father and herself on the brink of the grave, the whole liberally punctuated with exclamation marks. Still not convinced that the reader has grasped the drama of the thing, the author then tells us how the woman leaves the room, stooping and white-faced (even her shawl trails behind her) and her head shaking; her coughing can still be heard as she goes down the stairs. At this point, as everybody knows, the Master turns to Franti and says

in a voice that would make anybody tremble: 'Franti, you are killing your mother!' Everyone turned to look at Franti. And that scoundrel smiled.[1]

Here too the excerpt ends with a device very similar to that of Manzoni. But the similarity is only in the construction: an adjective (acting as subject) and a predicate. Seen in relation to its context, the expression is found to be very different. First of all, it occurs just when the reader is waiting for something unexpected, or for a closing sentence to relieve his emotions which have been assailed for so long by the massive accumulation of pathetic effects. The adjective describing the subject shows a heavy, undiscriminating judgement, which becomes somewhat ridiculous if compared to the poor boy's real crimes. Finally, 'smiled' cannot be compared with 'replied': for Franti to smile at that moment is the final and wickedest act that he could ever perform, and the sentence foreshadows nothing at all. Franti is a scoundrel. Full stop. Seen in relation to the whole, the expression is melodramatic and would describe a Iago rather than a wild youth from the suburbs of Turin. Placed as it is, at the end of a crescendo, the sentence is not a funeral chord but merely the banging of a big drum. The piece does not become any more trivial, because it was trivial from the beginning, but a stylistic device which was so restrained and so effective in the original, here is seen to be utterly wasted and

1. Similarly here, the Italian original '*E quell' infame sorrise*' cannot be literally translated and the quality of the construction is lost in the English.

deteriorated beyond hope of redemption. Any educative value that the excerpt might have is compromised by the uncouthness of its communication. This page, which is pointed out to young Italians as an example of fine writing, thus turns out to be irremediable Kitsch. Its one saving grace, one may suppose, is that the scholarly allusion was not intentional.

But when the intention is evident, then Kitsch, Midcult's banner, is waved around with glorious ostentation. The semi-abstractness of certain religious art, which cannot refrain from portraying a Madonna or a saint but smuggles it through in pseudo-geometrical shape for fear of being mistaken for an oleo-graph reproduction (thus developing another and worse form of modern-arty oleographism) – this is Kitsch; Kitsch too is the winged figure on the bonnet of a Rolls Royce, a pseudo-Greek element inserted for purposes of ostentatious prestige in an object which ought to obey the more honest criteria of utility and aero-dynamics; Kitsch at a lower social level is the Fiat 600 disguised as a racing car, with red horizontal stripes and, instead of normal bumpers, two barbs in imitation of speed-track cars; and so it is again, still in the car world, when you see that display of deep fins in the bodywork of a car, reminiscent of the spiked chariots of the barbarians, though somewhat corrected by a presumptuous, avant-gardish modelling; Kitsch too are the transistor radios with infinitely long antennae, which are perfectly useless for reception but indis-pensable for prestige because they look like the walkie-talkies used by the American army, which have been immortalized in innumer-able films of war propaganda; the same is true of those sofas up-holstered in a printed material reproducing Campigli's little women – not because the style of Campigli, in being taken over by the masses, automatically becomes obsolete, but because taking those figures from their proper place and inserting them in a context which does not require them makes them instantly vulgar; Kitsch again are the reproductions of abstract paintings on ceramics, and the coffee-bar decorations which re-do Kandinsky, Soldati and Klee.

Translated by Benita de' Grassi di Pianura

Dacia Maraini

HAVE YOU EVER BEEN TO MUNICH?

'Do you have a lot of lovers?' He raised one white heavy leg. Anna sat down beside him. Facing the bed there hung a full-length mirror in a gilded wooden frame. 'And what about your husband?' When he saw that she had risen and was standing there in front of him lost in thought, her hands on her hips, he fell silent. Awkwardly, he began to get undressed, keeping his back turned. 'What's the matter? You're shaking.' 'I'm a bit on edge,' he answered. Anna let Franz take her hand and direct it down towards his groin. For a moment she seemed to see Giacomo's face as it had looked that morning, unexpectedly adult and disappointed, full of rancour. She thought of telling him to stop before it was too late. She looked at the boy's head, still obstinately lowered. 'I don't want to get pregnant,' she said. She got up and went into the bathroom. She felt him gazing absently and curiously at her breasts, her bare stomach, her legs. 'What does your husband do all day?' Anna saw him get off the bed, bend down to look for his slippers, and go and shut himself in the bathroom. She began to get dressed. 'Do you notice my German accent?' Franz looked at her with green listless eyes. Facing the bed there hung a full-length mirror in a gilded wooden frame. Anna waited for him to get up and make for the kitchen. She saw him open the refrigerator door and take out a bottle of Coca Cola. 'There are some cream biscuits, do you want one?' Anna watched as he picked up two crystal glasses and examined them against the light to make sure they were clean. 'Do you two still make love?' Anna grasped the box, tore the paper, broke open the packet and began to eat the biscuits two at a time. His eyes were half-shut and he was frowning. 'He's in love with you.' He went towards the kitchen to get the ice. Anna smiled. She took his hand and placed it on her knees to show that she wasn't at all afraid. But Franz pulled his hand away as if he didn't want to expose it to her gaze. He took off his black sweater, pulling it over his head. He folded it in four and put it in a drawer in the built-in wardrobe. Then he took off his trousers, held them by the turn-ups, put the legs together, shook them and draped them over the back of the chair. 'You said your husband . . .' Anna watched him raise himself on the bed, reaching towards the blinds and pulling the cord with both hands. 'What's the matter? You're shaking.' 'I'm a bit on edge,' he said. She looked at his taut smooth back, his soft hips. His legs emerged from his body like two cylindrical columns, identical, white, without muscle. He dropped to his knees to mop up the spilt liquid. Anna smiled.

She got up. Meanwhile the washbasin had filled with hot water. She dropped the soap on the floor. She began to dry herself, looking out of the window at the traffic in the road and the row of plane trees, dull and slatey green. Franz came back into the room, carrying a glass of Coca Cola. He looked briefly at her. Anna looked at his naked body, stretched out on the sheet. His smooth white legs, his brawny arms, his stumpy workman's hands, his thick stiff neck, his perfect face with stereotyped smile. 'Tell me about your husband.' Anna sat down next to him. She took the glass Franz was holding out to her. She watched him jump down off the bed and bend down to look for his slippers. 'Do you really love him?' Franz looked anxiously at the crumbs dropping on the bed and hastened to hand her his clean handkerchief for her to use as a napkin. 'But if you love him, why aren't you faithful to him?' Anna looked at the clock. When she came back into the room she found Franz sitting on the bed, his legs stretched out and his back resting against the carved wooden bedhead. Anna lay down close to him. 'Is your husband well-off?' He bent down to take off his shoes and his white cotton socks. Anna sniffed the fresh smell of bergamot mingling with the greasier sharper smell of fried onions. 'Have you ever been to Munich?' His teeth were small and each one separated from the next. His green well-shaped eyes were lustreless. Anna saw him take a pair of clean, pale blue trousers from the wardrobe and a dark green shirt with small black flowers. They stretched out on the unmade bed. Franz had put the glass of Coca Cola on the floor. 'How old is your husband?' he asked. He reached out his hand to stroke her back. They went down the stairs together, he first and she following. Anna remembered, as she noticed Franz's smart wavy hair, that she hadn't even looked in the mirror before they went out. And to hide her dishevelled hair she tied a handkerchief round her head. 'Are you thinking about your husband?' 'Not particularly.' 'But you're in love with him.' Anna saw him stop in front of the mirror and run the silver-backed brush through his hair.

She watched him as he picked up the two crystal glasses and examined them against the light to make sure they were clean, poured out the brown liquid and went towards the kitchen to get the ice. 'He's about my age, more or less,' she said. Smiling, he looked into her eyes. He bent a white leg. He stood up. Meanwhile the washbasin had filled with hot water. He dropped the soap on the floor. Anna looked at his nice dull face that for a moment seemed to come to life with an intelligent expression. 'But if you say you love him, how can you . . .?' Anna tore the paper and began to eat the biscuits two at a time. His stiff straight neck, with its sprinkling of chestnut curls was as immobile as if it was made of stone. 'But what does he have to say about it?' Anxiously Franz looked at the crumbs dropping on the bed and hastened to hand her his clean handkerchief for her to use as a napkin. Outside the windows the garden was growing dark and dense. Above, the grey clouds reflected the nocturnal brightness of the city. Anna gestured with her head. The glass of Coca Cola was about to spill over the bed. Franz grabbed it in the nick of time. 'If you're unfaithful to him you can't love him,' he said. He shook his head feebly. Anna watched him take a pair of clean, pale blue trousers out of the wardrobe and a dark green shirt with black flowers.

'Do you have a lot of lovers?' He reached out his hand to stroke her back. Anna looked at the clock. She too began to get dressed, picking up her garments from the floor with hurried movements. She observed Franz's handsome naked body stretched out on the crumpled sheets. Franz laughed, laying a hand on his chest. 'I'm on a slimming diet,' he said. Anna watched as he picked up the two crystal glasses and examined them against the light to make sure they were clean. 'There are some cream biscuits, do you want one?' His eyes were half shut and he was frowning.

First he took off his black sweater, pulling it over his head. He folded it in four and put it in a drawer in the built-in wardrobe. Then he took off his trousers, held them by the turn-ups, put the legs together, shook them and draped them over the back of the chair. 'How long is it since you and he were married?' Anna let him take her hand and direct it down towards his groin. 'What's the matter? You're shaking.' 'I'm a bit on edge.' She saw again Giacomo's face as it had looked that morning, unexpectedly adult and disappointed, full of rancour. Franz was silent. 'Where in Germany?' 'In Munich, at home.' Anna counted the spots of Coca Cola on the white carpet. Franz stretched out his legs. The glass of Coca Cola was about to spill. Franz grabbed it in the nick of time. 'I've been a mechanic and a night watchman. I've been a model for romantic magazine stories and I've sung in restaurants.' He got off the bed and began to get dressed, slowly and awkwardly, keeping his back turned.

'Tell me about your husband.' He raised one white heavy leg. On the glass shelf stood a row of pots of face cream. Every time a train went through the underground the pots clinked against each other with the sound of porcelain. 'Is he in love with you?' His eyes were half shut and he was frowning. Anna watched that wide flat calloused hand. She felt him moaning and trembling. She began to dry herself, looking out of the window at the traffic in the road and the row of plane trees, dull and slatey green. Franz came back into the room carrying a glass of Coca Cola and a box of biscuits. 'I've been a kept man, too. Have you seen all this valuable stuff?' He handed her the brand-new box of biscuits. 'I'm on a slimming diet,' he said. Looking at him closely, he wasn't as slim as he seemed at first sight. 'There are some cream biscuits, do you want one?' Anna saw him stand up and make for the kitchen. 'Do you want some ice?' He had smooth white legs, a vulnerable stomach, a broad smooth chest, brawny arms, stumpy workman's hands, thick stiff neck, perfect face with stereotyped smile. 'Have you ever been to Munich?' His teeth were small and each one separated from the next. 'He must be my age, your husband.' He put the glass of Coca Cola on the floor. Anna felt him gazing absently and curiously at her breasts, her bare stomach, her legs.

They went down the stairs together, he first and she following. Anna remembered, as she noticed Franz's smart wavy hair, that she hadn't even looked in the mirror before they went out. To hide her dishevelled hair she tied a handkerchief round her head. 'I used to be a mechanic,' he said. 'I wasn't much good. I'm not even a good model.' His eyes were half shut and he was frowning. 'Is he in love with you?' Anna took the whole box, opened it and began to eat the biscuits two at a time. She looked at the house, a little liberty style villa with imitation battlements, a band of majolica below the roof with a motif of angels and bunches of fruit. Franz came in again carrying a box of biscuits and a small bowl of ice. The two plaster greyhounds that stood by the garden gate were sparkling. Anna listened to the sound of his steps on the gravel. They stretched out on the unmade bed. Franz had put the glass of Coca Cola on the floor. He bent down to unfasten his shoes and take off his short white cotton socks. Meanwhile the washbasin had filled up with water. He dropped the soap on the floor. When she came back in she found Franz sitting on the bed, his legs stretched out and his back against the carved wooden bedhead. She took the glass he was holding out to her. 'Is your husband well-off?' His body suggested an over-protracted adolescence. She sniffed the fresh smell of bergamot mingling with the greasier smell of fried onions. Franz was bending over the stove. 'I'll make the dinner,' he said. Anna glimpsed a plate of clotted and congealed sauerkraut in the refrigerator. 'It's red cabbage, do you like it? I eat it because I'm homesick. Homesick for Munich. Have you ever been to Munich?' Anna saw him go into the bathroom and come out again almost immediately. He stopped in front of the mirror and ran the silver-backed comb through his hair. 'There, it's nearly ready,' he said. He took the lid off the pan. He was enveloped in a cloud of steam. The cabbage was separating in the red liquid that covered it. 'Are you still thinking about him?' Looking at him closely, he wasn't as slim as he appeared at first sight. Anna watched as he picked up the two crystal glasses and examined them against the light to make sure they were clean. 'I'd like to be a parachutist. In Africa maybe.' Anna tore the paper and began eating the biscuits two at a time. Franz looked anxiously at the crumbs dropping on the bed and hastened to hand her his clean handkerchief to use as a napkin. 'But if you love him, why are you unfaithful to him?' He raised his eyes to look at her. Meanwhile the washbasin had filled with water. Franz came back into the room with a glass of Coca Cola in his hand. Anna observed his naked body. She let him take her hand between his and direct it down towards his groin. 'Do you really love him?' Anna looked at the clock. For a moment she seemed to see Giacomo's face as it had looked that morning, unexpectedly adult and disappointed, full of rancour.

Anna saw him get off the bed, bend down to look for his slippers, and then go out and shut himself in the bathroom. 'I eat this stuff because I'm homesick,' he said. She sniffed the fresh smell of bergamot mingling with the sharper and greasier smell of fried onions. 'Are you thinking about your husband?' His nice dull face seemed for a moment to come to life with an intelligent expression. The two plaster greyhounds standing by the garden gate stood out white against the shadowy pine trees. Franz stretched out a hand to stroke her back. He took off his black sweater, pulling it over his head. He folded it in four and placed it in a drawer in the built-in wardrobe. 'You said your husband loves you,' he said. He took off his trousers, held them by the turn-ups, put the legs together, shook them, draped them over the back of the chair. His handsome stiff neck with its sprinkling of chestnut curls was as immobile as if it were made of stone. 'He's in love with you.' Anna grasped the box, tore the paper, broke open the packet and began to eat the biscuits two at a time. 'I don't want you to get pregnant,' he said. Anna smiled at him. She took his hand and placed it on her knees to show that she wasn't afraid. 'Are you thinking about your husband?' He stood up. Meanwhile the washbasin had filled with hot water. Anna looked at his naked body. She took the glass Franz was holding out to her. Through the windows the garden was growing close and dark. Above the houses, the grey clouds were reflecting the lights of the city. Anna made a gesture with her head. She began to get dressed, picking up her garments from the floor with hurried movements. 'What does your husband do when you're not there?' Anna felt him look absently and curiously at her breasts, her bare stomach, her legs. Franz held out the glass of Coca Cola. 'I used to be a mechanic. I wasn't much good at it,' he said. He placed a stumpy calloused hand on his stomach. 'I eat this stuff because I'm homesick. Have you ever been to Munich?' His handsome stiff neck with its sprinkling of chestnut curls was as immobile as if it were made of stone. 'But you're in love with him.' Meanwhile the washbasin had filled with hot water. Anna took the glass Franz was holding out to her. She saw him jump down off the bed. 'Is my German accent very noticeable?' Franz raised his green listless eyes to look at her. 'You said your husband loves you,' he said. When he saw that she had risen and was standing there in front of him lost in thought, her hands on her hips, he fell silent.

Translated by Pamela Swinglehurst

Bruno Fonzi

IL NORD

Since the war the city of Turin has almost doubled in area; yet the visitor returning to the suburb known as Il Nord after an absence of many years will be surprised to find how little it has changed. Its position may be partly responsible for this – the most low-lying part of Turin, the least protected against the vagaries of climate, the dampest and coldest in winter, the most sultry in summer. But there are no doubt other reasons.

The inhabited area of Il Nord is bordered by a row of workers' apartment blocks, built thirty or forty years ago. Beyond this, and the artificial canal 'Pellegrina' with its steep gravel banks, is a vast area of uncultivated land extending into the distance, bordered by a line of grey poplars along the river. For most of the year it is immersed in fog.

Half-hidden by an elbow in the canal, and on the road flanking this flat land (a secondary road which even today is still not asphalted), are the remains of a building known as 'The Factory' – a title attested by the writing in large cement letters *Premiata Fabbr . . .*, which are still on the façade. It was burnt down some years before the events related here, and what remains is only a part of the ground floor, charred and darkened by the fire. Traces of what once were the walls or fence around the factory mark the extent of the property, which was occupied for several years by a group of persons who made their living by sorting and classifying rubbish. But this was some time ago. Since then, the ruins were further reduced by people in search of bricks or other second-hand building material; and the few rooms with boarded-up windows were now inhabited by Rosario Trifiro and his friends, who had emigrated from Palermo.

In spite of living in this part of Italy for some years, Trifiro had been unable to find regular work (his frequent spells in prison for nearly half this time may have been partly responsible for this). But recently things had improved, chiefly due to his liaison with Antonina Frigese (the wife of Signor Amato), who had encouraged him to return to his earlier occupation, exercised at intervals in the Palermo days – the acquisition of old clothes from charity organizations which distributed them free, and their subsequent sale. Every Saturday at dawn he was to be seen in the shafts of a handcart loaded with these crumpled garments, followed by Antonina who pushed behind, taking them the seven kilometres from 'The Factory' to the little piazza and three small streets behind the old arsenal, where itinerant vendors did a brisk business all day.

One Saturday in late September, the warmth of an Indian summer had attracted a larger crowd than usual. The stall was thronged with customers all morning; but they gradually drifted away in the afternoon, until only the vendors remained. Rosario and Antonina ate their provisions, which they had brought in tins, and drank their water from an old beer-bottle. Rosario then stretched out under the cart to sleep, while Antonina sat on a small chair at the side, keeping an eye on their possessions and staring moodily into the distance. The silence in the piazza was occasionally broken by the cries of small children running about. She sighed, reflecting that her own children, Maria and Santo, were spending the afternoon alone together, and that Santo would, as usual, be bullying and belabouring his small sister. . . .

In the big open space in front of 'The Factory', Santo gave his step-brother Peppino a punch, and Peppino clasped him round the waist; kicking and struggling, the two boys fell to the ground, Santo still pummelling hard (Peppino was the legal son of Trifiro, Santo the illegitimate). Suddenly, Peppino let out a shriek of pain and relaxed his hold; whereupon Santo got up, panting but triumphant, and disdainfully surveyed his adversary, who had begun to cry.

Although Peppino was a year older, and correspondingly taller and heavier, he was of a milder disposition than Santo, and mentally a later developer. When Santo was not molesting his stepsister Maria, he easily mastered Peppino, giving him a trouncing several times a day.

Aroused by the cries of Peppino, their old grandmother, Filippa, strode furiously out of the house and entered the fray (she was not really grandmother to all of them, but was generally regarded by the family as such). Santo was too nimble; evading her grasp, he skipped away, followed by the imprecations of the old woman, who could only give vent to her wrath by seizing Peppino. But seeing his condition, his grubby, tearful face, the dishevelled hair which she had washed and combed only that morning (she had even tied up his shoes for him), she realized who was the true culprit. She attempted to pacify the howling Peppino, brushed down his clothes, blew his nose in a filthy handkerchief (an operation he could perfectly well have performed himself; but being backward, he was always treated as a small child). She had spent half the morning delousing his hair, and she now continued automatically arranging it with her hand.

It was the lice which were at the back of it all. Santo had started school the year before, and had been sent home several times, after the school sanitary inspections, for being lousy. One afternoon, a small car had stopped at 'The Factory', and an athletic-looking lady of about twenty-five had alighted, a 'social worker'. She brought with her a tin containing a white powder which, she assured them, would destroy the lice. They had viewed this with some scepticism, but had tried it out on Santo, arguing that he was the only member of the family likely to be lousy, '*because he had picked them up at school.*' If the powder had any immediate effect it was not for long, because he picked them up again immediately afterwards from his brother and sister, with whom he was always in close physical contact, fighting with them by day, sleeping with them by night.

The visits of the 'social worker' now became regular occurrences, once every three or four weeks. She would come in and talk to the two women, Antonina and old Filippa, who regarded her with some apprehension, the first sitting on the bed, the second on one of the two chairs they possessed, replying to her many questions laconically or not at all (Rosario had told them not to open their mouths in front of her). Only with their eyes did they occasionally betray their feelings – 'she smokes', 'crosses her legs', 'wears clothes which show off everything', etc. But they were somewhat mollified by her other offerings, medicines, tonics, patent foods for the children, a pair of shoes for Peppino (which, in spite of his feeble remonstrances, were given to Santo, for whom they were too big). The lady soon realized that Peppino and Maria were most in need of attention; she suggested that Peppino should be taken to a certain place, an institute, whose long and difficult name was soon condensed and simplified by the family into '*Secòggecu*'.[1] Here he could be visited by the family, he would have proper medical attention, and they would have to pay nothing.

After this, their evening conversations, arguments and heated discussions were concerned exclusively with the '*Secòggecu*' (family problems were always debated during supper; it was the only time when they were all together). Rosario and Antonina had always grumbled about having an extra mouth to feed, all the more as Peppino was 'nothing to them'; but it took some time to persuade old Filippa that he should go to the institute. He was her flesh and blood, the son of her daughter Consolata, the wife of Rosario Trifiro, by another man, born to her during one of Rosario's periodic incarcerations. Old Filippa was much attached to the male grandchildren and considered she had a special responsibility for Peppino, who had been put in her charge by his mother not long after he was born, and Consolata had had to leave for an unknown destination with Rosario, who had just come out of prison.

It took them nearly a month to persuade the old lady, but at last she agreed, and set out herself with him one day for the institute. The 'social worker' had provided exact written instructions for the somewhat complicated journey; but Filippa had memorized them with a peasant's meticulous care, so that she need not show

1. Sicilian dialect: 'white powder'.

the paper with the name and address of the 'Centro Medico-
Psicopedagogico', which she was incapable not only of pronounc-
ing, but of reading. She put Peppino in his 'Sunday best', and made
an attempt at enlivening her own funereal garments (that eternal
black kerchief around the head and shoulders of the Southern
peasant women, causing them to appear in a state of perpetual
mourning), putting on a new pair of holeless stockings which she
had ironed – a sartorial flourish which unfortunately could not be
appreciated, because her skirt came down to her shoes.

After a last set of instructions and threats to Santo to look after
his sister, and above all not to hit her, she took Peppino by the
hand, and they set off down the road together, the boy following
obediently, but stumbling slightly, because he was not accustomed
to wearing shoes. . . .

Crouching by a hedge in the field, Maria saw them leave, and
then looked apprehensively towards Santo, who was also crouching only ten yards away. As the two figures grew smaller and
smaller in the distance, he was waiting for them to disappear altogether. It was one of those hot Italian middays when everything
is quiet, and even the birds are silent; the great plain of Il Nord,
dominated by the giant skeletons of the high tension pylons and
their traceries of cable, seemed to shimmer in the heat.

When the two figures were out of sight, Santo crept towards his
sister with the movements of a cat stalking its prey. The little girl
realized the hopelessness of flight, curled herself up and waited.
He came right up to her, and began repeating the proposals he
had made that morning, when he knew they would be alone most
of the day. Again he received the same refusal, a furious 'No! No!
No!' Undeterred, he continued with a combination of blandishments and threats, until he suddenly lost his temper and struck
her several times on the arms and shoulders. The anguished shrieks
of the little girl rang out across the plain. He waited until she had
calmed down and then again began his importuning; but she
summoned up all her strength and returned the same obstinate
refusal. Overcoming his inclination to hit her again, he seized her
bodily, turning her this way and that, reorientating her, as if

searching a vantage point for renewing the attack. 'All right, I'll buy you an ice-cream then. One of the big ones.'

She became quiet and stared at the ground. Thinking his blandishments were successful, he redoubled his offers, ardently, passionately, irresistibly. But her sudden silence was dictated less by the thought of the ice-cream than by the fear of further blows. He took hold of her arms and pulled her towards him; then, when she grudgingly capitulated, he pushed her towards the artificial canal, at the point where it was lined with blackberry bushes. Although she knew what this meant and moaned in anticipation, her resistance was over and, resigned to the worst, she let him do what he wanted. He pushed her though a small hole in the hedge and crawled in after (although the children had bare legs, and often bare feet, these bushes had given them hides like leather). On the other side of the hedge, beside the grass border of the canal which was now swollen by the September rains almost to the level of the banks, she made a last show of resistance, 'No, no, I don't want to !' But her words carried no conviction; she allowed him to pull up her tattered skirt, while he authoritatively told her to lie down . . . here, surrounded by the stench of foetid weed, human excrement, the buzzing of flies, in this waste land on the edge of a great city. . . .

In the distance, Santo saw his friend Vigin running towards him; he was accompanied by his grandfather, but he took no notice of the old man's instructions not to go too far ahead. Vigin often came here in the afternoon with his grandfather, and the two boys played together. They rarely spoke to one another, indeed did not even know one another's names; but Vigin instinctively recognized Santo's authority and always obeyed him. This afternoon, they plucked two branches from the hedge, denuded them of leaves, and fashioned two long flexible whips. Armed with these, they approached a low crumbling wall, the scene of their favourite sport – lizard baiting.

Vigin's grandfather sat down on the embankment; opening his newspaper, he pushed up his spectacles on his forehead and looked

at the boys, making vague sounds to recall his grandson. 'Here . . .
boy . . . not with that . . . Neapolitan . . . .' Failing to make any
impression, he lowered his glasses and began reading, muttering
irritably, 'Huh ! Neapolitan . . . Naples ! . . . God-forsaken place !
. . . good-for-nothing wretches ! . . .'

Santo and Vigin skirted the stone wall carefully, so as not to
disturb any lizards taking the last of the summer sun before their
winter hibernation. Then suddenly Santo's stick fell like a flail,
and one of the little creatures dropped off the wall, its white belly
uppermost, its tail threshing the air . . . but at this moment, from
the other side of the hedge, came the despairing cry of Maria, 'Oh !
oh ! oh !'

Santo, who had been waiting for this, threw down his stick,
and darted over to the hedge, while Vigin followed at a distance,
curious to see what the cry was about. But Santo turned on him
and ordered him peremptorily to stay where he was. Vigin stopped,
mystified, staring at the hole in the hedge through which his friend
had disappeared.

On the other side Maria was lying on the ground, weeping and
shivering with cold and disgust; she had just pulled her legs, which
were blue from long immersion, out of the canal. Around one of
the emaciated calves, a large black worm-like reptile, a leech, was
winding itself, gently waving its head to and fro in anticipation
of a tasty meal. Trembling with excitement, Santo put out his
hand and plucked it away; it left a dark purple stain on the leg,
from which a trickle of blood began to flow (there were two more
stains of the same kind on the other leg). He gazed admiringly
at the leech, then placed it in a tin in which two others were
writhing in a few inches of water – the spectacle of all three together giving him untold delight.

Taking advantage of his preoccupation with the tin, Maria
started to crawl surreptitiously towards the hedge; but he turned
quickly and seized her by the ankle. She yelled and struggled, and
he tried to persuade her, this time more gently, that if she would
do it again, once more, *just* once more, it would be the last time;
he swore it would. To solemnize this oath, he moistened the fore-

finger of the hand which was not holding her ankle with saliva, and traced a Holy Cross on the parched ground. If she would do it once more, he would buy her that ice-cream, the biggest there was. 'On Wednesday, you'll have it. I swear you shall!'

When he found that this form of persuasion was still ineffective, he began pummelling her again, pinching her bottom so hard that she howled; he followed this up with a number of hard blows to the chest and shoulders, abusing her, 'You tart! Tart! You're nothing but a dirty little tart!'

Once again Maria resigned herself, weeping gently; she let herself be led back to the canal, where he again lifted up her skirt and made her immerse her legs in the dirty water....

The evening air was sharper, and the croaking chorus of the frogs arose from the muddy banks of the canal, as Santo walked back, clutching his tin of leeches firmly in one hand, his sister by the other; she stumbled along, shivering with cold, her naked legs still bleeding. When they arrived at the built-up area, the sun had gone in behind the big mountains which marked the western end of the city; the street lamps were still unlit, but the popular quarters were alive with people and vehicles, and some of the shop-windows gave out a feeble illumination. They stopped first before a *profumeria*; then, to admire some wireless sets and electrical appliances; then, in front of a *delicatessen* shop. All these new and glittering wares were fascinating; but the pleasure was tempered for Maria, who now felt a little better as her legs warmed up from the exercise, by the arbitrary selection of Santo. They had to stop where, and for as long as, he wanted.

Only a few of the old peasant houses still stood in this street, the main thoroughfare of a suburb which the expanding city had surrounded and engulfed in the last twenty years. The old houses had either been destroyed by wartime bombardment, or demolished to make way for the big blocks of workmen's flats. In one of the few houses surviving from the beginning of the century was 'Dr Lovisetto's Old Pharmacy', as the black metal notice-board announced.

Santo went into this shop, instructing his sister not to follow, but to wait for him outside. She stared moodily into the drab shop-window, in which a stuffed marmoset and a dead snake embalmed in a crystal vase jostled dusty boxes full of corn-pads which were ten years out of date. Inside, in a penumbra impregnated with the oppressive odour of medicines, a dirty gilt-bronze bust of a late nineteenth-century gentleman with a small pointed beard, and the legend 'Dr Lovisetto' beneath, peered down from the dusty shelves; while Dr Lovisetto jun., the present *genius loci*, a bald and wrinkled sixty-year-old in a dirty white shirt, served a couple of customers. When he noticed the dishevelled head of a small boy only an inch or two above the counter, a ferocious guffaw, intended as a welcome, burst from his catarrh-filled lungs. 'Ah! Ah! Ah! So here's my leech provider!'

He beckoned the lugubrious-looking child into the back of the shop, where he poked in Santo's tin with long, gnarled fingers, fishing out the leeches individually, raising each to his myopic gaze, praising their size and beauty. He then placed them in the majolica vase where they were conserved for the few customers who still believed in this old-fashioned cure – some well-fed greengrocer suffering from high blood pressure, perhaps, or an elderly Fiat worker stupefied by arterio-sclerosis . . . .

With a frown of childish concentration on his face, Santo watched, his eyes moving from the chemist's face to the hand which accomplished the transfer, delighted by the old man's compliments about the quality of his leeches. When they returned to the front of the shop, the chemist gave the tips of his fingers, which had touched the leeches, a tap with a wad of cotton wool soaked in ether, and then placed a nicotine-stained finger on the key of his prehistoric cash-till. 'Five times one hundred,' he said. 'Here we are! A nice five-hundred-lire note for you!' The drawer creaked open, he selected the dirtiest of the five-hundred-lire notes and handed it to the boy. A benefactor, a philanthropist, a humanitarian, he regarded himself – paying one hundred lire for something which he could sell for barely three hundred! 'And the wretch doesn't even say thank you! What savages, these troglodytes! Yes, he goes off without even saying good evening!'

Followed by Maria, who now found it hard to keep up, Santo almost ran along the pavement. From the moment when his hand had closed on the five-hundred-lire note (which he had not expected), all else was forgotten in the glory of possession, a joy so intense that it was almost painful. It was the first time he had not only possessed – that is to say actually held in his hand – but touched, a bank-note. Hitherto, the only money that had come his way had been in the form of coins, small denominations of five or ten lire – although once or twice, after he had launched out into the leech business, he had handled a hundred-lire coin. Bank-notes he had rarely seen, glimpsed occasionally in the hands of his father or mother (more often in those of Carmelina), and always fleetingly, furtively – for there was something secretive about money in their house. Its possessor kept it jealously guarded, concealed in a small bag hanging around his or her neck, night and day, between shirt and skin.

The five-hundred-lire note clutched tightly in his fist, which was thrust deep in a pocket of his tattered shorts, Santo continued half running, apparently unaware of his sister, or deliberately ignoring her, as she cried out each time they passed a *gelateria*. He had now decided not to buy her an ice-cream – not because he didn't want one himself, nor because he was avaricious (he did not know what avarice was), but because he could not bear to think of that wonderful five-hundred-lire note being reduced into smaller denominations. For him, it was to be the first of a series of increasingly larger and larger bank-notes.

He remained deaf to his sister's entreaties; and the little girl, who had at first thought he was simply trying to tease her, began to believe he really intended not to reward her. Her cries turned to supplications, and she clung to his coat and arms, trying to hold him back. He threw her off and went on, still ignoring her. When she became even more importunate, he gave her two or three cuffs – not very hard because he could only use his left hand, the right being still occupied with the five-hundred-lire note, but enough to make her weep. He went on rapidly, not looking back at her.

Evening had come and more people were about. Most of them

were on their way home to supper, and they paid little attention
to the tearful girl limping along beside the frowning small boy
who was deep in thought. But Santo suddenly stopped, as if he had
received a blow; and when he went on it was without the same
urgency and sense of mission. He suddenly recalled his words:
'On Wednesday, you shall have it, I promise.' The words echoed
in his ears, and although he tried to drive them away, to suffocate
them, they persisted. A superstitious fear possessed him, and he
suddenly saw himself groping about blindly in the meadow while
Maria and Peppino teased him, punched him, pinched him,
knocked him down, without his being able to see them or hit
back. A violent hatred of his brother and sister welled up within
him.

They were now almost at the end of the houses. He stopped
before the last bar and turning to Maria, who had come up beside
him continuing her lamentations in a more subdued tone, gave
her a heavy blow on the back – to avenge himself, as it were, for
what he was about to do. She shrieked and began crying again –
but she quickly stopped when she saw he was going into the bar.
She made as if to follow, but he turned and told her to wait. Then
truculently, with that half-aggressive, half-defensive expression on
his face which he invariably adopted when dealing with persons
he did not know, he entered. He bought a small ice, the smallest
there was, and a big one, the biggest there was, reluctantly handing
over his five-hundred-lire note to the girl behind the counter, who
regarded it with complete indifference as she gave him the change.
He went out carrying the ices, one in each hand, and gave the
smaller to his sister, who became delirious with happiness as she
grasped it. Then very slowly, Santo in front, Maria five or six
paces behind, licking, sucking, silent, temporarily at peace with
one another, the two children continued their way home.

A heavy mist had come up from the canal, and the light of the
few street-lamps was fainter. Somewhere out in that lonely plain
of *Il Nord*, in a silence rendered all the more pervasive by the
chorus of the crickets, or near the canal by the lapping of the water
and the croaking of the frogs – somewhere out in that dark space

something secretive was going on, something furtive, shameful ...
criminal perhaps ....

Near 'The Factory', this false peace was suddenly broken by the
screams and cries of the two children, and the infuriated voices of
their parents cursing them for coming home late. ...

Translated by Anthony Rhodes

Mario Luzi

THE JUDGE

'Do you think that yours is real love? Examine
carefully your past' he insists
shooting right into me
his elder's glance, between mocking and strangeness.
And he waits. While I look into the distance
and nothing comes into my mind but
the sea firm under the flight of the seagulls
scarcely varied between the rocks of the island
where a naked land casts shadow
with its hillocks, or another, prepared for sowing,
casts shadow with its clods and a few threads.
'Yes, I may have sinned greatly'
I reply at length, grappling myself to something,
even if they are my faults, in that heathland light.
'You ought to weep – to weep – for your misunderstood love'
his voice begins again with a squally
whistle, passing high above that plain.
I listen to it and do not even wonder
why it is he and not I there on the bench
engaged in judging the evils of the world.
'Could be!' I reply, while my thoughts already stray,
while the street catches fire scale by scale
and here in the bar the full daylight still
shines in the two pupils of a girl who takes off her overall
for the hours of leisure, and the man who has taken over from her
puts on a white jacket and comes
towards us with two full glasses,
cold, to put them, one here, one there, on our table.

BUT WHERE

'It isn't here any more' – insinuates a surprised voice –
'the heart of your city' and it is lost
in the maze, already dark –
if there were not a rainy
light of coming spring
visible above the high roofs.

I don't know what to answer and I observe
the bees of this ancient viridarium,
the gilders of angels, of chests of drawers,
the workers in metals and ebony,
close one by one the old caves
and spill out, a little gay, a little afraid, into the small streets
    surrounding.

'It isn't here any more – but where?' I wonder
while the accidental and the necessary
fight in the mind's eye
and I think of myself and of my companions, of the
broken conversation with those souls in torment,
of a life that makes no sense, of the loss
of their swarm of thoughts in search of a pole.
Someone yields, someone resists in his faith stretched tight.

                              Translated by *Gavin Ewart*

Vittorio Sereni

THE GREAT FRIEND

A great friend who would rise up above me
and carry me wholly in his light,
who would laugh expansively where I would scarcely smile
and love strongly where I would hint my fondness . . .

But the years pass, and only the eye that foresees is calm
losing at its reappearance
the boat that passed first under the bridge.
He knows the messengers of chance,
can call them by name. He is the knowing soldier.
Did not the morning seem born for something else?
And the wing of the lime
and the steep path that suddenly strayed into green shadow
– did they not lead towards something else?
But on ground suddenly hostile at the expected point
the quota grows red-hot.
Like the late schoolboy
– nor any more from the menace of the barred
door do the flowers and wings distract him –
I follow him, I am in his shadow.

SITUATION

The force of the commonplace,
sad.
The jet of the hose in the grass
unnoticed sigh.

The garden in the dusk.
Chairs in a circle, deckchairs.
Familiar glances interweave; only one is evasive.
Generally calm.

On the reverse of the commonplace
the vesper bells. Unheard.
For centuries and centuries at this hour
clothes still warm
with blood and sensation.
And round about the swallows in their thousands.

I am all this, the commonplace and its reverse
beneath the vault that darkens more and more.
But can do nothing against a single look
from others, confident in itself, that lights itself
from my own look
against the guilty eyes,
against the furtive steps
that bear you away.

Translated by Gavin Ewart

Franco Fortini

LUZI

Some years ago, after reading one of the most beautiful poems of recent years (*Notizie a Giuseppina*), I wrote of Luzi:

Luzi's main preoccupation – the pursuit of dignity and spiritual integrity – has actually become a limitation in his poetry. Literally, today, one cannot aim at this dignity and integrity through the medium of poetry without enormously increasing the mystification with which our society surrounds any work of literature . . . Until the *Primizie* Luzi's hard realities of death and absence had elements of that false asceticism favoured by so many intellectuals. An asceticism, that is, which is neither more nor less than the defence of privilege on someone else's behalf; a defence of small-town petit bourgeois Rosicrucians, far removed from industrial life, who see their traditional field of action reduced from day to day by the ideological exploitation of the masses. For these intellectuals, awareness of values, agoraphobia, esprit de corps and historical and political *unawareness* are all one.

Some of the poems in *Primizie* foreshadow very different subject-matter. They are serious attempts to come to terms with a world full of contradictions – until then kept at a distance . . .

In the general tendency towards a discursive form – which has affected all writers, even including more sharply 'defined' poets like Montale and Ungaretti – the contradiction between the restored (or even increased) capacity for communication and the 'cultural' poverty of what inspires it, becomes more and more evident . . .

The poetry which has its source in the literature of the 'spirit' and in the culture (always on the defensive) of the petit bourgeois who, behind the walls of the towns of Central Italy, are obsessed by their own anguish – without being able to voice the anguish of those with another background, and their struggle to recognize or overcome it – this poetry succeeds, in its supreme effort to conquer aphasia, in mimicking 'communication'. But until now it has not been able to communicate more than that effort itself.

I did not realize, then, something that became obvious with the publication of *Onore del Vero*. For Luzi (and, in general, for the poets whose outlook is similar) the events of the War and of the post-war period ('*tutto l'altro che deve essere . . .*') the 'world situation', had made them understand – and not just through the violence of the 'facts', but through the actions and the 'committedness' to which men were driven by them – not only real life but also the *moral* value of something that could not be turned into poetry, that resisted expression, that was not dreamed of in the philosophy of Mallarmé.

Not that Luzi, and a few other poets, had not known, even in the days of their 'hermetic' books, the basic difference between confession and poetry, between communication and expression; but poems had been considered capable of dealing in exact detail with the whole of religious, moral and intellectual life. Now it slowly became clear that to strengthen the *appearance* of communication, and at the same time to show its utter impossibility, would be to arm oneself with a most powerful weapon of 'de-realization', of 'estrangement'. There were several precedents, above all in the whole tradition of what we call the 'ironical twilight'; but Luzi (differing in this from Parronchi, for example, who went so far as to 're-do', with astuteness and ingenuity, a certain kind of 'tender' minor poetry of the Italian late eighteenth and early nineteenth century) could not take this way out. He wanted to proclaim the unreality of this life and at the same time its supreme religious dignity. The word must be able to deny the presence of the object at the very moment of evoking it. But not, as in many recent resurgences of surrealism, to give rein to the absurd or to 'solarize' the inexpressible. Rather, to overcome any immediacy, to dissolve the last solid resistance of *things*, and at the same time to postulate a state beyond expression itself : '*la conoscenza per ardore o il buio*'.

The word (and the man who utters it) becomes, for Luzi, the central term of a ratio : the ephemeral is to the word as the word is to the eternal. Thus Luzi has no need to construct another world, he can look round him, describe other objects, accept other realities, exercise his syllogistic reasoning.

All the same, this bringing in of 'otherness', and with it this recognition of the irreducibility of 'yet more otherness' to poetical terms, Luzi only gains at a price – a scaling down, a sort of historical-geographical retreat. The world that is the background to this humble return, the world restored, after and together with its negation, to the traveller, is a world impoverished; in the double sense, Christian and non-Christian, of the word 'poverty'. It is no accident that the images and objects used for these meditations on the ephemeral and the state of grace are almost all taken from the semi-rural world of poor communities, from the small towns that have been passed by in the hectic rush of the modern world; as if Christianity had taken refuge in the countryside, returning to the amorphous '*volgo disperso*', among rustic deities and saints.

It is true that, unlike so much 'agrarian' Catholic literature, reactionary and vulgar, and also unlike so much more, equally worthless, that is vitalistic and decadent, these examples of regression are presented as allegories of the human situation. Luzi's *Notizie dall' Amiata* are not the terrible temptation of a moment ('*la morte, la morte che vive*') and one of the accidental results of 'existential' communication, as in Montale, but an aspect of life that Luzi has chosen. However, Luzi's setting does not escape – in his choice of 'situations' – the morbidity and the equivocal vengeance that one finds in the landscape and the situations of Fellini's films. The poet's privileged position is underlined by the very distance which he establishes between himself and the kind of people he writes about. His '*poveri*', pre-bourgeois (or at least pre-modern), make no demands on him – asking only his prayers. The only poem that contains an explicit reference to political events is about the struggle for independence of the Cypriots, and even this is typical. Luzi is sensitive to these 'rearguard' actions, in this case even to a struggle for independence (in itself, there is no need to add, a necessary one), as he is to the economic and cultural 'rearguard' of Italy. Nor need one add that for the Christian there are neither avant-gardes nor rearguards; to name is to choose . . .

But – and this seems to me the most important thing to understand, and one which explains why Luzi, with all his limitations and even because of them, is a true poet, one of the very few of our time – this 'scaling down' of objects, this *'miseria'*, is expressed with a characteristic 'monolinguism' which is no longer in the tradition of Petrarch and Leopardi, and represents another attempt at the 'noble vernacular'; a language that is almost colourless, unexpressionist, 'average', and yet never colloquial. 'In a civilized nation this language exists,' Luzi himself has said, in a revealing phrase contained in an article of 1958, a reasoned attack on the neo-dialecticists. A nation, he means, that does not contradict itself, progressing by fits and starts and yet remaining stationary. It is true, one must pre-suppose a real classless society; and it is easy to make fun of this weary, punctilious Tuscan 'poverty'. But what does this linguistic theory mean in practice? It means a man holding the balance between feeling and reason, between what is private and what is public – a man who believes in communication, a man relatively all of a piece, relatively 'committed' (compared to us, that is). This imaginary man is neither the person who writes 'I' in these poems, nor is he Luzi. Luzi, in his work, remains what he was and what he has become, and what I have tried to suggest that he is. He is, on the contrary, the man that one imagines if one 'prolongs' (so to speak) this figurative language.

In the state of Italy today this 'linguistic' ideal, and this humane proposition, are so radically opposed to the world of neo-capitalism as to become a proposition that aims higher than illusory reformism and, paradoxically, relies on human integrity. This impoverished petit bourgeois; humiliated, scorned, ideologically tied to his spiritual 'honour', bears witness, in the works that present him, to something that is essential to tomorrow.

SERENI

The poetry of Sereni only slowly became distinguishable from the other verse written between 1935 and 1940. When I consider the poems in his second book[1] I must admit that there was certainly something more in the young pre-war poet than his friends of those days, in their affectionate companionship, were able to recognize.

But without the war and Italy's defeat Sereni would scarcely have emerged from the limitations of an educated belles-lettres-ism. The cloudy lakeside seasons, the memory of a death, the sense of his own transitoriness, the presentiment of a threat to the things and people most dear to him – all of these were in him from the beginning, as they were in many young men of his generation. It was the cloud within which they moved, having no contact with other truths. All the same – luckily – something prevented Sereni from building up an ideological defence against events, like the one that was being prepared by his Florentine 'hermetic' friends, who mistakenly saw in him, at this time, a kindred spirit this side of the Alps. This defence would have been Catholic idealism, literature regarded as the whole of life, the denial of 'worldliness'. Sereni on the other hand – the elegiac, autobiographical Sereni – seemed then more defenceless, without metaphysical pride. But his was not an isolated case; rather, it was the result of a certain tendency of his class and his cultural background, in that place and at that time. In short, Sereni's moral and cultural antecedents lie in positivism that is basic in Gozzano and Montale – and that is, first and foremost, the denial of idealistic optimism and Catholicism; antecedent and therefore decadent, to the extent that scientific positivism was, in historical reality, overcome by the mythologies of totalitarianism, the European tendency for the Northern bourgeoisie to be led astray by their moral bankruptcy.

The Milan of Sereni's youth – I mean the Milan of the University and its cultural life – maintained, or renewed, contact with a European culture different from that of the Florentines or Romans; but those young men were destined to see it fade into darkness, as the war drew nearer. Sereni had to learn from the 'spirituality' of the hermetics the idea of '*purezza*', so foreign to his revered Gozzano; but, for him, there was no aristocratic excess. The world

1. *Poesie* (1942).

about which his poems do not speak is not that hostile or 'sinful' world of the newspapers; it is, quite simply, something that does not interest him. Sereni set out to make poetry by slightly correcting the traditional sentimental psychology. The facts of experience, neither character nor yet spirit, were not incarnate in symbolic objects (as in Montale at that time), nor were they built into 'metaphysical' architecture (as in Ungaretti). There was the foundation of psychological narrative, of late nineteenth-century tradition: in this respect (even if this is exaggeration) one has been able to speak, in Sereni's case, of the novel. In one way Sereni does reduce as much as he can his own visual field, taking care not to let himself be distracted by the clamorous novelty of the avant-garde, accepting situations and the traditional occasions for the 'diary' type of lyric (sleep, a journey, a memory) but this would have carried him into prose, into a 'notebook' or a *journal intime*, and so to that world of opinions, of chosen ideologies and passions into which – and this was his tribute to the vices of the intellectuals of his time – he had a horror of penetrating. Here then was the discursive, elegiac movement of his verse, in a minor key, that showed the influence of the 'twilight' ethos. And, as its natural counterpoint, a formal decorum, springing from a quite different source, a votive offering to his forebears and that Neoplatonism that, in Italy, seems inseparable from a certain love of words. Sereni rejected the 'music of angels' – but he could not help echoing it.

Reduced to arranging the few 'tones' of a psychology, to rejecting faith, history and blood, working for formal rigidity, at his best he would have produced results of great charm, like those of *Frontiera*. There are poems of Sereni before which (and this happens with many other poets of the immediate pre-war period) one asks oneself: Who is speaking here, and where? But it so happened that the march of events painfully involved the *'esile mito'* (slender myth) of a young Italian writer with the sand and sun of the war; that his reserve, his self-absorption and imaginary capitulation to life were objectivized in a national, historical defeat and in being a prisoner. Troop trains carried Sereni through those fields of roses of south-east Europe that, in a young man's poem, he had already seen in his imagination, from a window of the Orient Express. Fighting, as a test and as 'reality', was ironically always deferred; he reached Africa – but as a prisoner of war. Thus, long foreshadowed in the poetry of the 'decadents', the state of being conquered, of the man '*in forza altrui*' (in another's power), was first seen in the persons of the Greeks who passed before the young Lieutenant Sereni, and soon after in the Algerian prison camps. Death, already a gentle shivering on the shores of the lakes of Lombardy, was recognized as a 'second death', a condition of absolute emptiness, in the absence of finality which is the life of prisoners.

From that meeting of a psychological predestination and a historical realization spring the poems of *Diario d'Algeria*. The nostalgia of the first juvenile verse was succeeded by a sullen gloom, a blind rage, an anger without object, beneath an appearance of perplexity and stupefaction. And the flavour of his poetry is compounded exactly of that relationship between tenderness and anger, between the lakeside idyll, the visit to Hades, and the arid life of the prisoner. The ghost that touches him on the shoulder is the most complete image for that phase of Sereni's poetry. That dead man '*alto sulle ali*', like the figures on war memorials, asks him to '*pregar per l'Europa*', that is to say : for history. The refusal of the prayer and of the '*musica d'angeli*' is the strongest protest against any 'liberation'; '*perfetto il cerchio*', liberty is being a prisoner, victory is defeat.

In the poems that Sereni has published in the last few years, one apparently sees that technical process of the tonal sensibility that can be called '*velature successive*' (meaning in depth). But in each of them, even in their external form, respectful even to the point of irony to the literary conventions of the nineteenth century, you discern a corrosive claw, as it were the deep wound of an incurable present. The poetry has its beginning beyond the same psychological complication, so compact, sensitive and complete that it becomes, now and again, strictly private and ceremonial; even beyond an elegiac tone, a cadence that is prudent and gentle. But beyond all this, which is Sereni's character and biography, there is an extraordinary balance and the hidden power of a *refusal to obey*. I mentioned the marks of irritation, like a rash, that the world of today leaves on Sereni's verse; almost imperceptible allusions (hidden in a whirlwind of phrases or purposefully made clear in a journalistic cliché) to the world of the 'Little America' of Lombardy. But there is a certainty that he never did, and never will, tame this world with the gay audacity of youth – the audacity of a man who discovers an irreconcilable difference in a face that once showed love. Something has happened, something has gone, and left an empty blank behind it. The result is not nostalgia for it, or complaint – rather, a controlled anger, an amazed beginning again of existence. '*A fare il bacio che oggi era nell'aria/quelli non bastano di tutta una vita . . .*', lines typical of the new Sereni, with their false romantic melodiousness, their false image, and all their power, by contrast, centred on negation. '*Di tutta una vita.*' The kisses of a whole life, a life, after all, that has been lived, that still exists and is, as it were, annulled by something else – by another life than cannot be grasped, by a double nourished by that life's blood – that then moves it, in its turn, towards a larval state. Survival has lost the sinister implication that it used to have in the sands of the desert. '*I morti come noi*' know now that they are dead, and return to their own homes. In no other modern Italian poet had the denial of hope been less hopeless, less accompanied by the consolation of the non-existence of the world or of vital or infernal perspectives. In Sereni objects and beings, even the affections, remain; but as it were veiled, made of wind. They are not denied; they are diminished. From time to time a flash, a start. It is no accident that almost simultaneously, Montale, Luzi and Sereni used the image of Purgatory. But while Luzi's purgatory seems to have been drawn by Blake ('*chi pronto al balzo, chi quasi in catene*'), in Sereni it is a chilly twilight of the senses. In his most recent poems Sereni is the true heir of Montale, the heir of the 'barque of the dead'. That Sereni no more than Montale succeeds in objectivizing as the historical destiny of a class the '*tradimento*', the theft of which he feels himself the victim, is clear. But only in this way can he guarantee for himself the continuation of a cold armistice with a world that grows ever more in-human. Beyond that the possibility of a 'double focus' would cease; he would be rejected entirely either by the living or by the dead; condemned to recite the nth degree of the delirium of verbal arbi-trariness and of the will-to-live of the lyric, or to consume the last riches of the soul and find himself 'without visible means of sup-port', in the deep opacity of prose and rationalism. In him – even if this happens with the *diminuendo* of a poet who comes 'after', when the bodies have already been carried off the stage – another time is singing, after Saba and after Montale, another generation of 'European' Italians, in which the individual's surrender at dis-cretion and that of a class or historical category are mirrored, are mingled; and though they do not rejoice in it, neither are they conquered.

Translated by Gavin Ewart

Ottiero Ottieri

This is an extract from *L'impagliatore di sedie*, an experimental novel in a kind of cinematic style, partly in dialogue, partly in 'traditional' novel form, partly in the manner of a film script. The book deals with a week in the life of an industrialist who spends Monday to Friday in Milan and the weekend in Rome. The episode related in this anthology takes place on Wednesday.

THE CHAIRMENDER

Carlo unzips Sonia's dress down one side and deftly slides his hand into the opening and upwards. Sonia lolls on to her side with Carlo's hand under her, stabbed through and yielding with pleasure. She moans.

Carlo: 'But what hours do you work?'

Sonia, moaning: 'Nine to half past twelve. Three to seven.'

'And what do you do?'

'I'm a secretary.'

'And this afternoon?'

Carlo's other hand glides down from her shoulder towards her breasts, and Sonia's body begins to emerge out of her dress.

Sonia: 'This comes off my holidays.'

'I don't believe it.'

Suddenly she is offended. She pulls her dress back round her.

'Oh! So you don't believe me?'

She breaks away from Carlo, out of reach of his hands. Perching at her end of the sofa, she is genuinely offended; while Carlo, cross with himself for spoiling the mood, gets up and walks round the room, furnished with television set, corner cocktail bar, and an

aquarium bright with tiny fish, plants and greenery and little
stones on the bottom. He gazes at the aquarium.

'What do they eat, these little fish?'

Sonia answers him from the sofa.

'Water ... Well, darling?'

Carlo goes back to the sofa, coolly. Expertly he takes her hand
in one of his and with the other strokes the inside of her thigh.
Once again Sonia whimpers at the surge of pleasure.

Carlo, the seducer now, asks quizzically: 'Have you a lot of
clients?'

'Very few.'

Carlo, getting excited: 'As a secretary, do you mean? Or here?'

For the second time he has touched on the delicate question of
her work. She turns it over in her mind, content to take her time –
this handsome, sensual, stylish woman. She moves away from
Carlo again, so as to think more clearly; she crosses one leg over
the other.

'Very few clients, because I'm choosy.'

'You choose the ones you take a liking to. Me, for instance –
you've taken a liking to me ...'

'No. I choose the best.'

Slyly Carlo groans to simulate both lust and a rational interest
in the conversation. But Sonia knows her job and realizes she must
find some way of spinning this out.

Sonia: 'Do you like striptease?'

'I love it.'

'What?'

'I'm crazy about it.'

Sonia puts on a record and goes and sits on a low pouf, wide
and round. She starts by languidly taking off a shoe. Then the
other. She undoes her right suspender, with the stroking, lingering
movements, the slow rhythmic peeling of the striptease.

She has trouble undoing her left stocking. Carlo sees her forehead knit as a nagging thought pricks at her again.

Sonia: 'Nowadays I choose the best.'

Carlo, from the sofa: 'How d'you mean, the best?'

Sonia, pausing: 'What?'

Sonia carries on with what she is doing. Now her legs are bare, and she kicks them up, first one then the other, in a slow rearing arch, while her hands move to the zip fastener. She slides it down.

'I'm not clear what method . . . how you choose.'

Sonia has grasped the bottom of her dress. Now she grows animated.

'When a man comes to see me, I try to get him to introduce me to someone better off – either one of his friends, or a relation, or his boss. Everyone knows someone better off than himself. Bit by bit . . . and the next one can always pay me more.'

She pauses in her smooth-flowing movements, to peel off her tight-fitting dress. Now she is in her petticoat.

'If I know a chap from a firm, I get him to introduce his boss. I must move up all the time. I can't waste my time, like so many others. I can get to the top. My friends have got to be the really important men from all the various firms.'

'If you meet a branch manager, you try to get to know his general manager.'

Not to be put off, and slowly easing off her bra straps to the rhythm of the music, Sonia retorts:

'One from out of the top drawer's worth more than three below him. I just want to do a little work and improve my position all the time.'

'Sure. And aren't you doing it? You're great – you deserve to get on.'

'In three years' time I shall have just five boy friends, but all . . .'

Sonia's petticoat flops to her feet.

Carlo: '. . . from out of the top drawer.'

Sonia: 'What?'

'Do you prefer them from any particular line of business? Where have you got your best contacts – in the car trade or the chemical firms?'

She has her hands up round her back to undo her brassière. She thinks for a moment.

'Cars.'

She remembers that this is the moment to turn her back, while the secret of the bosom is unveiled.

'So you might make the chairman of Fiat.'

'He lives in Turin.'

Carlo isn't watching her face now.

'Have you done any market research?'

Suddenly Sonia turns and shows her splendid bosom.

'What?'

Carlo's eyes are fixed on her.

'You did say it was through the branch manager that you got to know the general manager?'

Sitting on the pouf in her pants, Sonia reads his mind in a flash.

'I'd show him the door. Come here.'

She puts out a hand to him. Carlo gets up slowly. He takes her by the arm and they go out of the room towards the hall.

Sonia: 'And you? What do you do?'

'Me? Nothing.'

'Are you engaged?'

'No.'

'Have you seen my flat?'

The hall gives on to the sitting-room where they have been up to now, and on to a kitchen, a bathroom, and a bedroom to which they are now heading.

But Sonia wants to show him the kitchen, neat and shining as if no one had ever cooked anything in it. Carlo looks round admiringly.

Then he is taken into the bathroom with its pink majolica. Here Sonia slips on a dressing gown. Carlo is surprised. Wearing the dressing gown, Sonia looks at herself in the mirror. And she feels sad. She stares at herself again, fiercely, conscious only of herself and the thought that has sprung from the reflection in the mirror. And she feels sad. Left to himself, Carlo sits on the edge of the bath. It's as if there is a listless eternity ahead of them. Carlo sits thinking.

'Yours is a difficult career.'

'In four years' time I shall be all right.'

'How d'you mean – all right? How d'you mean?'

Sonia, at the mirror, does not answer. Carlo touches a fold in her dressing gown and runs it up and down between two fingers.

Carlo: 'You've got to push your way up in the world ... up ... And just like anyone else, you need to get some capital together.'

Sonia, turning round: 'Are you going into town afterwards? Where are you going?'

'I don't know.'

Sonia leans against the little frosted glass window. She lets Carlo come up close to her. She puts her arms round him.

They embrace, to keep each other company. Carlo speaks into her ear.

'Do you ever go out?'

'Where?'

'Out in the street.'

It is as if they need to be together; as if, standing there with their arms round each other, they need each other's support. But Sonia tears her arms free and grips him with her legs. He looks at his watch: then he swiftly opens her dressing gown and fastens on to her. The bell for action is ringing in both their heads.

Translated by Graham Snell

Goffredo Parise

The extract below is taken from Parise's novel *Il padrone*, considered by many Italians to be the outstanding literary work of 1965. Told in the first person, it is a Kafka-like nightmare about office life. 'I', a young man from the provinces, slavishly yearns to resemble his boss, Dottor Max, whose own aim is to create the 'perfect', happy employee, with all loyalty and affection channelled into the firm. Sexual urges, for instance, have to be controlled; later in the novel 'I' has to marry a mongol, so that she will offer no counter-attraction to the firm, and in return he is rewarded with a car and a flat with all mod. cons.

THE BOSS

Here I am in my new office, happy and at work, a small part of a productive whole, namely, the firm. Dottor Max has kept his word. He said that he wanted me near him, and now my office is directly opposite his, separated only by the corridor. It's a tiny little room, made out of Dottor Max's private bathroom : the toilet and the washbasin have been removed, and now there is me, plus a chair, a table, an ashtray and a hat-stand by the window. I must admit that I don't have any real work, since Dottor Max has said he wants to put me to use in the most varied fields of the firm's activity, for the moment only as an observer, as the office he has assigned me indicates. He also assures me my time will come, my time of maximum efficiency and maximum productivity, and I'm whole-heartedly preparing myself for it, indeed I'm already prepared and even a little impatient because I spend many hours doing nothing, just sitting in my chair and thinking intensely of my future.

I know all too well there's a rumour going around – spread chiefly through the efforts of Balloon – that Dottor Max has put his protégé to work in a latrine, but I pay no attention to these rumours and I agree with Dottor Max when he says that the new building (like its employees) is a place of absolute immorality. Besides, there's no difference at all, except in salary, and that's not great, between me and those employees who have spacious offices with glass walls and air conditioning. They don't realize, in their meanness, they are dependants of the firm the same as me, despite their offices. That the level of prestige and of outward appearances doesn't count for a thing and, indeed, it merely increases their own meanness in the eyes of the world and of Dottor Max. First of all, I'm grateful to Dottor Max for having displayed such moral coherence, in giving up his private bathroom for my sake. These were the very words he said to me: 'It's immoral for me to have a personal bathroom. Why only me, and not all the others? So this space might just as well be transformed into an office, and this office will be yours. You are too intelligent to take offence, and for that matter, you can choose. Do you prefer to stay near me, here on the second floor, where we can constantly exchange views and you can keep me company a bit, or do you want an office all to yourself on the upper floors? You're free. Choose.'

I didn't have to think twice, and I answered: 'You choose, Dottor Max' (instinctively I felt that I could call him by name like that). 'All I want is to work and, naturally, to occupy an office that is arranged in the most rational way considering the work I'm to do. One place or another, it's the same to me.'

This answer made a profound impression on Dottor Max; I don't know whether it was favourable or unfavourable.

'What? Don't you have a preference? There are plenty of people around here who make themselves ill about the question of their office, and they must be satisfied. I satisfy them, but at the same time this fact gives me a clear idea about them. And my idea is as follows: if they are so fond of having a showy office it can only be for one of two reasons: either they are demanding of me, that is of the company, an exterior sign of respect and consideration, as if to say that, working in such an office, they are also entitled to a salary that is the office's equivalent. Or else they want it because they are driven by what you might call a psychological desire to become part of the ownership, the firm: that is, to feel themselves for eight hours of the day the proprietors of a part, however small, of the firm. In this way they reveal an aspiration to ownership (but also an attachment to it) which might seem unpleasant, but at the same time pathetic. Because they will never be owners, or bosses, despite all their efforts, and they will have to be content with admiring their office and themselves inside that office until they become confused with it, not knowing that the office is my property and that they, confusing themselves with that glass, that furniture, that air conditioning but, what is worse, with the essence of all these things, automatically become mine, precisely like those things. In either case they are what they are, namely my hirelings, all the rest is illusion. Now, as far as you personally are concerned, I'm grateful to you for having accepted this office. You've given me the opportunity of freeing myself from a burden, the immorality of having a private bathroom, to be precise. Just what Balloon, Diabete and others you will meet are dying to have.'

'But it was convenient for you, there, opposite your office . . .' I objected. 'I wouldn't want to . . .'

'Yes, it was convenient, but what does that mean? If a man doesn't know how to renounce things, if life, in other words, becomes reduced to a frenzied race for comfort, where will we end up? I can perfectly well walk a few extra steps to the end of the corridor and use the general bathroom for this department. Though this may cost me a little psychological sacrifice, and even an hygienic one (you never know who uses this bathroom, it's at the disposal of everyone and, as you know, there's no place like a bathroom as a receptacle for infections and diseases despite all our antiseptic precautions), I'm glad to make it. Basically my policy with the employees is this: you want to have fancy offices and private bathrooms? Very well, I'll give them to you, if you really want them. Unlike you, I have a very simple, anonymous office and use the same bathroom as everybody else. In other words, I behave like an employee and you behave like big general managers or even like bosses. Except that between me and you there is a little difference: which is that, on the contrary, I am the boss and you the employees. However, I frankly don't understand how it can be all the same to you.'

'But you've said it yourself, Dottor Max! I know perfectly well you're the boss and I have no illusions about ownership. I am the first to believe, precisely because it was you who hired me, that I am your property like everything here. But if you ask me my preference anyway, well, I'll tell you: I prefer to stay here. First of all because the office is small and cosy, silent, and I felt at home here right away, from the minute I sat down in this chair. And then because, if you'll allow me to say so and to go back for a moment to the question of ownership which is the basic concept in this conversation, it's much better to be close to the boss's sight than away from it.'

'So you consider yourself my property?' Dottor Max interrupted me with a smile.

'Yes, at least as long as I'll be here with you, in this firm. But since I hope to stay here for ever . . .'

Suddenly Dottor Max made a grimace of contempt and I was left with my sentence in mid-air.

'You're an imbecile! Shame on you! Don't you know this kind of talk is slavish, racist, ignoble? Do you really believe one man can be the property of another man? What are you saying?'

'Why . . .' I stammered.

'You're a free man, you understand? And you must behave as such. You're not the property of anyone, except of yourself. And, least of all, my property. That would be the day!' and with this he pounded his dry hand with its long nails (I was seeing them for the first time) on the desk: 'And stop smoking! How do you manage to see in here, with all this smoke?' and he went out, slamming the door.

'Dottor Max!' I shouted in a voice choked with emotion, and I rushed after him. But Dottor Max had already gone into his office and the red bulb over the door indicated all too clearly that he didn't want to be disturbed. I came back into my office and, distraught, opened the window. The smoke (but by now it was too late) went out in a single cloud that dissolved along the panes of the upper floors. I closed the window again and sat at my desk with my head in my hands.

I was in despair. What was to be done? First of all, I thought: why am I still sitting in this chair of which I've become fond (which now has nothing more to do with me), in this office? Why not, as would be only right, abandon the office at once, cross the vestibule, descend the steps and go out into the street? Now I'll get up, just one minute more and then I'll get up. I started to rise, but it was as if I were nailed to the chair; I couldn't move. Perhaps it was the sudden weakness that had seized me, the fact is that, as I tried to get up and couldn't, suspended, so to speak, I started thinking again:

And what if I didn't move from here? If I refused to leave? After all Dottor Max hasn't officially fired me, he hasn't sent me away, he didn't say anything like that to me. Perhaps something will happen. Why the hurry? My dignity? But is it more dignified to leave, displaying in this way a foolish touchiness that will lead to no good, or to remain seated and stick it out? In any case, by showing that I am remaining in my seat, despite that rage which seemed all too plainly definitive and dismissing, I am showing a coherence to my own words. For the moment I am Dottor Max's property. To get rid of it, he, physically, objectively, or someone acting for him, has to drive me away: make me get up physically from this chair (and I, like an ordinary object, like this ashtray, this chair, this table, this hat-rack, won't put up any resistance), take me out of the office, and from there, put me in the street. We'll see. I'll keep my promise to my parents: I'll be a part of the firm, I'll work and I'll earn, I'll marry and start a family, I'll have a house, with modern furniture, radio, television, refrigerator, washing machine and everything that's needed. I'll go on holiday in the summer in the three weeks due me, if they are due me, like everyone, like all men in this world. I won't move from this spot, I'll grit my teeth and I won't hear anyone's words any more and, in any case, I repeat: I'll be coherent with myself; now

I am Dottor Max's property and it's up to him to decide, not me; I must stay here and do what all the others are doing, what everything that's in here is doing: men, women, furniture, typewriters, electronic machines, and all the other objects here ...

At that moment the door was flung open and Dottor Max appeared: 'Forgive me, but then you must already have realized I'm a hysterical type. Not exactly hysterical, but I have so many, so very many thoughts and worries. Especially moral ones. When you're in my position you live in an eternal dilemma. To be a man and at the same time a boss isn't easy. This is also a moral problem because the two conditions present, in fact, contradictory moral problems. Forgive me, really. As for the smoking, you can smoke as much as you like, I certainly won't be the one to forbid you to, but watch out if you see my father. He doesn't want smoking in here and I don't smoke myself. I used to smoke, however; at one time I smoked forty cigarettes a day. Then I stopped because I realized that I was doing it to oppose my father, not so much because I liked smoking. If I liked smoking, I mean if I were a hardened smoker, I would still smoke, don't you think?'

'Yes, smoking is a bad habit, and it's not easy to give it up,' I answered mechanically, in a faint voice.

'Besides, I liked your answer. You showed a coherence nobody else around here has. Nevertheless, remember that even if, very realistically and rightly, you consider yourself my property, the fact is you aren't; on the contrary, you are really free. I mean, you're quite wise to consider yourself that way and you reveal a common sense I, for one, didn't have at your age. All the same, consider yourself free. And, among other things, I wanted to tell you: it won't be necessary for you to punch the time-clock. Let the others do it. But not you. This will give you – unlike the others – the moral freedom to arrive punctually in the morning, if not ahead of time. That is: you yourself will make a point of being punctual, not because of any threats of fines.'

I got up my nerve and said, smiling: 'Thank you, Dottor Max. But why all this freedom? I want to be exactly like the others, with the same obligations and the same rights.'

'You've already learned the words *rights* and *obligations*? What ugly words!'

'It's true, but they came to me spontaneously. What I meant is: I want to be like everybody else, without special privileges, which both of us might regret later.'

'True, but the words came to you spontaneously, as you put it. In any case, whatever you say. It's the same to me. And privilege isn't a word I like, you know? These are all definitions that don't sound well from the lips of a boy of twenty. Because you *are* a boy and you won't be offended if I tell you so. And why should a boy have things like rights, obligations, privileges on his mind? Think about playing football instead. I used to play football, what about you?'

'Me, too,' I answered, radiant. From the despair of a moment before had I now reached the point of talking about sports with Dottor Max?

'Then on Sunday we'll go to the game together, if you're free.'

I accepted. Dottor Max opened the door with a smile and – who knows how it happened to come into his head – he imitated the sound of a nervous tic of mine (from time to time, when in fact I'm nervous, I hold my right arm out, accompanying this movement with a kind of sob) as if to show me his affection, then he went out.

Since that day I haven't seen much of Dottor Max but, on the other hand, I have had more news of him from Selene, one of Dottor Max's secretaries. Selene comes into my office every morning, on one pretext or another. The first mornings she knocked softly (but I could see her through the pebbled glass door that gives on the corridor), then she got into the habit of simply walking in, casting rapid glances out into the corridor. These glances made me realize she doesn't always come for official reasons and she looks around to make sure nobody can see her coming into my room. Then she slips inside and leans against the hat-rack almost as if to mingle a bit with this object in case anybody went by in the corridor and glanced inside. Since she is very young and very

beautiful, for a while I hadn't managed to figure out the reason
for those visits of hers and I several times suspected she had been
sent to tempt me and then to report. Vaguely I asked some information about her from Diabete; he made a grimace of contempt
and said she's the mistress of this one and that one, all men I don't
know because they're in other departments. She's very young and
very provocative and I'm convinced that under her black sateen
smock she has nothing on but her bra and panties. For this very
reason I felt she might be a suspicious person since all the other
secretaries are ordinary girls, worn by their work or by the long
hours seated at the typewriter and obviously under their smocks
they wear a slip if not a sweater and skirt even. Instead, I believe
Selene doesn't wear anything at all and I'm amazed by this fact
because in our department there is also the mother of Dottor Max,
whose secretary Selene is, and there are other people who might be
shocked at that nakedness of hers. Can she be the mistress of Dottor Max? I've never been able to figure it out, Diabete dismisses
the possibility, and so do I because I think Dottor Max, with all
the worries he has, surely can't find time for sexual questions or
interest in them. For that matter I'm not – and don't want to be –
troubled by such questions myself, first because I have to think of
my work, and second because I don't want to betray the faith
Dottor Max has in me, and third because I don't trust Selene.
Nevertheless, a few days ago, Selene asked me a strange question,
obviously to excite me. 'I bet you've already drunk Sexy Gin.' And
in saying this she huddled against the hat-rack, evidently aroused.
A long silence followed during which I looked at her with my
throat suddenly dry, and she lowered her eyes. She told me that
she had been to the sea and, in fact, the sunburn is still visible on
her skin. This skin gives off the very same odour as Sexy Gin. Perhaps that's why she spoke to me about it. I looked at her for a long
time: her waist is tightly bound by her belt and her whole body
is tightly swathed in the smock; she looks like one of those girls
who appear on calendar advertising, her legs are so long, her
breasts turgid and erect, and her little round belly swells when
she breathes. That day she was aroused or troubled, her belly

trembled, tense with her slightly gasping breathing and it adhered so to the smock that I could clearly see the little hole of her navel. Still her face is the perfectly oval one of a little girl, and her nose, ears and mouth are very small, her eyes long and pure, her hair short and curly. These features of her face made me feel she must be a very reserved person. In fact she speaks little and with some difficulty, whereas her body, always moving to express itself without words, vibrates and shudders as if it were exposed naked to the wind.

'Yes,' I said, 'it has the same smell as you.'

Selene didn't answer and slowly slipped one hand into her smock until her long, dark fingers had reached her breast. From what I could see, she clasped it hard between two fingertips. Her fissure-like eyes and her lips a bit pouting made her look like a sleeping child, immobile, stirred only slightly by some rapid dream image. Her head dishevelled and abandoned between her shoulder and the wall, her body and her belly protruding, she stayed like that for a little while. Several times, for brief instants (the very instants when she seemed disturbed by a dream's images) she blushed violently and muttered some incomprehensible words. Then she woke from that kind of doze and looked at me, dazed and confused.

'Why? What smell do I have?' she said in a very weak voice. 'Do I have a bad smell?' and shaking the locks of her hair a bit, she started to sniff herself.

I couldn't resist. I got up from the chair and went over to her.

'Let me see if I'm wrong,' I said and was already about to sniff her myself, between the neck and the throat.

Selene huddled even further into the corner, furiously unbuttoned her smock, and her breasts appeared. The nipples were small, swollen, a dark red colour, and on one of them (the one she had touched before) at that moment a transparent little drop rose.

'Take it. If you don't it'll hurt me afterwards,' Selene whispered in a childish voice; with great delicacy, so that the drop wouldn't fall, she put her fingers around her breast and held it up to me. Almost automatically I bent over and collected the drop with my lips, then I drew back at once. I had approached her as in a dream but now I was perfectly awake and I was deeply ashamed. Selene, too, looked like a punished child; red in the face, she buttoned up her smock with trembling fingers. She went out at once, her head bowed, though she left her odour in my room.

Translated by William Weaver

Carlo Villa

La nausea media, from which these excerpts are taken, is in effect a highly polished diary. Its linguistic tricks, its images and its vocabulary are almost impossible to convey exactly in translation. The narrator, a white collar worker, the 'average' man, writes of his various *nausee*, or disillusionments: with his father and his father's family, his wife and marriage, his mistress, his job, his recreations, his reading.

DISILLUSION

I cannot sleep so I have got up; it is the middle of the night and Marisa says, 'Would you mind getting me a tisane'; well, why not, it is not worth both of us getting up; into the bathroom, into the kitchen, into the bathroom again because the water is turned off in the kitchen on account of the gurgling it makes when it's running (probably the ballcock wants changing); standing by the stove I think about my way of life and realize it is a bit distressing; I go and glance at myself in the mirror; I bustle about getting the drink ready, I take it to her and wait while she drinks it; a word or two and I turn out the light for her. I go back into the other room and become lost in gazing at the things all round me; moments like these when they occur are the most precious; there is no hurry and time is mine alone; my meditations can be unending for the night seems to stretch limitlessly before me.

Silence has fallen on the house; in the next room two female forms lie stretched out assiduously searching for each other: the baby girl will be having dreams in which the mother will be comfortingly present with her face and reassuring words; it's difficult to imagine the dreams of tiny children; and in the night the mother will be remembering with delight the wide-open eyes of her daughter crying for her and for her alone, and she will be imagining the day when the child can talk poperly and will shout out to her, 'Mummy, I've been playing with Tommy.'

Steel furniture which doesn't moan and groan in the night is to be preferred: some of those creakings make my blood run cold. Resolved: from tomorrow a greater faith in mankind, more respect not only for myself but for anyone else who when all is said and done does his best whenever he can: 'and it will be my intention to send you news of the outcome of my whole-hearted efforts just as soon as . . .' the whole thing with deeply felt respect, taking into consideration that twenty years of cosy home life and scholastic learning, followed by a year and a half of compulsory stand-at-ease — 'shun-slope-arms-by-the-left-quick-march-about-turn-halt' gives the citizen the highest polish for the benefit of civilization and naturally predisposes him to genuflection and to respect for lawn and lace: it is as clear as the sun.

Silence. Never interrupt our fellow men (not with a single word); these our so-called fellow men who make so many things compulsory for us. Instead, get used to being silent. Before answering let a moment pass (after all, there's no hurry) so that your questioner will have time to think: here's a really significant person full of intellectual resources, my goodness, he's the sort who will command respect.

Why should we always be polite so as not to make 'others' feel uncomfortable, why must we hasten to reply, smile and look pleased? We ought to have some sense of responsibility towards our dreams, so often unrealized through the fault of those same dear 'others', and is this then really the way to protect them? All right, impose discipline on yourself, at least in conversation stop wait a moment each time stop in this way the frenzy of always feeling embarrassed stop with all the cogent arguments within me propelling me on like a ball stop of dung, then will the others who speak without knowledge who are just showing off stop defer to us with the head respectfully bowed.

One might want to make a long distance call, some special number; one dials the code, places the receiver to the temple instead of

to the ear, 'Can I help you' the voice of the operator would say
and then one receives the shot, the gentle shock of death : perfect
manners. It is certainly not healthy to despise oneself like this;
but, here I am now in the most evocative period of the night,
where it is as easy to pass the time in thoughts of death as it is
with two friends.

*

From time to time a positive desire for suicide comes over me, as if
it were some voluptuous mistress; a longing that comes back again
and again, heady and exciting. A pale and mysterious lover with
deep eyes and without make-up. I like the idea of suicide because
it is a purification of self and a way of revenge on all those who
are always trying to get at one.

Suicide is like hot wine full of cloves; a wine that titillates the
nostrils and then goes down the throat; it seems to re-arouse sym-
pathy and re-create confidence amongst friends, it confounds
enemies, news of it gets around everywhere immediately and it
settles debts however great and however long-standing; suicide
reveals the pleasures of our days for what they really are; it allows
us to end our lives as we please, without having to wait for some
inconvenient or unpleasant circumstance; you can choose the
room and the chair best suited for it. The most convenient lighting;
if you like you can play your favourite gramophone record. It
allows a minute, final examination of the situation. What other
type of death allows that? The battle casualty dies without having
any say in the matter, death by drowning is unprepared for and
there is all that water; burning alive, with all one's skin aflame,
must be quite horrible; the victim of a car crash lies for hours
beneath the cape of the nearest policeman.

Suicide is a private death, a superior sort of death, the choice of
a connoisseur; one need be in no hurry and can take hours, even
days, over it; it can be savoured to the full and then postponed for
the rest of a lifetime. I would say that the fact that suicide may
not succeed does not matter because by giving oneself up to

thoughts of it from time to time one simplifies one's problems just as much.

*

I am making love with Marisa on the sofa at the pension. She goes to shut the window, and I lie stretched out watching her; after she has tucked the bedclothes round the baby she comes towards me with her flaccid breasts showing through her open dressing gown; but the demands of the flesh are great and I am thankful for the swelling of my organ. Lost in the happy land of profusion and prodigality, in the world of glittering weeklies with their pages of enticingly coloured advertisements and long-legged women, a prosperous land of a thousand and one nights, I am seized with a fear that the whole thing is make-believe; and then I become sure that I just do not understand reality when it is proved to be real, not even my wife who now seems to me to be a piece of data and to be considered only as such instead of how I should like her to be.

I still cannot see myself supporting a wife and daughter; I know nothing about wives and daughters. Is there anything wrong in making a second choice? The past does not fit me any more and my short life is now, happening now and no one has the right to tie me down for ever, even the most patient of wives, the smallest of daughters. Caprices and whims are quite natural. The choice is always there, I am just not making it. But putting things off is useless, it becomes a deadening pastime. Why so much bother over breaking a contractual arrangement? Perhaps because of the emptiness and the pain of being alone at night in this now over-organized world of today. How can one reach a decision without making serious inquiries? A sort of inverted vitality, this, where decisions are reached not from having explored the other ways of life which exist but because of squalid taboos: Just to be able to change one's viewpoint and not always to have one's neck in one fixed position!

In my greed for activity during these days of holiday I leave Marisa astonished; I keep saying to myself who knows what I wouldn't have been doing if I had stayed at home. Whenever she becomes amorous and tries to make up to me, I turn away from her, thus I cannot pretend to myself on those occasions when desire finally gets the better of me, that she takes me by storm.

The nervous system has got used to periodic quarrelling and abstinence. I make her pay for the thousand uncertainties which haunt me by my long and gloomy hesitations between one love-making and the next, yet in spite of our differences these acts are consummated by her with passion because she is easily aroused at such times.

In the periods between our lovemaking her body leaves me cold and until my energies are recharged she does not excite me at all.

Here we are then in this small room scratching away at each other from morning to night; she always in the same cotton dress, going around without make-up, her hair untidy, and showing a lack of that imagination and enchantment which it seems to me ought to be the prerogative and aim of sex.

A fortnight without any opportunity or excuse for running away from her; without any place where I can shut myself up and be alone; and so every stupidity is magnified and reaches irrevocable proportions. Oppressed by my moods she becomes more and more insecure, caught between my extremes of humour she knows she cannot count on anything for certain and doesn't even try to open up, to say what she feels, and I, to get the better of her, go on saying nothing, too.

A moment ago there seemed to be an opportunity to talk, but then it was gone, everything becomes useless and there seems nothing to hold on to. In the end I tried every way of starting up a profitable conversation with her: no good, she has learnt nothing, the idea of communication just passes her by, let alone that of my being a normal human being, and her, too, or of it being at all possible for us to get on; there is no way of giving the right answer, whilst I have this great need of someone to talk to and not just for the encouragement that one gets from hearing the living voice, let me make it clear, but for the cheering warmth that imagination gives to conversation, because in the end, if two people must live together, what else matters but to be able to discuss and exchange ideas and make life bearable by dint of a little fantasy? Be exclusive, become indispensable by answering questions that an outsider would have difficulty in understanding; a sort of private stage and school of acting with its own simple rules (and don't let unformulated thoughts weigh you down nor lead you into the whirling cerebration which slowly but surely build up the convolutions of madness).

Oh indeed we make love from time to time, but it's all too openly programmatic and collapses suddenly emptied of all emotional significance (and involves me in fantasies having nothing to do with her which make my orgasm come even more quickly after which I return once more to the gloomy self-pitying defensive).

And so, in a relatively short time, with all our encounters inhibited like this (whilst day and night fantasy urges me to repetition) it seems like the cloth of Penelope, woven and unravelled in a night, binding us ever more tightly together without there having been anything between us other than elementary contacts for ordinary purposes which really should not justify such a profusion of high principles, moral obligations, and rights and duties all round.

Very well, more faith in long term projects, let's extend our consideration even to individuals; and in fact as I happen to be lying down, stretched out comfortably, it's enough for the moment to accept domestic tranquillity, enough that the baby in the next room is calling her skittles by names, dressing them up for school and scolding them, enough, for the moment at least, to make me forget so much repeated selfishness, because provided it is undoubtedly more comfortable, when all is said and done, it seems more heroic to go on consciously as I am than to make a clean break (and clear out).

She just doesn't say anything and I keep aloof, so if there's a problem it's never thrashed out, and I don't know how to go on. We are silent for days and there is only one reason for it, and a silly one at that, so why then doesn't she ask me what it is? I would like her to show some interest in my powers of dialectics, it would be hard for her, but it would cool us both down, we'd gradually become less angry with one another, less formal, until finally as has happened on other occasions, we would put our arms around each other and make it up.

*

I walk slowly beside the massive walls; in the distance closed factories; incessant rain; someone's there, but it's only shadows, glittering asphalt and tall street lamps; excruciating cold and hunger; find some shelter, stretch myself out in the warmth and, above all, in the dry, but just keep moving; somewhere there will be a place to take cover, maybe just round the corner; I just want to sit down; an open doorway would do; a little room, and some stale bread, that would be delicious; I pass beneath high overhanging balconies and they offer no protection. Shutters and windows are hermetically closed. The unbelievable rain will stop at dawn, it always happens like this; but go on, one can't stay out all night. Try the first door you come to, ring, it doesn't matter if it isn't a grand one; but they are all bolted, evidently to keep people like me out as well as the wind, the cold and any wild animals that might escape from neighbouring circuses in the night; if one was to break one's way in one would be taken for a thief.

Here's luck at last; one's open, but the cold comes in, too, put your back to the door so that others don't take advantage of it; tramps; once I'm comfortable, everyone else is too; and then, being so miserable and lonely, I don't want company or people to see me now that I am beyond help.

On a floor above a telephone rings faintly; someone answers it, they are not asleep then, voices, perhaps it is an hotel? Hurried footsteps, people are about, they may even have bread. I've got to screw up a little courage; what will be the best way of confronting these strangers, what sort of tale would be most acceptable to them? Would they look at me with disgust or forbearing? But in any case I shall have the right to something and maybe they will know this. I am hungry and ashamed of it: but it ought not to be like this. Take a good look at yourself: sodden and not shaven for who knows how long; all benumbed with cold: I am at the end of my tether. Go on; climb up there, take a risk, what can happen to you? In spite of everything determination makes me feel bold and strong; but I still don't like to beg. There, now the first step is taken; worn out stairs, year by year life passes over them; polished by relentless feet, unending successions of beggars: sooner or later we're all linked in a gigantic ring: the origin of the species; in front of me there is a faint light, a horrible smell, though after such cold a little warmth is pleasant; but what a stench! in the shadows one can begin to make out shapes stretched out on the floor like so many sacks of jute: I shall not be able to leave now, to run back outside would attract attention and I just do not have the strength: pain is insupportable when the body is healthy but as soon as one gets ill one quickly gets used to it and one thinks only of a little relief and not the cure; and would it really matter if I sleep here with all these people, just one night?

Translated by William Clowes

Cesare Vivaldi

STRIPTEASE

La bionda ballerina
da pochi mesi femina
danza ad orchestra piena...'
POMPEO BETTINI

1

Lily Niagara unbuttons the perfumed clothes of sleep. She gathers to herself a net of wounds and feigned caresses.

Faces in the purple shadow like sheets of paper in the field where children avoid the noonday sun.

A drum roll. She takes one step forward. A drum roll. She steps back. Rhythm of an elastic garter stretched and released.

White flesh and black hair: the naked silk of the body in a cone of light. And the triumphal upheaval! The breasts thrown, as it were, into the air. Their escape from the thunderous laws of gravity.

2

Child faces in the field where a shadow of purple paper avoids the noonday sun.

Elastic garter rhythm of a step. A roll stretched forward and back: drum released.

As it were thrown in the triumphal gravity of the air laws thunderous the white upheaval of the breasts. Naked light of the cone of a body of flesh escaped from the silk of the black hair.

Lily unbuttons a feigned Niagara of wounds. The perfumed clothes of caresses gathers in a net of sleep.

3

Drum of roll of a stretched step that elastic advances and retreats released.

Thunderous light in the black escape of the air : thrown cone of a triumphal breast. Laws a white gravity of flesh like silk in the upheaval of the naked hair.

A sleep of wounds gathers a Niagara of perfumed caresses. Lily who unbuttons feigned nets of clothes.

Where sheets of paper avoid the sun in the field of purple shadow turns a girl child.

4

The white laws of gravity. Avoidance of the breasts of light with the black upheaval of the air ! Flesh and hair of silk thrown, as it were, to the triumph of a body made naked in a thunderous cone.

Perfumed nets gathered caresses of wounds : a lilac Niagara of clothes is unbuttoned from sleep.

On the purple field of faces paper children avoid the shadows.

To the drum rhythm of a garter : a roll stretched and released that advances and retreats by a step.

5

Unbuttons the nets from feigned perfumed wounds of clothes gathers caresses of sleep Lily Niagara.

Girl child of purple shadow avoids of faces the paper of the field.

A step advances and retreats of a drum roll. Rhythm of elastic stretched and released of a garter.

Laws a black gravity of flesh thrown in the white thunderous cone of light. Naked upheaval of the breasts, escaped, as it were, from the body in the air of silk of the triumphant hair.

Translated by Gavin Ewart

Giorgio Bassani

THE SNOWS OF YESTERYEAR

1

Among the dozen or so young men, who, in about '37, made up
the gang of the so-called *sfatti*[1] with which Ferrara was blessed at
the time, as far as I know – and this view is also held by the photographer Uller Tumaìni, known to his intimates as *'al duturét'*[2]
and a better connoisseur and judge of these matters than almost
anyone – as far as I know, Mario Spisani, who then answered to
the name of Pelandra, never cut too brilliant a figure. True enough
– friend Uller is wont to concede – at the time, in '37, Pelandra was
also setting some pretty high standards for shiftless and corrupt behaviour. But let's face it – he instantly amends – who would ever
venture to draw a comparison between him and, say, *sfatti* of the
calibre of Geppe Calura or Edelweiss Fegnagnani? A man can take
all the 'dope' he cares to, he can fornicate till his 'backbone lique-
fies', he can even reach the point where, without having the least
vocation for it, he occasionally 'gets in by the back door'. But this
has only limited importance. Because in this field of endeavour too,
what is it that counts if not a man's manner, his bravura; in a
word, his authority?

Uller was dead right. Authority, self-confidence – that is what
Pelandra had always had too little of.

From the age of twenty to twenty-five – I repeat, till about '37 –
there was not a thing he denied himself, to my knowledge. An out-
and-out wencher and gambler, a consumer of cocaine in large
quantities or, in its absence, of any manner of concoction, Pelandra
– like Geppe Calura and Edelweiss Fegnagnani in their day, and
Marco Giori, Eraldo Deliliers and Gigi Prendato afterwards – made

1. i.e. cads, rotters.
2. Equivalent of 'Doc' in Ferrarese dialect.

plenty of mischief. Yet when did Pelandra ever possess the calm and tranquillity, the peaceable arrogance flaunted by the older generation of masters and then by his contemporaries, their not unworthy disciples? Even at the time he was ashamed of himself, is that it? Even then he felt remorseful? In the light of the events following '37, it may be that this was really so. His yellowish face as at about noon he neared the Café Borsa in Corso Roma, not to mention his brightly shined shoes with points like daggers – he called them Parisian shoes – made him look as though each step he took was an effort, but more of a moral than a physical one; and then there was that grin of his, forcing back into an uncertain quiver, the corners of his livid lips stained with nicotine and condensed coffee (a humble, warped grin but at the same time pervaded with a vague presumptuousness, as if he meant to say: 'All right, I'm a wreck, I know it, but a terrific specimen of a wreck, aren't I?'): well perhaps even then some sage might have had it in him to see that this character was not actually as irrecuperable as he appeared to be; and hence to foresee what was then ripening.

A conscience is something you cannot invent for yourself. If you have one it's there, and if you don't you cannot hand yourself one: it's like courage.

So the fact is that, towards '38, in an unexpected development that abruptly revealed to them that Pelandra had always had a conscience, the community learned that he – yes sir, that young loafer with the coffee-and-cream complexion (the friend of young Giori, of Marco namely, and of that other reprobate, that Deliliers who, after having ruined Dr Fadigati, the ear, nose and throat specialist, and driven him to drown himself in the Po, absconded to Paris with money and a car) – had suddenly decided to get engaged. And in all earnest, I mean: it was no trick! The family of his betrothed – she was one of the Pasettis who lived in via Romei – were small landowners, all devotion to home and church; and she, Germana, was a small slip of a girl neither good- nor bad-looking, brought up by the nuns in via Colombara and then, after she was sixteen, kept strictly within the privacy of the home. And he, Pelandra, who from the moment he had got engaged did not seem the same fellow, had changed as from night to day. Everything testified to a radically new order in his way of life, to a kind of conversion.

2

He had changed as from night to day; he was literally a different person.

The passion he used to put into his vices before – an unregulated passion, lacking all style and such as to make his fellow-debauchers turn up their noses, for they, accomplished profligates that they were, had always been able to take drugs and brothels in small doses – apparently he was putting all that into cultivating the gentle pleasures of normal, respectable folk.

He had composed his differences with his '*grimo*' and '*grima*',[1] the intimidated old couple who were constantly worried about him, their deceitful, idle and spendthrift son, so different from the other one, their second born who, at twenty, was already working for a bank and earning his living; he had requested and received authorization from the Venice Insurance Company to act as commissions clerk for them, and soon had drummed up plenty of trade for himself. When, on his rounds, he had to pass through the Café's portico, he never sat down. He would exchange a few words with his customer, and off he would go in sober haste, paying no attention to the sarcastic winks directed at him by the fellows lounging at the tables with their legs spread out and hands resting on their groins.

Not a Sunday ever passed without Pelandra's being seen, complete with his betrothed on his arm, approaching San Carlo for midday mass; he, long and lanky and bent slightly forward so as to allow her, Germana, to cling to his coat-sleeve; and the betrothed's parents bringing up the rear, they too arm-in-arm; all four of them already united and compact like a single family. And in church, at the moment of the Elevation, if his kneeling came as a shock, it was still more stupefying to see the seraphic smile that,

1. Ferrarese underworld slang for 'father' and 'mother'.

at one o'clock, upon coming out of doors, he would affix to his puffed-up neophyte's face. 'What an experience to be virtuous!' that smile of his proclaimed. 'How good one feels.' The spiritual pleasures of the mass were soon to be followed by other delights almost as spiritual, namely those of noodle soup, boiled beef, diluted home-made coffee and, finally, the game of rummy for which – as a contrast to the still pool of the hours spent hand in hand with the betrothed, both of them looking down through the panes of the best parlour's window at the garden slowly invaded by dusk – would converge conspiratorial hordes of relatives from all over town. It was patently obvious that besides these things he had also discovered, through divine grace perhaps, that certain ineffable something which makes life really worth while; and that by now everything touched his heart, everything left him feeling grateful. He even went and had his teeth fixed by a dentist.

A model fiancé. Thereafter for ten long years, from '38 to '48, he was also no less exemplary a husband and a father.

The career he made for himself at the same Insurance Company did not turn out to be too sensational, but it was more than adequate: right after the war he was promoted to the post of sub-agent and then, in '47, to that of agent. Even though he was not enrolled in the Christian Democrat party, he diligently took part, with his Missus, in the cultural debates organized by Catholic Action in the home of Count Chiozzi in via Santo Stefano. And during the meetings, though he never took the floor, he always proved to be an attentive and thoughtful listener. In the meantime he had lavished upon his wife the gift of four children, two boys and two girls. And my, if it wasn't impressive to see the air of subdued pride with which on Sunday afternoons, while the rest of the town, craving entertainment, hurried to the movies or the football stadium, he accompanied his loved ones on their stroll along via le Cavour, back and forth two or three times from the Castle to the Station! His financial situation, which was not too brilliant though it steadily continued to improve, did not as yet permit him to have his own home, which is why he accepted, on behalf of himself and his family, the hospitality of his parents-in-law in the house in via

Romei. Very soon however the cohabitation was to end; that is if it was true – and it certainly was – that in the spring of '48, right after the elections of 18 April, the well-known and highly respected insurance agent, Mario Spisani, featured already as the owner of an instalment-plan flat situated on the fifth floor of one of the many low-cost buildings then going up around the Aqueduct. For which he had forked out some four million lire of his hard-earned savings, no doubt.

And it was also perfectly feasible that he was not the sort to refrain from providing his family, whenever necessary, with some form of amusement that might even be quite expensive.

The Spisani couple did not go to the movies more than once every two weeks, but when they went, it was to the better, top-rung cinemas, and they duly occupied the best seats. Nor did any summer ever go by – except for those of '43 and '44 which perforce they had to spend in the Pasettis' rural homestead in Formignana – without their passing August in some resort; one summer in Pievepelago in the Modenese Appenines, the others on the Adriatic at Viserbella : places not frequented for having fun in, obviously. For how can Viserbella, for instance, ever compare with Rimini or Riccione or even Cesenatico? But at least there the sea, the sun, the fresh air – plus the chance for a young father not to look silly, as he zealously builds castles and garages of sand for his children or as he hastily conducts them behind the beach sheds as an induce-ment to relieve themselves of pipì or popò – are superior to those vaunted by any other holiday spot in Italy.

3

It is Uller Tumaìni, the photographer, who reminds me of these things whenever I return to Ferrara and drop in on him.

I have never known just where '*al duturét*' lives (Is he married? Does he have children? It does not matter . . .); and were I not sure, whenever I remember to call on him, that inevitably I will find him in his 'studio' in via Garibaldi or, failing that, though of late less frequently so, in a little café tucked away in via di Porta

Reno, who can tell whether I would succeed in finding his home?
There he is invariably, as I say, in the doorway of his shop, standing in his white doctor's coat left unbuttoned over his meagre
chest; with his face just as bony and cadaverous as ever, his black,
impassive, slightly veiled eyes, and his small, crooked, lined and
puckered mouth: the very image to my mind of loyalty, even
physically so. He must surely be somewhere between fifty and
sixty but, perhaps protected by the very circumstance of his con-
sumptive thinness (when he was young, he had a life expectancy
of only a few years; and yet so many other fellows, much healthier
and sturdier than he, have been dead for some time now), he looks
anything but old. He still retains the air of an aged youth which
he had twenty-five years ago. And how can anyone not be grateful
to him for that too?

What I like about him is his always being even-tempered, and I
enjoy stepping in to have a chat with him.

We find ourselves in a small room measuring no more than nine
foot by twelve. Uller sits behind his desk; I am opposite him,
seated in a tubular chrome armchair. Through the front window
we are afforded a clear view of the persons going along the pavement. And since Uller never turns on the electricity (he does not
like it, to the point where even at night he wears sunglasses), we
feel justifiably that we are invisible. There they go, all those
people. Attracted by the front window's light, turned on there of
course, and also by the photographs on display: there they are, the
assorted faces – the innocent, trusting, unsophisticated faces of our
townspeople! They're young, they're men or women, they're old;
they're folk of every condition and age who, as the years pass, grow
even more unfamiliar to me. But Uller is remarkable. Having always stayed here 'mounting guard', and having never travelled,
well it is hardly surprising that he knows who this or that person
is.

However his favourite subject is and remains the golden era of
the *sfatti*: the decade from the thirties to the forties, the epoch of
Geppe Calura, Edelweiss Fegnagnani, Marco Giori, Eraldo Deliliers, Gigi Prendato and their ilk. And of Pelandra too, who for ten

years, from '38 to '48, did everything he could, poor thing, to become a perfect fiancé, a perfect husband, a perfect father; and finally one day, thereby fully justifying the attitude taken by Geppe Calura and Edelweiss Fegnagnani, for they had never taken Pelandra too much into their confidence, he disappeared from house and home, from Ferrara, maybe from the world, without leaving anything behind, not so much as a word, a note, nothing, not even a trace of a dead body.

'Is that the way for a man to act?' deplores *'al duturét'*, sagaciously nodding his small, dark, neatly pomaded head from side to side. 'Not even a trace of a dead body,' he adds in dialect.

What actually was Pelandra's fate is something Uller does not know. He has always limited himself to receiving and passing on whatever he is told, without adding anything of his own to the information. Death by suicide in the Po? Fallen in action in Algeria while fighting with the Foreign Legion? Or still living, is he, under an alias, in Paris, Venezuela, Australia? Any of it might be true, and it is obviously not this that he is interested in ascertaining. What interests him is the human aspect of the case, the moral aspect. Because a fellow simply cannot, holy Mother of God – Uller even goes so far as to profess – turn overnight from a devil into a saint! It's a thousand times better to sin, repent, then sin again, then repent anew. It's a thousand times better to lead a double, triple or if you like quadruple life, than to . . . 'No, no,' he exclaims: 'there are certain values in life (and the Family is one of these) that a man cannot fail to revere.'

Yes, I know all that, and I give my approval to it, as I patiently wait for him to get down to the facts.

Actually things probably proceeded in a way that is not exactly like his account of them, but the scene of 'the severing of the last bond' or 'the get-away', which each time Uller describes in almost the same words and with a poker face that would be the pride of any Chicago killer (it's no more than an anecdote, come to think of it, and not even a brand new one), still to this day the scene has the power to grip my heart in a peculiar vice, halfway between fascination and fear.

The action is set in the parlour of the Pasetti home – Uller starts to relate. It is a Saturday afternoon in October 1948.

The flat is empty. The parents-in-law went out with their four grandchildren and the maidservant, she pushing the perambulator in which lay Alcide, the latest born. Up at one of the windows giving on to via Romei, Germana watched them as they turned at the corner into via Voltapelletto, bound for the Montagnone.

Now in the parlour she keeps vigil over her sleeping husband, stretched out full length, long though he is, on the sofa. She is a small woman of past thirty by now, but pretty enough and not too badly laid waste by four consecutive childbirths. What is she thinking of as her husband dozes and a pale ray of autumn sunshine settles obliquely like gilt on his fattened posterior? This is what she is thinking (as she herself says in telling the tale over and over afterwards to half the town): that by the time she will have finished mending her elder son's, Fabrizio's, woollen sock, it will be four o'clock, and at that point it will devolve upon her to say to her spouse, 'Wake up Mario, it's time.' The movies await them, the lush movie house with seats upholstered in red felt, the Salvini where today they are showing *The Best Years of Our Lives*.

Except that at ten to four, the ex-Pelandra wakes up. Of his own accord.

'What time is it?' he asks, sitting up and yawning.

'Ten to four,' she replies with a glance at the wall clock. 'You slept, did you?'

'It tasted good that risotto with the peas we had,' he murmurs. Germana smiles.

'You liked it?'

'I'll say I did. Who prepared it? You?'

'Yes. Mummy always tries to keep me out of the kitchen, but this morning I had my way with her, I did. Poor Mummy!' and she sighs, lowering her head to the sock which is almost finished.

Silence. Germana is thinking about the new apartment she and her husband will take possession of in two weeks, right after the day commemorating the Dead. Meanwhile Mario has risen from the sofa, he has gone to the window overlooking the garden and, what with his girth because he has put on weight, he blocks it almost entirely.

'I'm going out for a second,' he declares calmly, without turning.

'Where to?'

'Down below, to the tobacco shop on the corner. I feel like smoking.'

Bewildered, Germana has raised her head.

'Like smoking!' she repeats after him. 'Since when have you got into that habit? I don't...'

'Meanwhile you can get dressed,' he says, interrupting her and moving off. 'Can you be ready in five minutes? Remember that the show starts promptly at three forty-five.'

And he disappears.

Five minutes pass, then ten, twenty, a half hour, an hour, two hours. The Pasetti in-laws, the children and the servant return from the Montagnone towards six o'clock. They're all a bit flustered, the children's cheeks are nice and rosy. They find Germana all decked out in her tailleur and her hat with the veil, dressed to go out. She is in tears. She tells them sobbing that Mario went out two hours ago to buy some cigarettes because he felt like smoking ('Smoking!?' exclaim the parents in one breath, staring), and that since then he hasn't returned.

And what if something has happened to him? – Germana continues to lament. He went out in his old, worn-out jacket. Her heart tells her that something happened to him.

Translated by Vera Wygod

Alberto Arbasino

FIGARO UP FIGARO DOWN

It seems a rare thing to find an opera with an 'internal production' of its own as detailed and precise as *The Marriage of Figaro*. Sufficient for the singers to follow the indications implied in the words they speak and in the sounds coming up from the orchestra rather than explicitly stated in the stage directions, and all will go well. Nor is there any need for a stage manager. It is rather odd, therefore, for two such notable directors as Visconti and Vilar, who have enjoyed the greatest triumphs and suffered the most deplorable failures on the opera stage, to decide simultaneously to lay their ugly hands on this opera.

The criteria they adopted could not be (and rightly) more dissimilar: Vilar's emphasis on Emptiness or Bare Bones on the one hand, and Visconti's preference for Fullness, or Putting Things On, on the other – both of them wrong. But the former has profited from a superb performance at La Scala: after a mercurial overture, so fast that each phrase seemed cut off in the middle, Scherchen conducted admirably, serving the excellent singers (Freni, Cossotto, Lorengar, and enchanting they all are) with a truly inspired passion. Visconti on the contrary suffered from a diffuse musical mediocrity at the Costanzi Theatre, on top of his own lapses in taste; a disagreeable combination: after an overture clearly devoid of distinction, Giulini did not do a thing to keep his ragged orchestra in line, the singing was so-so, there was nothing distinguished about the Cherubino of Dina Galli, the most sublime arias passed off indifferently, and I really do not think that the absurd audience, rushing as it did to attend the event as a matter of snobbery, could have realized to any extent – even if it had wanted to – what there really *is* to this opera, a work from which the authors of *Falstaff* and *Der Rosenkavalier* have taken so much (and unashamedly at that), and why it is so beautiful.

Transposition of place and time, and fusion of styles, in the theatre are pathetic and hateful survivals from the thirties, like the surrealist exhibitions, the Viareggio prize and Marlene Dietrich. And it is also quite clear why these things turn out to be so tiresome: if you mess around with a well-known opera the life goes out of it (who is going to laugh when he sees a *Figlia di Jorio* against a Versailles background, or a *Phaedra* where all the characters are black?). On the other hand, if you do not know the opera that has been the victim of this game, what does it matter for example to an Italian audience if the most outrageous liberties have been taken with Lortzing's *Zar und Zimmermann* or Gilbert and Sullivan's *Princess Ida*? (No more than a version that was all winks and nudges of *Beatrice di Tenda* or *Oberto conte di San Bonifacio* would matter to a Dutch audience.) These are some of the easiest tricks however; and it is understandable that there will always be someone liable to fall for them; after all, there is no shortage of the type of 'user' prepared to listen to an *Encyclopaedia Britannica* salesman.

But both in Rome and in Milan this year's watchword seems to have been: 'Strip the *Marriage* of its rococo'. Which is like saying: 'Strip *Medea* of its neoclassicism, *Pelléas* of its impressionism, *Lulu* of its expressionism, Mascagni of his realism, and *Tristan* of its Wagner.'

For Vilar Stylization and Rarefaction have thus been bad counsellors. For the scenery his decision was to transform into straight lines and right angles what was round and curled in the styles favoured by Eugene of Savoy and Giandomenico Tiepolo, though he did retain the gilt cornices.

The only trouble is that other people had the idea before him: all the decorators and furnishers who had taken on the job of putting Vienna to rights after the bombardments of the last war did exactly the same. His plain walls adorned with plaster oblongs are thus to be found in every hotel or ministry rebuilt after the State Treaty of 1955; and the furniture and lino he invented can be met with in every department store (even in Frankfurt and Cologne) in the Department for Simplified Tradition provided for those housewives for whom Swedish furniture is not sufficiently *gemütlich*. It is only his pseudo-ascetic prejudice that leads him to keep the stage clear even when it would not normally be; just a chair, a pouf, and that is all, in those immense empty rooms. In this way you get the impression that the Folle Journée takes place during a removal, that at any moment now Gondrand's men will come in to roll up the last carpet or bring in a chest of drawers. And the singers, poor wretches, do what little they can; for instance, when the Count and Cherubino must each of them hide behind the only piece of furniture there is, a tiny chair no bigger than a piano stool, the limitations of such a production are harshly shown up in all their absurdity. But as a rule one is not greatly bothered because there is really no direction to speak of, and the singers make the same customary gestures that the libretto lays down itself: 'What a slap!' (there is really nothing else you can do after being slapped), 'Come and kneel down' (you must kneel), 'I'll get behind this' (there's no option), 'Now he turns up those sleeves over his elbow' (there's nothing left but to suit the action to the word), 'Here's the bonnet' (you can hardly hold out a coffee-pot).

Hence the deep feeling of nostalgia for Karajan's production at La Scala some twelve years ago: it was the most perfect ever heard, not only in terms of singing and orchestra control (and you can check on the recorded version if you wish), but also for the restrained elegance of the décor: rooms and pavilions on a human scale and in Salzburg taste, just like the surroundings where Mozart's music was born.

Extending it over a huge platform is as nonsensical as confining *Norma* in a small dining-room. Coupled with the contrived Spanish background, this is Visconti's basic error.

There is an exact precedent here: Wallmann, who stages *Un Ballo in Maschera* and, seeing in Antonio Somma's libretto that 'the action takes place at the end of the seventeenth century' and 'the scene is laid in Boston and surroundings', follows through to the very limit. Hence (Boston at the end of the seventeenth century) wooden huts and Puritans with black sugar-loaf caps, cod fishermen and woodmen, and redskins at the gates; and then there is Amelia, straight out of *The Scarlet Letter*, and *Ulrica*, destined for the trial of the Witches of Salem. Not even André Breton in his wildest dreams would be capable of making a chorus of pilgrim fathers sing:

> We're busy loving and dancing
> In our happy homes
> Where life is only
> A lovely dream
> Nights of precious moments,
> Of heartthrobs and songs,
> Why don't you stop your flight
> On a wave of delight?

I find it equally difficult to imagine Esther Prynne at grips with a page Oscar who warbles to her:

> You'd like to know
> What he's put on
> When it's something
> That he wants kept secret
> Oscar knows
> But won't tell
> Tra la la la
> Tra la la la.

And that leaves aside that for me 'And what an uproar about this strange business/and what talk there'll be in town' inevitably calls to mind the Oltretorrente district of Parma with its Lambrusco wine and Culatello sausage, rather than Arlington or Revere in Massachusetts or the Back Bay of the Charles River.

Here is what Visconti has done. Even though the Barber comes from Seville, and that city is in Spain, he has moved back there a poetic world that had already crossed the Pyrenees with Beaumarchais and undoubtedly becomes Austrian and rococo with Mozart, no more and no less than *The Sun Also Rises*, though set in Spain, is American and not Spanish, and *A Farewell to Arms*, notwithstanding its Milan setting, is American and not Italian (just as *Tempo di Uccidere* is an Italian novel and not Ethiopian).

The sets are vast and evocative of something else altogether. First we have a laundry without windows (there is only a little one, absolutely tiny, although according to the libretto it is 'the most comfortable room in the palace'), and it seems to be urgently awaiting the arrival of the Miller and his Wife with their dance from *The Three-Cornered Hat*. Secondly there is a picture collection that recalls Velazquez and Goya and Pannini and 'Senso', that portrays not just sexual gallantry of a high order but a Leonora in the true Verdi manner, dying under terrible curses, with her dagger stuck up her behind. The room of the third act has turned into the patio of the wicked landowner in Eisenstein's *Thunder over Mexico* but invaded by Berber women from Tripoli enveloped in striped garments, in search of Governor Volpi. The garden at the end, on the other hand, is the Bomarzo park of monsters *tout court*; all that is missing is Dali photographed with his moustache in the mouth of a Chimera. And no one denies that this kind of set-up makes a certain impression on the stage; an Aïda against the background of the Parthenon would also make a certain impression if you so wish, or a Tosca who flings herself from the statue of the Virgin on top of Milan Cathedral. What I find second-rate is the caprice of gratuitous contrivance, not justified by a poetic excuse inherent in the opera : all the more ominous because Bomarzo's charm, second-rate as it is, is a fairly accurate test of second-rate taste. Sufficient to see on whom it makes an impression : retarded surrealists, dressmakers, photographers of bright American magazines, minor poets specializing in sylvan 'follies'. . . . In the quizzes where they award top marks to those who say they like the 'right' poets, and serious penalties to others who still send the kind of postcards beloved by servants and soldiers, Bomarzo has for some years ideally occupied the same place (100 penalty points) that had previously been the fate of Cocteau's films *Mythes d'Oreste Revisités* or *Orphée*.

And if the formal Bourbon halls that are so ill-chosen a substitute for the gay Habsburg boudoirs are to be filled afterwards, there will be no getting around the use of kapok padding. As a remedy for, and consequence of, the would-be Spanish setting Visconti sees himself forced to multiply the instances when boots are polished, pillows fluffed up, bedclothes folded, and napkins ironed; cases such as the sewing and weaving labours of the 'Locandiera' and 'Smirne', the curtains of the 'Gattopardo'; the twinnings between the House of Rushes and the Frette linen factory; and the throwing of rosebuds in time to music, and even peones marching past; in a paroxysm of domestic activity, sitting down at table and getting up again, that is both annoying and cumbersome, and, in the end, tiring: precisely because all this bustle, recalling as it does Pico della Mirandola, accentuates even further the disproportion between background and event rather than softening it; and the result is Toti dal Monte.

The most beautiful and amusing play of the season, however, was to be seen at the Cometa Theatre. *Oh, les beaux jours* is an extraordinary *pièce de boulevard* magnificently written by Beckett with the verve of a Shaw or Swift in their moments of blackest felicity. It is marvellously played by Madeleine Renaud who has never been seen to act so well. There is nothing reprehensible in this grotesque pairing. The great actress, irritating as she has always been with her intolerable rococo airs and graces, here approaches the sublime in contemporary acting (and she sticks to it with determination all through the evening), once she is pulled away from the rustle of exaggerated gallantry, and cruelly immersed, affectedness and all, in the shifting sands, mock-heroically existentialist, of the new Dublin Wizard. But truly paradoxical (and commendable) is the fact that, once in Hell, this ostensible Louise de Vilmorin feels 'quite at home', like a counterpart of Sarraute in her Louis XVI *fauteuil*: in spite of the indignation of the puritans and purists to whom this wordly 'facing up to' ultima ratio is insolently frivolous.

And on the other hand the wistfully inconstant tittle-tattle of this ridiculous lady *bien parisienne* immersed in her sand up to her nipples, and later up to the wrinkles of her neck, with her horrible drooping flesh and the bits and pieces in her bag and her little souvenirs and her poetic swoons – and generally speaking anything else which makes it unpleasant to be there – singularly fits in (better than any Lenten gloom) with the essence of the impeccable despair of this last baffling incarnation of the secular prototype of the Garrulous Irishman. More 'virtuous' if possible than the previous visions; because meanwhile an Ironic Dubliner, capable of presenting himself disguised as a Parisian clochard disguised in his turn as a charming young lady and a regular at the *dîners en ville*, is a 'turn' of high-level illusionism apt to throw the suspicion of childish facility even on his own antecedents, from *A Tale of a Tub* to *Ulysses*. Then, starting as he does from the most sensational 'limitation of means' ever tried as well as a systematic and radical Negation of Certainty, he comes out in a paradoxical explosion of Creative Fertility aimed at Nothing, only comparable to the proliferation of objects not just in the theatre of Ionesco but even more so in Beckett's own *Comment C'est* (though the ingredients he starts with there are apparently only darkness, mud, a cord, a can opener, and a sack perhaps full of cans) or in Maurice Blanchot's review: 'immense' notwithstanding its essential preoccupation with Nothing, the affectation of Uncertainty of Everything, and that is all.

It has after all been admirable to see the Cometa's audience in its bovine fashion fall into the Wizard's traps, taking at its face value his apparent (and very spurious) paradox that 'there is nothing to act, nothing about which and with which to act': deceptive and *trompe-l'oeil* like the classic Paradox of the Cretan Liar ('All Cretans are liars,' said the man from Crete). Very few of the ladies in the pit will have recognized that this existentialist sham apple tree is probably the most realistic comedy they have seen these last few years; and there is really nothing to distinguish them from that lady, immobile on the stage, who makes (by definition) their own *limited* speeches, with the same *limited* gestures, toys with the same equally limited objects or souvenirs, has the very same very limited worries, and is herself up to her neck in their very same sand. But there has been an even surer sign during the days that followed that the comedy 'has got home', when you heard them, in the restaurant or at the café or at home, going back to what they remembered and just repeating and slipping into their everyday talk (where they fitted in perfectly) any number of Beckett sayings: '*Ah, le vieux style . . .*', '*Pas de douleur . . .*' (or maybe the other way round: '*Oh, les vilains jours . . .*', '*Ah, le nouveau style . . .*'), just as a popular song 'sticks' when people come out of the cinema and everybody is humming the tune without realizing it.

I cannot, however, dismiss the critical insinuation of a wicked lady: she maintained that the play is odd and goes down well precisely because it is a drawing-room text acted out in Hell. If *Occupe-toi d'Amélie* or *Un Fil à la Patte* were to be acted similarly by actors immersed in sand or mud up to their necks – maintained this wicked lady – the effect would be precisely the same: neither more nor less.

Translated by Alexander Fainberg

Ignazio Silone

VISIT TO A PRISONER

I watched them grow out of the distance along the deserted dusty road – two constables of the military police and, handcuffed between them, a ragged barefoot little man who moved with a hopping and jumping gait, as if attempting to dance some clumsy jig. Perhaps he was lame from birth, perhaps he had just injured his foot. Framed by those two pillars of the Law, their black uniforms funereal in the harsh brightness of summer, the little man made me think of an animal captured in a ditch, pulsating with life and earthiness. On his back he carried a bundle from which there came, in rhythmical accompaniment to his hopping, a squeaky noise rather like the cry of a cicada.

I had been sitting on the front doorstep with my spelling-book on my lap, struggling with the mysteries of vowels and consonants, when I first noticed the approach of this pitiful and comic figure; and the unexpected diversion he provided threw me into a fit of giggling. As I looked around for someone else to share my amusement, at that very moment I heard my father's heavy footsteps coming through the house.

'Do look, isn't he funny?' I said, laughing. But my father shot me a stern glance, swung me to my feet and dragged me by the ear to his room. I had never seen him so displeased with me.

'What have I done wrong?' I asked, rubbing my sore ear.

'You must never, never make fun of a prisoner.'

'Why not?'

'Because he can't defend himself. And then because, for all you know, he may be innocent. And in any case, because he's to be pitied.'

Without saying another word my father left the room, and I remained alone with a new kind of perplexity. Vowels and consonants and the intricate relationships between them had ceased to interest me.

That same evening, instead of packing me off to bed at the customary hour, my father did something very unusual : he took me with him to the piazza. And instead of standing around with his friends near the premises of the Mutual Aid Society, as was his habit, he sat down at a table outside the 'Gentlemen's Café', where various members of the local gentry were taking a breath of cool air after the sultry day. The district magistrate was sitting at the next table, engaged in conversation with the doctor.

'What's the charge against that man they arrested today?' my father asked the magistrate, with whom he was on friendly terms.

'Stealing,' the magistrate answered.

'Where is he from?' my father wanted to know. 'Is he a tramp? Or just out of a job?'

'He works at the brick factory,' the magistrate said, 'and it seems he stole something from his employer. Has he stolen from you too, by any chance?'

'That's strange,' my father said. 'Judging by the way he looked when I saw him, barefoot and ragged, I'd have thought him to be a victim of theft rather than a thief.'

The spectacle of some such unfortunate creature, handcuffed and escorted by *carabinieri*, was at that time quite common in the road where we lived, because prisoners arrested in any one of several villages within the jurisdiction of our district court were obliged to pass that way; and since no transport was available, they had to come on foot.

The older part of our village lay huddled against one side of a hill surmounted by the ruins of an ancient castle, and consisted of a vast beehive of peasant hovels, a great many stables, byres and pigsties hewn out of the rock, a couple of churches and a few derelict mansions; but in recent times, as the population grew, the village had spread downwards into the valley, along both banks of the river; and our street, being the main artery connecting it with the Fucino plain, was a busy and noisy thoroughfare. It was a dirt road, as uneven and treacherous as the bed of a mountain stream, with ditches and potholes that were full of mud and snow in winter, and of blinding dust in summer. The houses, mostly two-storeyed, that lined the street were defenceless against the mud, the dust and the noise, to the production of which, being largely inhabited by artisans, they in fact actively contributed.

Every morning, at the first light of dawn, our street would witness a procession of goats and sheep, of donkeys, mules, cows, carts of every shape and size, and of peasants on their way to their day's work in the plain; and each evening until late the same procession of men and beasts would straggle past, visibly weary, in the opposite direction. During the intervening hours both sides of the road, in front of the houses, were occupied by artisans – carpenters, cobblers, blacksmiths, coppersmiths, cartmakers, coopers, dyers – with all their working gear and equipment; while, in between, long lines of little mule-drawn carts laden with 'red earth' would file interminably past. The 'red earth' was quarried by very primitive methods from a poor and ancient bauxite mine in a near-by mountain, and from there transported to the railway station. No one, in the whole of the village, knew what became of it afterwards. Very often, in bad weather, a cart would topple on one wheel into some ditch that the mud had concealed from view, and the whole procession of 'red earth' carts would be held up for hours, amid the shouts and curses of the drivers.

It was a big event for me when, a few years later, my father agreed to take me with him to Fucino for the first time. I felt grown up all of a sudden. He woke me very early; it was still dark, but he had already fed and watered the oxen and got the cart ready in front of the door. I was also amazed to hear, from another part of the house, the sound of the handloom, of treadle and shuttle. My mother was at work already. But she came at once to sit beside me while I ate my breakfast of bread and milk, and to give me some final words of advice. I remember that she warned me severely not to sit in the sun when I got to Fucino. 'Nearly everyone gets sunstroke the first time they go to work in the fields,' she told me.

Then she came out with me to the cart. Every detail served to increase my trepidation. In the pale light of dawn the huge bulk of the oxen, the primitive simplicity of the things loaded on the cart – the plough, the sack of hay, the casks of wine and water, the basket of food – and the sudden, ritual and yet unexpected crowing of the cock, all seemed to me tokens of the earnestness of the life into which I was about to be admitted. We had to set out so early because our piece of land was about five miles away, towards the centre of the Fucino plain, and it was wiser, both for us and for the oxen, to reach it before sunrise.

As everyone knows, a bullock-cart moves scarcely faster than ordinary walking-pace. But this slowness of the cart suited my mood, the mood of a boy who is being permitted for the first time to take part in adult life. I watched the peasants ahead of us and behind us in the procession of carts and cattle, and I tried to hide my feelings and behave as they did. I was struck by the fact that, even among friends and familiars, they greeted each other only by the barest nod. It was a working day, not a ceremonial occasion. I did not even mind the fact that my father, plunged in his own thoughts, spoke scarcely a word to me; this was proof that for him too I was no longer a child. One unexpected discovery for me was the sight of our village when, having gone some distance into the plain, I turned to look back. I had never before seen it like that, as a whole, spread out in front of me and, as it were, detached from me, dominating the valley. It was almost unrecognizable: a piled-up jumble of houses in a cleft of the bare mountainside.

As we made our way farther into the plain, the crowd of peasants, carts, mules and donkeys began to dwindle, sorting itself out to right and left, until in the end we remained almost alone. Only then did my father suddenly realize that he had forgotten to bring a supply of tobacco. From his reactions I gathered that this was something very serious. How was he to get through a whole day in the sultry air of the plain with nothing to smoke? Not even the poorest peasants would have dreamt of doing such a thing.

The sun had already risen, and we had already gone too far into Fucino to think of turning back. I felt particularly mortified by

the fact that my father kept repeating: 'Never did I forget it before, never, never.' Did that mean the fault was mine? I felt
overcome with dismay. A cloud had suddenly darkened the day
that was to have been so memorable for me. On reaching our plot
of land my father unharnessed the oxen from the cart and yoked
them to the plough without uttering a word, without as much as
a glance at me. The long dusty poplar-fringed avenue was deserted,
as were the rectangular spaces of the fields adjoining ours. So
there was not even a hope of finding some acquaintance willing to
share his tobacco with my father.

When he was ready to start the oxen going on the first furrow,
my father called me.

'Here, take this coin,' he said, 'and offer it to anyone you see, in
exchange for a cigar or a bit of tobacco.'

By now the sun was hot and it was hardly likely that there
would still be people on the road. My father took off his coat,
lifted the iron goad and shouted at the oxen in an angry voice. I
sat dejectedly on the grassy bank of the canal that separated the
field from the road. I watched my father bent over the plough
behind the oxen, moving away slowly and then returning, and
then moving away again, tracing straight ash-coloured furrows in
the soil that was blackened by burnt stubble. He ploughed on in
silence, keeping the same slow, even pace, although the sun was
beginning to scorch. There was not the faintest breath of air to
sway the rows of giant poplars that fenced the field on all sides;
the waters of the canal were muddy and seemingly motionless,
as if stagnant. Although I was sitting in the shade I felt almost
stifled. I was overcome by a vague sense of nausea and somnolence,
and began to think I would have done better to have stayed at
home. But towards midday my father's voice startled me out of my
torpor. A man astride a small donkey was coming slowly along
the road in our direction. They both appeared to be almost wafted
on the dense low cloud of dust raised from the ground by the
animal's invisible feet. I ran towards him, showed him the coin,
and straight away proposed the deal, pointing out my father at a
standstill with the oxen halfway through a furrow.

'I haven't got a whole cigar,' the man answered, 'only a half one.'

'Never mind,' I said, walking alongside the donkey. 'Take the money and give me whatever you have – oh, please, don't refuse.'

'And why should I have to go the whole day without smoking?' he asked. 'Is your father a better man than I am?'

'No, of course not,' I said. 'It isn't that. It's just that he can get so annoyed and upset by a thing like this that for twenty-four hours afterwards he won't speak a word to anyone.'

'So much the worse for him,' the man retorted. 'Who does he think he is?'

I still kept trotting along beside the donkey, but I was beginning to despair. What could I do to get hold of that half cigar? I cast appealing glances at the man, but he parried them with a cool watchfulness that masked, I felt, either mockery or compassion; but which of the two it was I could not decide. Never before had I seen, at close quarters, a man as gaunt and sunburn-dark and wizened as he was.

'We've got some good food in that basket,' I said. 'You may have my share if you like. In the cask there's cool wine from our own vineyard. Please stop for a moment, please come and see for yourself.'

But the man remained obdurate; indeed, he seemed to be amused by my predicament. I was on the verge of tears.

'Please,' I kept repeating. 'Please.'

'Here,' he said suddenly, handing me the half cigar. 'I'll make you a present of it.'

'But won't you take the money?' I protested.

'Not for half a cigar,' the man said. 'You don't sell a half cigar. Either you keep it for yourself or you give it away for nothing.'

I didn't insist, because I was in such a hurry to boast of my prowess to my father.

'Strange,' my father commented, when I had finished reporting my triumphant negotiations. 'You should at least have got the man to tell you his name.'

A few years passed. One evening I was sitting on the front door-step with a book of Latin fables in my lap, when I saw a man go by, handcuffed between two constables of the military police. It was that very same man of the half cigar. I recognized him instantly, without hesitation, and at the shock of recognition I felt a violent thump in my heart. I ran off to look for my father and tell him what had happened, but he was not in the house. I ran to my grandmother's, and then to the piazza, but no one had seen him anywhere. At last, after some time, I found him in the byre, water-ing the oxen. I must have looked very upset, because at the sight of me he immediately asked if I were bringing bad news from home. Yes, indeed, I said; and poured out my tale.

The next day was Sunday. On coming out of the church after Mass I found my father in the piazza, waiting, as we had already planned, to take me to the magistrate.

'Tell the story yourself,' my father said. 'After all, you know the man, I don't.'

There was not very much to tell, but I put all the pathos I could muster into the telling of it. The magistrate listened with a smile. When I had finished, he explained that the man had been arrested for stealing.

I was dumbfounded. I could have imagined him as being violent, beating up someone in a quarrel, but not as a thief.

'He must have done something to make the police and the magistrate think he was stealing,' my father tried to explain. 'Whatever he did must have looked like stealing, to them; but only God can know what it really was.'

The magistrate was kindly and gave us a pass to visit the man in prison. He wrote my name on it too. On the way to the prison my father said:

'We ought to bring him some little present. But what?'

'A few cigars would be best of all,' I suggested.

'That's a splendid idea,' my father said.

I can still remember that visit in every detail because, given my tender age, it was the first time I had ever set foot in such a place. The moment I crossed the threshold, my heart began to beat so violently that it hurt. The jailer led us to an evil-smelling little room into which a dim light filtered through the two iron bars of a tiny window. Here he pointed to a grating, open at eye-level in one of the walls, through which we were allowed to speak to the prisoner we had asked for. In order to see him, I had to stand on tiptoe. He remembered me straight away, from the first moment; and this made me very happy.

Translated by Darina Silone

Luciano Erba

DIGNUS EST ENTRARE

How much darkness on the fields of pumpkins,
how many hills on every plain:
Wingèd farewell
o that your flight may not be entangled with the robinias,
return where a white remoteness
already announces beyond the mountain your hosts,
return and, wings folded, tell of
the journey on the sides of my chariot,
steered with the freshest hands,
tell of the ghosts of the villages
like clothes blown by the wind
and of the August night as white leprosy
that devours the roads and cottages,
tell of the fields of oats,
the fields of stars,
and my new cheeks if a pallid haystack
takes away their fever !

IN THE IVORY TOWER

I would like to re-read
the adventures of the tin soldier, or
tell long stories about things
that we must leave. Distant
destinies of things: *in aeternum.*
Like balloons, sabres, whips
or animals, parrots for instance

(on the terrace we had an aviary,
I leant against the cages to see, some rust
came off on my forehead) or the biggest rabbit
that I stroked in the main square,
some feathers that may have fallen
from the Bersaglieri running through the streets.

To narrate and to describe : medals
clouds skies tapestries
figures that are born on the hair
lamed zain aleph
to D. in the mornings of June.

Translated by Gavin Ewart

Nicola Chiaromonte

A BRIEF LOOK AT THE THEATRE OF TODAY

When we speak of a crisis in the theatre, we forget that the great periods of flowering in the theatre have been very few, in fact precisely three in number, none of them lasting a full century – that of the ancient Athenian theatre, from the beginning of the fifth to the beginning of the fourth century B.C., of the theatre of England, France and Spain from the end of the sixteenth to the second half of the seventeenth century, and lastly of the modern theatre, from Ibsen to Pirandello. Great ages in the theatre are things of rare occurrence because it is rare for a society to accept, indeed actually to enjoy, being held up to judgement in public – or as Pirandello would have put it, seeing itself in the mirror. The whole beauty of the drama as an art-form lies precisely there. For if the dignity of man can be measured by his power to see himself as he really is, and at the same time, and in spite of this, to forge a noble image of his own destiny, no art-form can perform this with the same force and immediacy (I would add, with the same courage) as the theatre. This capacity for facing the truth unveiled and naked, when it is presented in a public performance, is clearly a quality not only in the dramatist but in society as a whole. In Athens the theatre was a public institution. And essentially, so far as it exists at all, that is what the theatre always is, a public institution, rather than a private enterprise on the part of artists and writers; the only question is to what extent it *does* exist and what amount and kind of recognition it receives. For this reason, the place which any people assigns to its theatre is the surest measure of its level of civilization. A society without a theatre, or which discourages the theatre, is a society barbarous and unsure of itself; I would add, a weak society.

Hence, what is needed is not to ask ourselves whether or not the theatre is in decline, as a consequence of the cinema or of modern life in general, but to make up our minds to want it. No other form of expression or spectacle is a substitute for it, and hence the theatre cannot die. Living in society, of its very nature, means enacting, staging, living out dramas of all kinds. The first and fundamental theatre is our own conscious mind, in the privacy of which we argue with our fellow-men, debating not only our own but their problems, and those of our life in common. It is here, before anywhere else, that the world becomes a stage and that drama is born. Whoever takes his relations with his fellow-men seriously gives dramatic form, in some degree or other, to his own life, and moreover, as we all know, he may find himself moving from farce to tragedy. Nonetheless, the full exhibition of these tragedies and comedies can only take place on the stage. So the reasons for sterility in the theatre are, above all, moral ones; they indicate a state of demoralization. And they are rather like the reasons which lead people to sneer at politics, on the grounds that, whatever you do, the world will always go on in the same way. The sneering and the feeling of discouragement are perhaps justifiable, but the conclusion drawn from them is a false one; for whether or no the individual actually takes part in politics, he is always subject to political forces; the choice lies between passivity, or some sort of participation, of whatever kind. The same is true of the theatre; the choice is between suffering it and actively co-operating with it. Choose which we will, the theatre is always with us.

Furthermore, the best way to keep the theatre alive is to give it continuity. Masterpieces come when they will. But it is hard for an author of genius to write for the stage if he cannot be sure of there being a theatre where his work will be welcomed. And this means not only actors, producers, sponsors and patrons (or a generous and encouraging government, as, in his own time, the Norwegian one was towards the rebel Ibsen); nor does it mean merely a combination of these favourable factors; it means also the existence of a well-disposed public, a public, that is to say, which neither panics if the dramatist presents its own situation to it as horrible or hopeless, nor gets indignant if he tells it it is absurd and hypocritical, a public, in short, open-minded enough to accept the truth willingly, whatever form it takes.

Now it is exactly the novelty of the modern theatre – the inspiring spirit of which is Henrik Ibsen – to have put on to the stage (for the first time since the Greeks, though in a very different manner) the tragedy of man struggling with the truth, man in his determination to dig down to the very depths of his own being and to come to terms with the world he lives in, deterred by no human taboos. From Ibsen onwards to Strindberg, Shaw, Chekhov and Pirandello the drama has come to be concerned with, not this or that conflict or this or that human case or human passion, but truth itself. Or rather, perhaps one should say, with the problem of truth – and in so saying we define the highly intellectual, or as the phrase goes 'cerebral', quality of modern drama, from the patriarch Ibsen to Beckett and Ionesco in our own day.

Truth in the theatre doesn't merely mean presenting true human cases and problems, it means the 'bringing into question' of the cases that are being presented, it means forcing the spectator to put the same question to himself as the dramatist has done, to debate it with himself and ask himself if the way the author resolves the problem is true or false, necessary or arbitrary. But more important than the resolution, of course, is the debate itself, that is to say whether the problem that has been staged is a real one, a problem of *ours*. It is the actuality and immediacy of the situation that has been brought on to the stage which counts in the post-Ibsenite theatre, not the mere verisimilitude or otherwise of the particular human case. An 'immediate' or actual situation is not merely one in which the characters are wearing our clothes (that is a secondary matter); it is a situation which really deals with *us* – with our way of life, with our moral condition, with the rules governing our conduct, with the very reality of our world indeed, or rather the ultimate assumptions on which that world is based – and poses the question whether they are truths or comfortable illusions. Since Ibsen, Shaw and Pirandello, it has been of less importance whether the actual plot shown on the stage is superficially lifelike or not; what is important is that it should be authentic – that is to say that it should spring inevitably out of our moral situation, and should correspond to a problem actually existing in our consciousness (even if, till the dramatist presented it to us, we had not been aware of it).

From this there spring two essential characteristics of the modern drama. The first is that, by forcing himself and his audience to question the meaning of what he is presenting, the dramatist himself becomes an actor in the play, involved personally in the action. He is felt to be responsible for the problem he is raising and as under an obligation to answer for its truth, for the way it is explored, and for its final resolution – responsible, that is to say, for the answer which he gives to the question he himself has posed. The second characteristic, a corollary of the first, is that the spectator also should be involved in the action, that is to say that he too should be out there on the stage, compelled to put himself the same questions as the characters do, to make up his mind as to the logic (or necessity) of their actions, and, finally, to assess the conclusions they come to.

Convinced as I am that modern drama has rediscovered, with Ibsen, something of the very essence of the theatre – that essence which embodied itself so splendidly in Greek tragedy and comedy – I am tempted to see in what I have called the 'presence' of the dramatist on the stage an analogy with the function of the Chorus in the Greek drama, and in the removal of the barrier between the presented action and the audience, an equivalent (even if only a symbolical and abstract one) of that direct participation by the spectators in the stories of Oedipus or Hecuba which a Sophocles or a Euripides did not have consciously to strive for, these stories being, in the fullest sense of the word, communal stories, the inheritance of the collective consciousness.

In any case, when Pirandello deliberately breaks down the barrier between the stage and the audience, bringing the actors in among the audience and the audience out on to the stage, confusing fiction and real life, it is not a capricious stunt on his part but the visible realization of a conception of the drama and a relation-

ship between the drama and real life already implicit in A Doll's
House and in Shaw's *Plays Unpleasant* – and even, if you come to
think of it, in the work of Chekhov, with his efforts to abolish the
distinction between the language of the stage and the language of
every day. And as for the famous 'alienation-effect', on which the
drama of Bertolt Brecht is based, what else is it but a way of con-
veying that the dramatic action is not there to provide illusion and
entertainment, but on the contrary to rub the spectator deeper into
reality, to deepen his restlessness and discontent with his own
situation. And to come to the most recent drama, the apparent
eccentricity and unreality of the plays of a Beckett or an Ionesco
spring from the same need on the playwright's part to present his
vision intact, without compromising with the conventions of 'nor-
mality', and to encourage the spectator to look for the meaning of
what is going on not in superficial likeness to life but in the inner
experience. I would go so far as to say that we measure not only
the originality, but also the authenticity of a modern play by the
presence or absence in it of some questioning of the world, of some
irony or (though this is less ideal) some intellectual *parti pris*
which transcends and justifies the external action and comes home
directly to the minds and hearts of the audience, forcing them to
relate what goes on on the stage to their own experience of the
world today. Of course, by putting himself in this posture, the
dramatist makes himself answerable for the logic of his own ideas
or *parti pris* and cannot get away – like certain playwrights I could
mention – merely on stunts and charlatanry; but there is no need
to worry about charlatans – in the theatre trickery is always shown
up.

However brilliant or artistically justified the dramatic inventions
of Pirandello and Brecht, the bizarre fantasy of Ionesco, or the
pessimistic assumption of Beckett, they are, in the final resort, a
matter of externals. What finally counts is the *spirit* of modern
drama, its determined laying bare of the soul of man, and the
technical freedom that goes with this, and these remain a living
reality. No longer, in the theatre, are we content to witness more
or less realistic, more or less striking and highly-coloured, dramas.

We demand from the dramatist not only (and not primarily) that he should be a master of plot, but that he should also make it plain to us why he has chosen a given story in preference to any other. Merely for him to say that it is the sort of story which might actually have happened, or which illustrates accepted notions, is no longer enough. In the theatre, even more than in the novel or the plastic arts, we want to feel the inevitability of the work in hand; we are ready to see an authentic dramatic action only in what seems to have general application or to illuminate our own moral world. What is happening on the stage must also be happening to and in us. Everything else, even if not mere boredom and emptiness, is only entertainment, of a more or less idle kind.

Truth and freedom are the watchwords of modern drama, as indeed of all authentic modern art. And, to speak of ourselves, if the theatre in Italy, though full of talent and of potentialities, has remained confused and uncertain up to now, and is still – despite the great example of Pirandello – not truly modern, it is, essentially, because the spirit of truth and freedom is still cramped and impeded in our theatre, handicapped by nineteenth century traditions and respect for public susceptibilities and social opinion – and, above all, because it has not really been understood.

The great new feature in the Italian theatre in the last twenty years has been the emphasis on the producer. We have producers equal to the very best in the profession, men capable of mounting spectacles which are almost too superb. This kind of progress is in danger of remaining sterile – of being only the same kind of progress as, at the end of the sixteenth century and in the following century, inspired Italian architects and scene-painters to create the form of the modern stage. No one knew what to use them for, those magnificent theatres of Palladio and stage-sets by Serlio – at the most, they were used for some trivial court-spectacle. And similarly, we possess first-rate producers but (generally speaking) no playwrights. Or if we are beginning to have a playwright or two, we have no actors trained in the modern style. Or finally, say we have (as we have always had) talented actors, we still do not have any actors with the practical vision required to found theatres, large and small, to spread the taste for modern drama. One thing we unquestionably do possess – as we possess an inborn feeling for the theatre – and that is a public which will go to the theatre when there is something to make it worth its while, even if it means a certain amount of effort. Experts can say what they will, I am convinced that there is a public even for really difficult drama in Italy; all that is needed is for this public to be educated. And in fact the experiment of educating it has been tried, sporadically; but it has never been carried through to a conclusion. For, of course, it doesn't educate the public to mix up lightweight plays (of the French and American type) with works of serious or modern intention – Shakespeare and Anouilh, etc. And indeed, I might add, it is not even the way to train modern-style actors. Similarly, it is not educating the public to give it (with the idea of dazzling and impressing it) lavish productions, enshrining trivial nonsense or empty box-office successes. Simplicity, if not actual poverty, of means is one of the basic stylistic principles of the modern theatre.

About the deficiencies of the theatre in Italy there is much that could be said. One essential question (to which, however, no one seems to attach much importance) is that of specialization on the part of theatre-managements, a question connected with the problem of repertoire. It was brought into the open by Strindberg in 1888, when he realized that to offer a play like *Miss Julie* to the big-theatre public, steeped as it was in Sardou and Dumas, was useless and absurd. The result was the proliferation of little theatres, more or less experimental in character, all over Europe.

This was not merely a consequence of the special requirements of the avant-garde theatre, it also had a practical basis, in two distinct ways. On the one hand it meant that theatre-repertoires became more specialized, so that the public was able to know more precisely what sort of production to expect from a given company – and this, which helped to split up audiences according to their particular tastes, was in itself an essential step in creating the right atmosphere for the new drama. On the other hand, it was, and is, clear that the plays of, say, Strindberg, Chekhov and Brecht, are quite unsuited to the giant scale of nineteenth-century theatres (the scale, in Italy especially, of the opera-house). And in addition to this there is the financial aspect. Plainly, one is bound to think twice before putting on a play of doubtful prospects in a large-scale commercial theatre.

The lack of specialized repertoires and specialized theatres in Italy is merely the outward sign of a fundamental deficiency – the lack of a true sense of style. Obviously there is one style for the *pochade* and another for tragedy, that goes without saying. But in the modern theatre the question of style goes far deeper than such crude distinctions. The demands of truth and freedom, which we have been talking about, can, in essence, be reduced to the demands of style. By style we mean rigorous selection in theme, in quality of language, in purpose, and in the whole conception of what is meant by drama. It means, also, clarity of thought and the ability and determination to carry through a dramatic action to its logical conclusion, reducing it to its essential unity. And if it means all these things, it also means an intellectual and moral rigorousness, a capacity for resisting wishful thinking or the fear of public opinion. Beneath questions of taste and aesthetics there is always, if you look hard enough, the question of intellectual integrity and moral courage – the real and substantial question in every field of human effort.

I will not, at this point, institute an inquiry into the present state of Italian society or its culture. I will merely say that we have been witnessing for some years a progressive enfeebling of the feeling for truth and the passion for liberty; and the worst of it is, this decadence possibly affects the intellectual classes, and the life of art and culture, more deeply than the life of society in general. Moreover, the phenomenon is not confined to Italy. Confused, frightened and bewildered as he is, the man of today seems to want merely to distract himself from his own condition, not to examine it. In such an atmosphere the theatre can only survive with difficulty. On the other hand, this same atmosphere, suffocating and demoralizing as it is, makes one even more aware of the *need* for the drama and of the liberation a free, thriving and truthful theatre would provide.

Translated by P. N. Furbank

Giovanni Arpino

L'ombra delle colline (1964), from which this extract is taken, is typical of Arpino's work in the way he uses an actual journey – the return of Stefano from Rome to his home in Piedmont – as a device for creating another sort of journey: into the past. The inspiration is the Fascist period and the war. Gradually important things emerge, such as the murder of a German soldier when Stefano was thirteen. We have the complex relationships with his father the colonel, with Francesco the farmer's son, and with Lu his Roman girlfriend, all in connexion with both the past and present.

IN THE SHADOW OF THE HILLS

'. . . All he'll eat now is salad, morning and night, and an egg every other day . . . Some of the fights we've had! And what hell to pay if I dare put anything else on the table. . . . But I know why it is . . . he wants to slim. That's what it is, I reckon. At his age! He wants them to put him into one of his uniforms when he's dead . . .' The maid, Caterina, chattered on about the colonel in the brief moment I was alone with her.

'And you?'

'Me?' she blinked, surprised, before turning and hurrying away, her hand fluttering to hide the straggling bunch of hair on the nape of her neck. 'Me – how do you mean? Go in to them now, go – it'd be as well . . . Don't leave her alone, that poor signora – or signorina . . . If he takes it into his head, there's no knowing what he might say to her . . .'

I followed Lu and the colonel on a tour round the house and heard them talking – they a room ahead of me all the time. When I moved along the corridor separating the two rows of rooms on the first floor, or when I shut a door behind me, their footsteps had already drifted away, their voices grown fainter on the other side of a wall. The fading light came filtering in through the windows which the colonel had thrown open one by one. Splashed with yellow, now that the lights had been switched on, the walls looked dingy, the corners of the chairs and tables stood out stark, and the upholstery seemed swollen with the damp pressure of the years.

The spring greenery in the garden thickened into darkening chaos; and the grass seemed to encroach even on to the drive, which narrowed to a pale ribbon between the wild bushes merging hazily into the farthest row of pear trees. From the balcony I peered at the hump of the hill down there, black with a profusion of nettles, like some enormous drowsy octopus. Among the branches of the pine trees that marked the beginning of the drive, the sparrows were gathering for the night in a chirruping twitter. And the plain stretched away in one long sweep, its different shades of grey merging one into the other as far as the distant back-drop of the Alps standing violet and gaunt now that the sun had dipped out of sight, although it still gilded every peak and with giant rays sliced a portion of the sky into segments of a dying blue.

They were talking, in there, the two of them, and perhaps at every complimentary remark from Lu on the house, on a piece of furniture, on a window with a view of the lawns and distant woods, the colonel was bowing stiffly, with a smile that was sometimes cloaked but sometimes held warm approval of a secret affinity at last able to declare itself, as if to a fellow accomplice.

Now a late tea was getting under way in the drawing-room, with a silver sugar bowl dug up who knows how, who knows where, in this higgledy-piggledy of walls, little alcoves, nooks and mouldering corridors, doors and swollen wardrobe timbers which creaked as soon as you touched them. On a little lace mat in the centre of the table the cups sparkled, empty as yet, but already Lu was playing her part, busying herself with little spoons and tongs, slices of lemon, a tiny jug of milk, talking and smiling graciously, or darting me a look with her eyes, as if to say, '. . . You knew about this but you still dragged me here without giving me time to change, without letting me have an hour at the hairdresser's though God knows I begged you in Turin. . . . You've brought me here empty-handed – and now I'd give anything to have a shawl to present to Caterina . . .'

Behind her, overhanging the sofa in their gilt frame, the two rosy eternal lovers of the English print were perpetually coming together in a brushing kiss – the woman with her eyelids half closed and her fair ringlets down the back of her neck, the man with a high, spotless cravat all round his starched winged collar . . . I realized I scarcely existed – I was a tolerated if necessary outsider called in to witness a pledge, a theatre enchanted with itself, with its own dignity, redeemed and free at last to put itself to the test, and to conquer. . . .

But Caterina, in the next room, was already bustling about and making a din as if she wanted to warn me of something, and I felt a sudden childish dread.

'Everything ready? Nothing forgotten?' she darted at me as soon as I went into the kitchen. 'Get cracking – it'll be all right for you to go! Look in the colonel's cupboard, upstairs. It's locked, but the key's in the top drawer of the chest of drawers . . . I'd have looked myself if I'd ever dared . . . I don't want the revolver hidden there! He's complained a thousand times about not being able to die – Our Lord does everything to make sure he gets left down here . . . You go and have a look – but make it quick and watch out . . .'

I went up the stairs, groping my way in the dark at each step. Floating up from the drawing-room came the mingled murmur of their two voices. I opened the cupboard doors, cautiously, so that they wouldn't creak.

All I could see hanging there in the empty cupboard, on a hanger, was his best uniform, the medals already pinned in place on the left of the jacket. The ribbons bearing the weight of bronze and silver hung one next to the other, exactly symmetrical. The trousers had been carefully folded, with their black band and the red stripe running through, and just rested on the newly-polished boots. A yellow envelope stood obliquely against one boot and bore the words, underlined and all too legible: 'My last wishes.' At the bottom of the cupboard, in a low pyramid of shadow, was a single box with two new-looking brushes and an immaculate kerchief, things which were obviously needed to keep in daily good order the uniform, the boots and the peak of the cap which was lying there on a little square of felt. For some strange reason, neither the light blue scarf nor the sabre was to be seen. He must have discarded them in deference to a precise picture he had of himself, lying in perfect repose, with not a hint of fussy tinkling tassels.

I closed the cupboard doors, trying not to let my mind wander, and going down the stairs I found myself, for no apparent reason, thinking of my mother. At the dinner table, her hand used to smooth the tablecloth in the area immediately round her plate, marshalling the breadcrumbs into a thin line, and then after a bit deftly covering them up under a knife or a spoon. Meanwhile the ripples in the linen would spread out, compelled to echo the movement of her manoeuvring fingers.

The two of them were still talking in the drawing-room.

'. . . Yes, you're right, a house like this would be worth looking after. . . . My wife, saintly woman that she was . . .' the colonel was saying. 'But now you must let me be frank with you, signorina. What I mean is, I shall be delighted to have your advice, delighted and honoured . . . but only when you've managed to get yourself married to that wretch of a son of mine. . . .'

Lu gave a dry laugh, which immediately deepened, and she hastily murmured something.

'. . . Yes, "wretch" is a word with many meanings . . .' added the colonel tartly. 'But in the case of my son – if you don't mind my saying so – well, I'd say they all applied equally well . . . But I leave it to you, my dear, to decide whether you should be benevolent or critical. . . .'

He went on: '. . . I know that Stefano has always been out of step, as they used to say once upon a time of a certain type of horse . . . And now it's my accursed fate to have my hands tied, and be robbed of all authority! But you . . . someone like you ought to be able . . . well, I really don't want to force you to talk about these things. Think of me as a has-been – it simplifies matters.'

'But why? . . . No, no . . . I'm the one who . . . Stefano is . . .' whispered Lu coaxingly.

And I could imagine her, on the other side of the door, her eyes intent, chin in hand, weighing up what she might confide that would make the conversation flow more easily, and their sudden unlikely alliance closer, more clearly defined and solidly based.

'Well now . . . via Giulia. You said you lived in via Giulia, didn't you? When I had lodgings in Rome, in the year 1912 – yes, that was it – 1912, after Libya – via Giulia was something, a territory . . .' The colonel's tone of voice had already changed.

I could hear Lu moving the cups and spoons on the table, the chinking sounds hardly penetrating the easy flow of the two voices.

At the bottom of the stairs, not knowing whether to go into the room or move away, I thought over the details of his face now that I had seen it again after too long a time.

A misty light had come into his eyes, dulling the steel in them – a light which almost by some mysterious design was to bring calm and obscure all that to him had once seemed deserving of immediate hate, of contempt. A careless gesture, or an ill-conceived word from someone – now he let them pass him by without pouncing with the acid punctiliousness that had been his wont.

At his temples where the skin hung slack and had cracked into a criss-cross of tiny wrinkles, the blood rose thinly to tinge that pale pale grey, a distant reminder of a Mediterranean ivory which the years had relentlessly overlaid with a blanket of ashes. His hands still trembled, suddenly, but almost immediately drew back together on to his chest, seeking repose; and his voice, cracking into piping shrillness, after a couple of words faltered back, its soaring flight already abandoned, wearily to die away.

His head would make a disdainful movement, turning sideways on when someone spoke to him, while his eyes wandered as if searching round to capture some hidden strength lying near at hand; but these were the mere mannerisms of an idle petulance, and now only on the offensive against the voices that haunted him.

Not having attained the wisdom of old age, uncomprehending one minute and shrewd the next, he held back warily so as not to have to erect further elaborate defences against a world which closed in all round him, ever more monstrous and mysterious. Solitary, he stood aloof from what molested and defied him in the evening of his days. He was like a doomed soldier in the desert without map or compass who still watches and measures his last drops of water, almost as if they would last for ever....

I stepped out from the veranda; the garden was now an intricate maze of obscure shapes under a clear sky, stabbed with a single star. I moved towards the drive; the thick, coarse grass had made the ground uneven and the bushes were so overgrown and straggling that they got in the way of the gently sloping view of the vineyard. The octopus swarm of nettles had spread from the hump of the hill down to where I was, like a mass of twisted girders with not the tiniest gap between them.... If no one was going to try and keep them down, after two or three years even the bottom of the drive would be completely overgrown....

I stood and thought of the German down there. By now I felt detached from his death. And the events of that long-ago afternoon – which I could still picture so vividly – were no longer part of me. I mused idly on how a hired labourer might try to put things right and clear the nettles, how he might pull them up and bury them, and perhaps his hoe might suddenly turn up a rifle, a little piece of leather, a button or a bone . . . But it was a vague picture which dwindled and melted away before it could produce even the faintest sensation of fear....

I turned back : by this time Francesco would already be waiting for me at the café.

Everything that Lu and the colonel were saying to each other I could guess from where I was, from behind the dark curtain of the drive. I knew the sweet contrived smiles that Lu could put on, I knew what chinks the colonel (anxious to find out all he could) would casually leave open in the conversation so as to gather snippets of information that would immediately provoke him to a violent tirade against me, about how I was spending my time, how I could have done things better, more thoroughly and sooner . . .

Perhaps Lu had taken out a cigarette, while Colonel Illuminati lit it for her. He had never approved of women smoking, but in his blind, passionate prejudice, he was prepared deep down to condone any frivolous weakness in someone he took a liking to and esteemed worthy of his old-world respect.

Without realizing it, they had left me completely to my own devices; and I found myself walking between overgrown beds of hydrangeas and zinnias, dawdling, even more alone – yes, like some ill-favoured examination candidate who had been banished from the classroom where the teachers were conferring about his progress, his aptitude and willingness to learn. . . . Suddenly I was seized by an obscure, indefinable joy.

There they were, walking slowly along by the stone balustrade in front of the house. The whistle of the train sounded from across the plain, and a moment later, in the distant darkness, the line of lit-up windows, barely discernible, sped into view without betraying another sound.

'. . . Well? Aren't you going to have a look round your old haunts?' the colonel asked me.

I looked at Lu, who gave me a gentle smile.

'. . . The signorina will stay here with me, of course,' the colonel went on, pleased with himself. 'She can sleep in the terrace room . . . What are you waiting for? Get along, get along to your worthy companions . . . Wasn't that why you came tearing up from Rome? But you're not going to get a key. I shall still be up, as usual, when you come back . . .'

And Lu nodded crisply, as if she wanted to send me on my way. I turned the car round, and there they were in front of me, relaxed and side by side, in the glare of the headlights.

'Watch the roads!' called out the colonel, savouring his triumph, his tone of voice both commanding and condescending. 'And don't gulp down all that filthy stuff they pour into your glass! Don't be your usual soak . . .'

' 'Bye, be careful . . .' called Lu, quite happy to take up the chorus.

The road suddenly dipped away between the old trees which loomed up one by one in the darkness. I felt I was fleeing like a thief, and already I was wishing I had stayed. . . . But perhaps it was this very rushing away that was raising my spirits, releasing inside me a joyful feeling of movement, tingling and mounting. . . . I didn't pause to probe my happiness; if I let it simmer within me, like some pulsing animal, I could make it last. . . .

Translated by Graham Snell

Carlo Cassola

THE RETURN OF MICHELE

Michele came in the afternoon. After the hugs and the tears (he could not help crying either when he hugged her) she realized how much he had changed. It was not that he had been fat before, but now he was just skin and bones. His aunt's cry when she saw him was due to fright rather than surprise and happiness.

She had made him sit down on the bench and had sat down beside him. She stroked his head: 'How is it that you have long hair?' Michele told her he had let it grow lately: they were not supposed to, but the officers looked the other way if one was about to go on leave. In fact it was as long as when he had left, but rather thin on top. With his pointed skull, his sunken eyes, his Roman nose and his receding chin he looked more than ever like a bird.

'Poor little Michele,' said his aunt over and over again, brooding over him with her eyes. Michele, still a little agitated, passed his hand over his hair to straighten it and lit a cigarette. The first puff put him into a fit of coughing. His aunt was alarmed but he hastened to tell her he was all right: 'If I had done at home all the things I have done out there I should have been ill a hundred times.'

'How can you say you're all right when you're so thin?'

'But I was thin before, too, Auntie . . . Only, at home I was always afraid I might be ill. And out there I have realized I am as strong as a horse. There you are,' he laughed, 'I am even unlucky that way. I can't even hope I might be taken ill and get out of that hell that way.'

His aunt clasped her hands: 'Jesus, Maria, help us, do,' and crossed herself. 'But you pray, don't you? You commend yourself to the Holy Virgin? There's no one else who can help us . . . But now you're here, you've come at last! How I've longed for this moment.'

'I'm here now all right, but in a fortnight I've got to go back up there,' said Michele with a nervous laugh.

'We'll go to see the Countess. This time she'll be able to do something, you'll see . . . But I haven't asked you yet whether there's anything you want! You will be hungry, thirsty . . . Nelly, go and get a bottle out of the cellar.'

'No thanks, Auntie, I'm not thirsty: I had a beer at the store,' Michele said rather defensively, 'I think I'd better go,' and he made as if to get up.

'You're right, you must go. Nelly, run quickly and tell them to put in the horse . . . Your poor mother can't wait to have you in her arms again. Oh, Michele dear, I couldn't believe my eyes when I saw you . . . But why didn't you write you were coming today, I should have come to meet you at the station.'

Michele shook his head: 'I had no idea when I should be coming . . . And up to the last minute I wasn't even sure whether I should go at all. There was always the chance that my leave would be cancelled. . . .'

Nelly came back and said Andrea's father had thought of putting in the horse of his own accord. They went outside with Michele, and his aunt told him: 'You must come here for a meal tomorrow, you and your mother. I'll send the cart for you.'

They went back into the house. Nelly's mother remained restless, wandered about the kitchen, took up her embroidery and put it down again; she also went up to her room but she came down again quickly. Nelly was different; she had sat down in a corner. The War had gone on for more than a year, but she could not yet imagine what it was like. She had heard people talk about it, she had read the posters on the walls, and once she had seen a troop-train go by; and by and by there had been some bad news; someone had died, someone else had been posted missing. Yet for her the War remained something far off, unreal almost. But now she had seen it stamped on Michele's gaunt face. Depressed, she stared into the dark hearth without saying a word. Her mother on the other hand did not stop talking. First about Michele, but then about other people as well. She was in a reminiscent mood; and at some point she started talking about the former owner of the estate, an old lady with a foreign name. She had known her because she had done some embroidery for her. 'And towards the end I even nursed her. After all she was alone, poor lady. . . . She had quite a few grandchildren, but not one of them came near her. Yet when she was near the end they all came quickly enough. And because they couldn't agree how to divide up the inheritance they sold the estate. I heard later that they didn't come to a good end; just fancy, one of them even killed himself. You see, Nelly, divine justice always comes in the end. If you neglect a relative you deserve punishment. You must help everybody, of course; but with relations we have a special obligation. . . .'

Nelly's mother had not only helped her own relatives, but also her husband's. A cousin, for example: 'Your father didn't even want to recognize her as a relative; she had been out of the country so long, and hadn't kept in touch with anybody. And when he took something into his head you couldn't budge him. Who knows: being in the service of Count Brando, perhaps he went out of his mind. Because Count Brando, I didn't know him but I've heard so many people talk about it . . . The very fact that he didn't want to take himself a wife tells you he was mad. Because a gentleman should first of all think of putting an heir into the world, don't you think! If only so that the name shouldn't die out. . . .'

Then she began talking about Michele again: 'God willing he's come back,' she said again. 'Our Lady has done me the favour.' She was talking as if he had come back for ever.

After dinner his aunt insisted that Michele should have a rest. 'Go to Nelly's room and stretch yourself out on the bed for a bit.' But he told her he would rather go out.

'Go with him, Nelly.'

'But Mummy, I must do the washing up.'

'Never mind, we'll do the washing up. You young people go out. . . .'

They went under the ilex tree, half-way down the slope. There was not a blade of grass all around: just a poppy or two that the scythe had sliced off at the same time as the grain, and which had remained to fade among the stubble. Michele stretched out on the ground and rested his head on his hands. Nelly was afraid he might be uncomfortable, but he told her he was used to sleeping on the ground. 'Even behind the lines you must make do with a bit of straw. . . . Was I tired last night! And yet I didn't manage to get to sleep: I had a sinking feeling all the time. . . . This morning though I woke up at ten.'

Now that he had rested after the journey he looked very much better. He had not shaved, but his beard was so scanty, and fair at that, you hardly noticed it. He had smooth cheeks, and now that he had had plenty to eat and drink, they were glossy.

He smiled at her: 'I feel as if I was drunk . . . but I've hardly had anything to drink. And my head has been going round since this morning. Ever since I put on civilian clothes. I feel light . . . as if I was naked.'

'But you are naked; you could at least have kept your vest on. You'll end up by catching cold.'

'No, I'm all right like this.' And he went on to open his shirt as well, uncovering a chest barely darkened with a fluff of hair. Even his forearms were white. Nelly was surprised: there was several years' difference between her and Michele, and ever since she had been small she had been used to looking on him as an adult, a fully grown man. Only now did it strike her how young he was. With that white skin of his, blond hair, fine bones and delicate mien he looked like a boy.

After a while he said to her: 'Do you know, my ears are buzzing. I'm so used to the noise of shooting that silence bothers me. Because even when they send us for a rest you can hear the sound of gunfire all the same. Ah' – puffing up his chest – 'how good this feels. Would you mind if I tried to have a nap?'

'Oh no, not at all.'

'And you? Why don't you lie down, too. . . .'

'No. I'm all right like this.' Michele closed his eyes, and she was anxious not to disturb him. She had qualms about changing position although, with her legs tucked up, she was sitting uncomfortably: moreover something pointed was pricking her thigh. To take her mind off she looked at the black trunk of the ilex: so big that you could hardly get your arms round it. Even the first branches were thick, and they spread horizontally. In fact the tree had grown thick rather than tall; and it was easy to climb, by way of certain projecting knots that formed steps. How often had she climbed up there as a little girl. They had spent hours up there, she, Dina and Andrea. They had a branch each, on which they would sit astride, or a platform of branches where you could be sitting, or even lie down full length. She herself preferred to swing from the fork higher up. Until Dina once told her not to get up there when Andrea was with them: he could see her legs from below.

That distant memory made her blush with embarrassment: how was it possible that she had not thought of it herself, that Dina had to tell her? And it was all due to her own stupidity, because she did things without thinking. The others knew how to behave, she did not, and did the most unbecoming things without realizing what she was doing.

She looked at Michele: perhaps it was also unseemly that she was there while he was asleep? But no, her mother had told her to keep him company. And after all, Michele was her cousin. . . . At any rate she pulled down her dress far enough to cover up her feet: she did not want him to find her in an unseemly pose when he woke up.

Michele was enjoying his sleep: his mouth was half-open and his chest rose and fell as he breathed. Certainly, to look at them nobody would have taken them for cousins. She was dark, he was fair; her eyes were black, his were light blue. . . . Finally she had regular features, a small nose, and a round chin; whilst Michele . . . Ivana had once said to her: 'How ugly your cousin is,' and she had taken it badly. Because she had never asked herself whether he was ugly or handsome: he being her cousin, she took him as he was. But it was also logical that a stranger should find him ugly. In fact Michele had irregular features, or rather, features that were badly matched: that big beak of a nose certainly did not go with his small eyes, thin lips and receding chin.

The pain in her thigh grew sharper, and Nelly decided to change position. It was not a pebble that had worried her, it was an acorn, small and sharp as ilex acorns happen to be. It was bound to have left a mark. She looked: sure enough, there was a scratch. . . . She became aware that Michele had woken up, and rushed to pull down her dress. 'I had an acorn just under my leg,' she excused herself.

'I thought you were looking for fleas' – and he burst out laughing. Nelly was ill at ease. She wanted to reply but he did not give her time: 'In the trenches all we did was killing lice. There are millions of them. We are also full of fleas, of course, but we hardly take any notice of them. The barracks are infested with bugs. On the one hand it's better: at least we've something to do' – and again he laughed. He pulled himself up and looked at the back of his hands, marked by pebbles and twigs. He told her to stretch out her legs: 'I can rest my head this way.' And when he saw her hesitating: 'Are you frightened something's going to bite you? Don't worry, I washed myself all over this morning. Mum had got a tub of water ready, and I said to her: Just think I'm a mule: take the scrubbing brush and groom me. . . . As for underwear, I had it boiled, because there's always the risk of bringing lice into the house. Damned creatures! We soldiers hate them more than the Austrians.'

Nelly decided to stretch out her legs and he lay down again, pillowing his head on her lap: 'There you are, that's how I like it,' and he shut his eyes again.

Nelly felt the warmth of his head and shoulders rather than the weight, and she wondered whether it was not all improper. For the only people she had seen in that position had been a pair of lovers. She looked round, worried: fortunately there was nobody about.

In the oppressive heat the countryside seemed asleep. Everywhere the harvest was under way but in one field the sheaves were piled up at regular intervals, waiting for the cart that was to carry them to the threshing-floor. The threshing-machine was already going round and would be coming to their own farm soon.

From afar she heard the machine's clatter. It stopped for a second, then started again. The reports became more and more frequent until they merged into a continuous steady noise. Nelly looked around: and right at the end she made out the dust rising above the faded green of the elms.

'Where are they threshing?' asked Michele, without opening his eyes.

'On a farm of the estate.'

'Ah.' He had worked as a stoker for a number of seasons: he had even done threshing on their own farm. Nelly remembered him in mechanic's overalls, his face black with oil. . . . When work was over he came into the house to wash, but he ate with the others, at the long table laid in the square.

One evening she had been at the door, drawn by the lively activity that was going on outside. Dina and the other girls were serving at the table, and the men permitted themselves a joke or two: especially with a certain Aida . . . until Michele had seized her as she was passing and had tried to put his arms round her. But the girl had wriggled free and fled among general laughter. Michele laughed, too; but afterwards someone had told him: 'You frighten the women. Of course, with a nose like that you wouldn't even manage to kiss them, to be sure. . . .'

At that time Nelly was looking at Michele through the eyes of her mother who worshipped her nephew. He seemed to her somebody then, that cousin who stoked the threshing-machine. Only now did she realize that he was a poor devil harassed by fate, and looking at that ungainly bird's profile she felt moved.

The hill rising above the land was split up into innumerable individual plots enclosed by hedges or low walls. Gradually, as it rose it grew bare and the top was downright rocky. Hence, whilst the plots lower down were densely cultivated, with fruit trees, rows of vines, and pergolas, those higher up were bare, and even the grass that grew there was stunted.

Her uncle's smallholding was right at the top. The path was

steep and on the last stretch turned into a flight of steps. Michele
went in front, taking the steps two at a time, and Nelly could
hardly keep up with him.

She had only been up there once or twice, and she hardly remembered the tiny oblong field with an artichoke bed shaped like
a wedge, and a wooden hut at the back. A wall separated it from
the plot below whilst a row of stones marked the upper boundary.

'You won't find shade here at any price,' said Michele. The only
trees were two half-withered fig trees. 'Shall we go into the hut?'

'No, I feel better out in the air,' replied Nelly. On that day she
had unwillingly agreed to accompany Michele; as usual her mother
had made her go.

'Then let's go behind those rocks.'

But Nelly turned this suggestion down, too. She preferred sitting
down in full view of some women working below. Michele remained standing for a bit, but in the end he sat down beside her.

'Button up your shirt, you're in a sweat, it might do you
harm. . . .'

'No, I'm not sweaty at all. Seriously, I never sweat. Not even
when I was a stoker, and there you really do sweat. . . . By the
way, when did you say the threshing-machine was coming?'

'Day after tomorrow.'

'Right then, I'll come over to your place, the day after tomorrow.
I want to ask the engineer to let me have a go at the boiler. I'm
getting bored with doing nothing,' and he laughed.

'But you haven't even been back a week.'

'Oh yes, but what can you expect, all my friends are away. . . .
It's just as well you're here.'

They had met every day. Either he had come to the farm, or they
had walked in the country. Michele was on familiar terms with
her, and called her dear, love, darling; he took her arm, put his
arm round her waist, even gave her a kiss or two. Nelly dared not
push him away, but these familiarities always worried her. She
might have thought that there was nothing wrong in it, given the
relationship; but her instinct warned her to be on her guard.
Besides, her feelings towards her cousin were contradictory: she

was a little sorry for him, and felt the need to comfort him, but on the other hand he frightened her and positively repelled her.

'You're always so quiet; why don't you tell me something?'

'What shall I tell you?'

'Something about yourself, what you do . . . You're a young lady now, things must have happened to you. I bet you've already got a boyfriend.' And when she remained silent: 'You can trust me, I'm not going to tell your mother. Well? Why don't you tell me?'

'But I've nothing to tell you.'

'How many boyfriends have you had up to now?'

'None.'

'I don't believe it. A pretty girl like you, you're bound to have had boyfriends.'

'I had one, but I didn't like him so I gave him the go-by.'

Michele looked at her: 'Now I know what kind of a girl you are: one of the quiet ones, who don't tell anything, not even to their girlfriends. But you could tell me all the same. In the first place I can keep my mouth shut. And then I'm off in a few days and I may not come back. . . .'

'You're not starting on that again.' The day before he had started talking about not coming back, and in the end he had burst into tears.

'Do you think the War is just a joke? It's hell, that's what it is. As far as I'm concerned, it's a miracle I'm still alive.'

'You must pray to Our Lady to help you.' She hesitated a moment. 'I always say a prayer for you, every evening.'

'You're a darling, Nelly.' He kissed her hand. 'But I'm afraid prayers aren't much use. And as for charms, your mother has given me three, and to listen to her each one is more wonderful than the other. But if a bullet comes at you, a charm isn't going to stop it, that's for sure.'

'We must make a move,' Nelly said timidly. 'Mummy will be worried. . . .'

'As long as she knows you're with me.' He was still squeezing her hand; and he started stroking her arm.

'It's funny, we've been together all the time these days . . . and before we never used to meet at all. We've spent more time together these last few days than in all the rest of our lives. . . .'

'Because you've nobody you can be with now. And you must make do with me.'

'No,' he replied, 'I didn't notice anybody before. I didn't even see you'd grown up, become a girl . . . but everything was like this. To think I wasn't happy before, I didn't like my life . . . Do you know I thought of emigrating? I got it into my head I was going to America. . . . But then I didn't pluck up courage. How stupid I was. If I'd gone to America I would laugh about the War now. But I've always done the wrong thing, in everything. There're so many chances I missed . . . with women, too. Shall I tell you something, in confidence? I've never made love. . . . Even when I liked a girl, I daren't tell her.'

'Why?' she said, surprised.

'Oh, just like that. I always thought I was too ugly . . . and no girl would take any notice.'

'But it isn't true at all, you're not ugly.'

'You're telling me that just to cheer me up . . .' He sat up sharply. 'Tell me honestly: would you sleep with me?'

'Whatever do you mean?' she said, blushing, 'We're cousins, and then . . .'

'There you are, you see, you find me ugly, too.'

'But no, I promise you.'

'Then give me a kiss.'

'Please, let's not start that again.'

'I can see I make you sick.'

She was irritated. She could not listen to him when he talked like that. She would have liked to ask him, 'What kind of a man are you?' But he looked so depressed that she felt very sorry for him. She said to him: 'What put that idea into your head? You're not ugly at all. You're a lad like the others. You could find a hundred girls if you wanted.'

'You say that but you don't give me a kiss.'

'If you promise to be good, I'll give you one.'

He promised, and Nelly closed her eyes, put her lips close to his, and pulled back quickly. She had not even had the time to feel the pressure. 'Now are you satisfied?'

Michele did not reply. He was more excited than ever. Finally he said: 'But if I asked you to make love with me, you would say no.' Nelly was silent, and he said: 'You see, you don't love me.'

'Whatever next: I love you all right, but as a relative.'

'But I am a young man as well: and the love of a girl for a young man is different. . . . Listen, Nelly: I shall be off in a few days, and if we make love nobody'll know. . . .'

'Stop talking like that.'

'Nelly, I want to so much . . .'

'Look, I shan't come with you any more.'

'Nelly, don't be nasty.' And the next moment he was talking about everyone being nasty to him; that nobody loved him; that no one cared that he had to return to the front in a week's time . . . ' "You do not see the hour of his parting, nor do you see the hour of his death. . . ." But I am twenty-seven, do you understand? Why must I die? I am young, I haven't tasted life yet at all . . . I haven't even been with a woman. . . . I don't want to die, it isn't right that I should die so young, without even tasting life. . . .' and he started sobbing.

She was also moved, for she realized how desperate he was. She pulled him towards her, pressed him to her, and began stroking his hair: 'Michele, don't be like that. Don't be so desperate. It's not true that nobody loves you. We all love you, Michele, I love you, I love you so much,' and she kissed his hair.

He held her tight. He was still sobbing, but slowly he grew calmer. They remained in each other's arms, until he lifted his face and smiled at her.

Then she kissed him: first on the cheek, then on the mouth. And she felt a great tenderness. . . . 'Little Michele,' she said to him. He seemed to her like a child, and there was nothing wrong if she held him tight and kissed him. . . . 'Be a good boy, Michele, my little one, you're here with me.'

But he had started pressing her and touching her. She felt him raising her dress, pressing one of her thighs. . . . 'Be a good boy, there, stop it. Don't do that, it's bad,' but by then he had broken away: a push with his shoulder made her lose her balance; and then he was on her, crushing her with the whole of his body. He was talking, too: he told her she was a good girl, that she should please him, that he did not want to die without having known love. . . . 'Make me feel it, Nelly, do'; and she was already beginning to give in when she felt him squeeze one of her breasts.

In a fit of rage, she groped for a stone with her free hand and struck Michele on the head.

At home they said they had climbed up on the rocks, and that he had slipped, knocking his head against a sharp corner. Michele joked about it, too: after escaping so many times in the War, he had run the risk of killing himself through a stupid fall: 'If I have knocked my temple it serves me jolly well right.' Nelly's mother was afraid he might have damaged the bone; but he said it was nothing, he did not even want to put on cold compresses. Nelly did not say a word.

Andrea's father came to fetch them with the cart. On the way mother and daughter did not exchange a single word.

At home Nelly wanted to go up to her room, but her mother stopped her: 'Now tell me what happened.' Nelly was taken unawares: she was sure her mother had believed the story of the fall. She turned white and had to sit down.

Her mother, still on her feet, was waiting for her to reply: 'Mind you tell me the truth my girl.'

'I . . .' began Nelly. 'Michele hurt himself; he's told you, hasn't he?'

'But I am not silly enough to believe that, oh no. Well, are you going to tell me what happened?'

'Leave me alone, Mummy,' and she tried to get up.

But her mother took hold of her arm: 'First you tell me what happened.'

Nelly felt too weak to resist. 'Michele tried to annoy me.' She replied. She raised her eyes, hoping that this would be enough; but her mother's firm expression quickly disillusioned her.

'I tried to make him stop, but he wouldn't, he threw me to the ground. . . . Then I hit him with a stone. . . . But I didn't want to hurt him, believe me, Mummy.'

'Indeed, when you almost killed him. You *are* a stupid girl. First you let him carry on; you even encouraged him, I shouldn't be surprised . . .'

'No, Mummy, I swear. He . . . had been familiar once or twice but I thought . . . after all, seeing that we are cousins . . .'

'You are cousins all right, but he is a man and you are a woman. Heaven help me, what a silly girl you are.' And as if to show the whole weight of her misfortune, she went to sit down on the bench.

'But I didn't know how to behave; I didn't want to offend him. . . . You told me yourself to be kind to him. . . .'

'And now you'd like to make me look like a procuress? How did I know what you two got up to between you when you were on your own? I trusted you, certainly, but I thought I had a daughter who knew how to behave. . . . And instead I should have known you were a fool! What am I saying – fool? You're shameless, that's what you are!' She shouted. 'You behaved like a hussy! Because it was you that led him on; it was you that made him lose his respect for you!'

Nelly looked at her, appalled; she wanted to say something but could not speak.

'What have I done to deserve this punishment?' Her mother pressed her palms to her temples and rocked her head.

'Oh Lord, what have I done wrong . . . to have to have such a hussy of a daughter! To make me blush in front of my own flesh and blood!'

'Mummy, no,' she stammered.

But her mother would not let her speak:

'A hussy, yes, a hussy; without a bit of shame. And don't come and tell me I haven't brought you up properly. Haven't I told you fifty thousand times to be modest, not to show your legs. . . . But you, you would never take any notice. You went about like a gipsy. . . .'

Nelly at last found the strength to react: 'And what about

Michele? He's a relative, he should have had some respect....'

'Be quiet, quiet, d'you hear!' Her mother yelled. 'When these things happen they're always the woman's fault. Nothing ever happens to a girl who behaves as she should. Nothing ever happened to me. There's never been anyone who didn't show me respect.'

'But I trusted him; how was I to know he had bad intentions?'

'Because you are a fool. All men have bad intentions. Only there's no need to give them the excuse. . . . But you, I can just imagine; I can just see you. . . . And don't you tell me it hasn't always been the same story with Andrea.'

'But Andrea has never shown me anything but respect....'

'Be quiet, quiet I say. Go away, go, I don't want to see you any more. Up to your room, go on!'

Nelly rose but had hardly gone up one step when her mother's imperious voice called her back: 'Come here.'

She obeyed mechanically. Her mother looked at her with her small eyes and took her wrist: 'Mind you don't let anybody notice anything, do you understand?'

'Oh, you're hurting me.'

But her mother pressed her wrist even harder and dug her nails right into the flesh: 'That's nothing to what I'll do if your aunt ever finds out. And now go, go away, don't let me see you again,' and she gave her a push that almost sent her flying.

Nelly slowly climbed the stairs. She went into her room and sat down on the bed. She felt a lump in her throat and a weight pressing on her head. Even if her mother had called her to supper she would not have gone down. And even if her mother had forced her she would not have eaten. She could not eat anything, with that lump in her throat.

But her mother did not call her. When she heard her go to bed, she went to bed herself.

During the afternoon she avoided going out although she knew Michele was not there. She had shut herself up in the house from the moment she heard the clattering of the threshing-machine and the curses of the men urging on oxen. The wheels had made a hellish clatter on the pavement of the square. Finally the threshing-machine had been brought up to the threshing-floor.

An hour later they had started work. Although the kitchen window was at the back of the house, overlooking the street, the rattle of the engine came in all the same. Every once in a while Nelly also heard a voice, or a shout. In the end she closed the window: better suffer the heat than be bothered by all that noise.

Luckily her mother was not in. She had gone out as soon as she had had her meal, to call on the Countess. She had gone to sing Michele's praises, naturally.

Nelly spent the afternoon knitting. This time she worked for herself, to make herself a pullover. Andrea's father had bought the wool for her one day when he had had to go to the market at Cecina. The light was bad and she had to light the lamp. The din of the threshing-machine reached her, muffled, through the window: it rattled steadily, without a break as if it was in a hurry to finish the job before dark.

Time was getting on, and there was no sign of her mother. Nelly decided to eat by herself. Afterwards she washed up.

She fancied her mother had been entertained to supper at the farm. Very well, she would wait for her a little longer, and then go to bed. True, with the din in the square it would be hard to sleep. They were capable of remaining at table, eating and drinking until midnight.

She pricked up her ears: she heard only female voices, and concluded that they were still laying the table. As for the men, they were probably having a wash. Nelly recalled how she had once walked into the farmer's kitchen and there were the men washing their faces, necks and arms in three basins they had put on a bench. There was only one piece of soap, however, and they had to pass it around.

Sitting there doing nothing she began to feel bored. She also felt the need for a breath of air after being cooped up in the house all day. She put the light out and opened the door. This way she was sure no one would see her. The table had in fact been laid in front of the farmer's kitchen, and there was only a single lamp dangling from a branch of the lime tree. The circle of light touched the centre of the table, leaving the ends in darkness.

One by one they began to emerge from the shadows and to take their places on the benches. Nelly recognized the engineer, the stoker and some of the farmers. There were at least twenty of them, packed tight round the table. The engineer and the stoker were wearing their overalls, but the farmers were in their shirt sleeves; one wore only his vest. As for the girls, they kept coming and going, and when they passed one another they said something under their breath and laughed softly.

Everything was as it had been in previous years, but there was no life in it. Perhaps the boys were missing. Nelly yawned: she might as well go to bed; she was sure not to be disturbed.

In the past Nelly had wanted to take part in the meal that followed the threshing but her mother had never allowed it. And with good reason, because every time there was someone who got drunk. And then the curses, the bad language and coarse jokes started flying around. . . .

Nelly shivered and went back indoors.

Translated by Alexander Fainberg

Nelo Risi

POEM 8

Life isn't really so bad,
my dear Leopardi, believe me, life
is above all a contest of love,
blows not excluded, hence
aggression not always open
but also a loyal dispute, is Tancred
and Clorinda with a little less Christian
piety, is our most sincere effort,
is the current that as it passes reduces itself
till it extinguishes itself in Nothing – and here
I take your point, Signor Conte.

POEM 20

To deny what we know
as if it did not concern us,
not to upset our neighbour
and ourselves even less,
to create a diversion
without alarm or shock,
never to come to the point –
so that somehow one can live !
This is the new Commandment.

POEM 21

Loud voices are needed,
uvulas of iron, today, to speak
a single gentle word of love.

Translated by Gavin Ewart

Paolo Volponi

The extract below is from *La macchina mondiale*. It is a stark, pitiful story, a study in mental abnormality. A young, uneducated, but not unlettered peasant from the mountains near Urbino has an obsessive interest in science and philosophy. He is provided with textbooks by a seminarist and sets out to write a thesis embodying his fanatical ideas, which gradually take the form of a religion for him. He believes that man is a machine created by beings who have not succeeded in realizing fully their aims and intentions; others in time will supersede the men of today, and machines will be invented endowed with thought and other miraculous powers, so that life will be wholly scientific and good and full of peace and amity among nations. This obsession later brings on a persecution mania and causes tragedy for his wife.

THE UNIVERSAL MACHINE

One day in the course of that summer I came across a silent youth bathing in the Canneto river. He was squatting between some ferns, his body was white, and his hands were under the water, and there was a rapt expression on his face, as if he were searching for a stone or something that interested him in the water. Perhaps what he was searching for was his fear, because his neck between his ears and shoulders was stretched and his chest was hollow, like a bowl, and at long intervals it moved slowly, all of a piece, because of the fear that oppressed it. Or it might have been because of the cold water; or he might only have been afraid of drowning, and not of me or anything supernatural.

I had gone to that part of the river to water the mule; the women with their baskets of washing had stopped lower down. I made the mule go into the water and began washing it, to dirty the water and see whether the white young man would come out and say what he was afraid of. I watched him moving in the water and making his way towards the bank through the deepest pool, where the stream that I was dirtying did not reach. He walked out of the water with body bent and holding one hand in front and the other behind him, and I realized that his fear might well be of his own nakedness, and most of all that whiteness of his that moved on him just like a living thing. A moment later he was dressing behind a clump of bushes; he put on a pair of tight knee-breeches and a pair of black cotton socks that came up to where the breeches were laced. He was a seminarist, all black and white, standing behind a clump of bushes with crushed chest.

I turned to him and said:

'You're a student, aren't you?'

'No,' he replied, 'I'm a seminarist.'

'Well, you're a student at a seminary, then.'

'Yes.'

'Then tell me,' I called out to him from the middle of the stream, 'supposing someone had a theory that men were not creatures of heaven, but machines made by other men, or rather by other beings that now lived elsewhere or were actually extinct, what should he do to try and prove it? Should he study the mechanical sciences or philosophy?'

The seminarist turned and faced me more directly, and said:

'But haven't you already been studying the works of some author who thought up those ideas?'

'No,' I replied, 'I've never studied at all.'

'Then I'm afraid study won't help you.'

'Why not?' I said. 'Are you too a slave of the nobility already?'

'No. But if it's really a genuine question that you're asking, I should say that a man who had that idea would be more likely to be a philosopher than anything else, and in that case studying or not studying wouldn't make much difference to him. But, if anything, the best thing for him to study would be theoretical philosophy.'

'Then stay where you are and wait for me,' I said. 'Stay there and wait for me, because I want you to tell me what theoretical philosophy is and what books to read about it. You've probably got some yourself, you've probably actually got one or two on top of your clothes there behind those bushes.'

I took the mule back to the Canneto side and then crossed over to the Montevecchio side. By the time I got to where the seminarist was he had put on a collarless striped cotton shirt. His chest was now heaving normally, and his wrists were crossed on his knees, and they were blue and white. To gain his confidence I sat down in front of him and said:

'Do you know the name of this river?'

He looked round behind him at the hill as if to make sure that it and the trees on it were still in their place, with the great green and blue shadows that they cast up there, where it seemed as if there were no human beings or even roads in the woods of oak and chestnut and holm-oak. Actually I had never heard of anyone living on Montevecchio and, looking at the mountain in the distance covered with the thick silk of those shadows, I had never imagined that there might be a village or houses anywhere on it. The seminarist turned back towards me and said:

'Here it's called the Cinisco. It's a little river that rises at Petrara above Frontone.'

'You're a clever fellow to know all that,' I said. 'Show me your theoretical philosophy book.'

'I haven't got it with me,' he said. 'And in any case it's only a small book. I haven't got to the senior stage yet.'

'But you know something about mechanical science?'

'No,' he replied.

'But surely you have some books about science?'

'Yes,' he said. 'About natural science and physics.'

He turned to his black brief-case, and I hoped he was going to produce a book about natural science right away. But he had no books with him, and all he had in his brief-case were four elastic bands, two to keep up his socks with and two to keep his shirt-sleeves in place.

Even on that first occasion I noticed that he had a feminine face, a very pretty girl's face, and that there were dark shadows on it, like those on his Montevecchio. He was shy and frightened, but tried hard to look at other people and trample down his fear, though he never lost his shadows. He kept stretching his arms and crossing them and looking at the blue veins on them, and gazing up into the air to entrust himself to the glory of God, as if to a great cloud or a buffet from heaven.

During the next few days he brought me a natural sciences manual, and then one by one he also brought me a dictionary, a book on theoretical philosophy and a book on physics, and he also brought me a life of a saint of the Tarugo, which is another stream that rises in Fenigli. This saint was San Martino dei Muri, who was an ambitious builder, so ambitious that he wanted to build walls so high that they reached the sky, but one day while he was building a church he found himself unable to put one brick on top of another without first kneeling and praying for grace to the Holy Spirit.

The seminarist told me that I should learn from San Martino's example and not imagine that I could work out my ideas about machines without the aid of the Holy Spirit. But I did not risk offending him by giving him the answer he deserved, because I had discovered that whenever I said anything that happened to offend him, though I never intended to offend him, it always made him shut himself up in his shadows and grow more stubborn than ever. Then, towards the end of that September of my twentieth year, he came to see me for the last time before returning to his seminary, and he gave me a box of compasses to design my machines with and a special prayer for scholars to address to San Giuseppe da Copertino.

During the winter, with the aid of the dictionary and the natural sciences manual and the exercise books that Liborio left me, I managed to write a few pages of my treatise. From my window I watched the snow piling up on the trees and bushes and the roofs of the pigsties, and watched the bored dog in its kennel mechanically stretching one leg after another. Who could have devised and made such a creature as the dog with its elementary mechanism but someone who was intent on making a machine and was meanwhile experimenting, making sketches, carrying out minor projects, concentrating on gathering experience, practising his hand and his mind before embarking on the construction of the more ambitious machine he had in mind?

I watched the sparrows hopping about on the window-sill, and thought how simple their life was, and drew it with a straight line. I used Liborio's compasses, but did not know yet how to make the drop of ink remain compactly on the nib of the drawing-pen. Often I dropped the compasses and drew in pencil. I copied illustrations from the natural sciences manual, from those of stones to those of human or animal limbs. Whether they were wings or arms, I always discerned their mechanical nature and noted how very simple they were, attached by an articulated joint, like the arm of a compass. I set up my compass on the table and on top of it I stuck a potato, on which I drew the eyes, nose and mouth of my creature.

I also studied words, and arranged them according to sound: culture, cultivate, continue, comfort; auto, automaton, author, automatic; genius, ingenious, genital, generate; and I noted that words were articulated in syllables and sound in a way that was itself a construction, a construction that assumed an autonomy of its own, that is to say, had no need to be sustained by my thought but by its own force and also its own design and structure constituted a thought in itself, that is, became a new, sensible thing apart from the meaning that each word had on its own account.

After these studies I found myself able to do my work more easily and I got it done in better time, that is to say, the jobs in the barn, cleaning out the stable, and feeding the animals. I examined the animals closely and observed their shape and features. I kicked the sow, and noted that its response was partly a grunt, but chiefly moving its head towards the place that was kicked.

After the barn had been cleared of grain, I used it to make constructions out of pieces of wood, putting them together, leaning one against the other, using grape boxes and broken chairs to stand them on. I made constructions that looked like skeletons, that is, skeletons of possible living creatures. Often I tied the parts together with string and left the bits of string between them, and other bits just dangling. I balanced one of these constructions on the scales, another I gave a funnel and yet another a chair or a fan from the honey separator or a pail from the cellar. Next day these constructions were different; the equilibrium I had created had changed on its own account, and often two constructions had merged into one, as a result of weakness or symbiosis, that is to say, because one design was necessarily complementary to another, and its complementary nature had felt the impulse to complete, if not yet to perfect, itself by merging with the other.

Thus during the winter of my twenty-first year I began writing my treatise. I found those four books tiring, mostly because the sentences were short and always broke off abruptly. There was no consistency in them, no logical flow leading towards movement, and later on they did not even confirm the movement they sometimes impressed on my thought. This reminded me of Liborio, who had to turn round and look at Montevecchio before he could remember the name of the river – he with his shadows and the mountain with its shadows.

I had to go ahead on my own, with few tools and few words, and force myself not to succumb to the fault of Liborio's books, which was devotion to the unity of the Prime Mover. This determination guided me like a globe. I had to dissect the parts of that concept, catalogue and grade them, and find for them a rational medium that would move and articulate them into the loom that I divined and that interested me. The movement of the loom that I found everywhere – its rhythm vibrated all around me – affected everything.

In that winter of destiny that enclosed me like a caul movement and stopping alternated every day and in everything; the stopping occurred suddenly after a moment's suspension of my thought or observation or even of the independent action of the object, tree or piece of earth, and often interrupted the movement itself. The movement and the stopping worked to the rhythm of the loom for which I was searching.

The astral loom that presented itself to me in the evening seemed to me to be the heart of the mechanism that I must study, so that, when I had discovered its unity, I might use it for an indefinite number of further constructions, the phenomena of which would be inserted into time and launched into astral space. In the face of this space and this time my lack of tools left me isolated, with a fear that might have left me empty, unable to measure anything, and hence in the position of seeing the handful of earth that I had gathered wasted, with no guidance in the face of the immense mirror of a thousand facets and prospects.

I had to limit my researches and try to design my loom. I needed books and physical and mechanical instruments, and I spent a great part of the day imagining them, and even got to the point of clearly seeing them in place at a spot that I did not recognize but to which I must make my way. In my impatience the books I had began irritating me. I grew irritated with the kind of books they were and the paper on which they were printed, and I began to fear that whenever I touched them they would leave a blot on my fingers, a blot of black mourning and a fatal infection, fatal, that is, to my studies. But then, in February, at carnival time, when people started moving about again between San Savina, Cupello, Fenigli and Frontone for the dances and the killing of the pigs, I too set myself in motion to pursue the plans my agitation imposed on me. Chiefly I went for long walks in order to pass in front of the villa of the Contessa Carsidona, or at any rate to reach a point from which I could see it. Meanwhile my curiosity was roused by the killing of the pigs, and I applied to help the butcher, and ended by becoming his accredited assistant, whose job was to hold the animal by the ears while he cut its throat and put his arm inside in order to pierce its heart.

I passionately wanted the butcher to start cutting up the beast immediately, so that I might see how life receded from the various parts during the last spasms while death spread heavily through every fibre. But the butcher would have none of this, and threatened me every time. I always had to wait till the slaughtered beast slumped to the ground, dead in all its fat, and then take it to the tub of boiling water.

Sometimes I had to get up at two o'clock in the morning to make my way across the fields to the farms where the butcher was working. Carrying a stick, I often walked across country all the way to the Frontone or Acquaviva roads.

In the cold I became increasingly aware of how my body reconstituted itself after sleep, and I watched my dark, automatic footsteps negotiating embankments and defying the gusts of wind and picking their way.

At about five o'clock on the clearest morning of that winter – powdery snow had fallen the previous evening and the north wind had made it keep its sparkle – I made out the two Megalotti houses standing out dimly in the darkness and saw the bus draw up in front of them.

When I got near I saw Liborio sitting inside next to the window, tall and solitary in his black clothing. His cloth bundle was in the rack over his head, and the hands he held joined in front of his face were whiter than the frost on the bus window.

He sat there motionless and did not turn his head, and he did not see me. The bus started up, and to attract his attention I struck the ground with my stick, but the snow was soft, and he could not possibly hear. I could not call out, because I was out of breath, both from running and from the surprise, and the ice on my woolly scarf kept my mouth shut.

The bus with its blue cage moved off slowly on the snow, and Liborio held his head as straight as if it were an instrument connected with the bus route, or to demonstrate his indifference, like a poor, predestined bird.

Good-bye, Liborio, I said, you think you are leaving this part of the world, but you are going to a still worse place, to live with your heart perpetually enclosed within that timid breast of yours.

Good-bye, I said, you'll see that I shall work for your redemption.

With the frozen scarf in front of my mouth I noticed a savour on my tongue and felt hungry, and it struck me that, if he had been free, Liborio and I would have been able to kill a pig and eat it whenever we liked.

Translated by Eric Mosbacher

Renato Barilli

CALVINO'S SHORT STORIES

Until some time ago the critics regarded Calvino as a difficult 'case' because of his unusual duality: for he seemed intent on following with equal devotion two quite distinct thematic streams: one ranging between actuality (autobiographical in tone) and the history of the recent events of the war and the resistance to Fascism in the light of widespread demographic and social myths (Il sentiero dei nidi di ragno, L'entrata in guerra)[1] showing, therefore, an obvious desire for engagement, and the other apparently moving in the opposite direction towards a fantastic, fairytale escapism where any ideological aim could only be redeemed by means of a remote allegorism to which Calvino himself sought to attribute an eighteenth-century origin – something between rationalism and illuminism. Now, however, the 'case', at least within the apparent terms of reference, can be considered definitely closed. One of the first consequences of the massive array of short stories which has recently appeared[2] is to make nonsense of the rigid bipartite scheme, inflating it from within, since even a cursory examination clearly shows that the previously recognized two categories can in fact be subdivided into many others. The vaguely neo-realist, the fantastic and pseudo-illuminist strains are augmented by unmistakable overtones of magic realism, Kafkaism (La formica argentina – The Argentine Ant),[3] nineteenth-century naturalism (La speculazione edilizia) and maybe even influences of the French avant garde novel. To avoid dismembering Calvino's narrative output into an innumerable series of divergent sectors

1. His first two books, the second being a collection of stories. See p. 35.
2. I racconti. This book includes all L'entrata in guerra.
3. Where English titles are also given the translations of the stories are to be found in Adam, One Afternoon. See p. 27.

we must recognize that his various modes of presentation and expression are no more than a consistency of 'phenomena' in the etymological sense of the term, and therefore admit that they relate to an underlying essence or substance, are accidental by nature, hence are subject to contingent pressures, influences of fashion and actuality, momentary moods and inspirations. And so the investigation must understandably change course. It is no longer a question of harmonizing what are at first sight divergent components and trying to establish the moment of equilibrium of each one, be it static or dynamic; one must dig down into the substratum which – and there is sound evidence to support the theory – will remain unchanged, though outward appearances may alter from time to time, causing accidental changes. The advantages of this second procedure are immediately evident. The poetic unity of Calvino's writing is guaranteed almost *a priori* and there is no need to wager on its future aspects and disguises or to dwell on some of them, declaring, at the risk of a prompt denial, that with them the author has fully realized himself and reached his optimum. On the contrary, one can adopt an attitude of pleasurable open-minded anticipation, confident that eventually some of the writer's basic characteristics will show through.

Of course, there remains the grave risk of having to define what is Calvino's essential narrative style. Still, the peculiarities that exist in it are so clearly evident that we can pursue this course surely and calmly. The core of Calvino appears to be an attitude of close attachment with keen curiosity to the world, things in general, animals and human gestures and actions. The writer looks at them with crystalline clarity, childlike innocence that is at the same time extremely prehensile and retentive; as if there were between the eye and the objects observed a clear transparent film, throwing them into sharp relief without blurring line or colour, hence providing a well-defined image. Linguistically, this accuracy of perception is expressed in the search for a precise, specific vocabulary, that is to say, which tends to move from the vague and abstract level of the generic to the species, the family until it aims directly at the individual. And in this urgent desire to reach a hair-fine, valid definition, Calvino undoubtedly has the merit of avoiding the deplorable mediocrity and generality of so much of our contemporary narrative writing (limitations which we have previously had occasion to regret in the cases of Cassola and Bassani). A mass of things pile up in his narration and ask to be catalogued, each to be given a specific place in the limited space they share with their neighbours. To borrow terms frequently employed in semantics, we might say that he uses a denotative type of language in which each word bears a clear, precise relation to one particular thing, one to one, and not a connotative language, that is to say, allusive, ambiguous, inspired by vague feelings. We must, however, be careful of drawing certain conclusions from these initial considerations: the passion for description which, as we have seen, possesses Calvino has not the panic, vitalistic sense at the root of the 'chaotic enumeration' of which Spitzer speaks, nor the nausea on account of the myriad contingencies and senseless aspects of creation that Contini pointed out in Montale. Calvino's experience is much more moderate, and in this sense akin to the 'mediocrity' predominant in our narrative writing; firstly, his linguistic zeal for defining things has nothing to do with expressionism, nor does he resort to specialist and technical terminology. A normal vocabulary is more than sufficient for him though he does his best to avoid the generic and the vague. Then, his descriptive lists never seem too long. In composition, Calvino never forgets to exercise a sense of classical moderation allied to a feeling for sound and rhythm which he tries to reproduce in incisive, fluent cadences and clauses.

That his position, despite appearances, is not radical or extremist is confirmed by a study of his psychological and gnoseological level in relation to the world. As far as things are concerned he is *sguardo*[1] – lenticular survey. A ready association of ideas brings to mind the new French short story, l'*école du regard*, Robbe-Grillet and Butor. But the comparison is completely superficial. The two French writers in fact, attempt a bold, extremely difficult and frequently ingenious trick, beyond the bounds of 'common sense'

1. i.e. look. regard.

and go in search of original relationships between an anthropo-
centric universe governed by reassuring gravitational laws and
objects, restoring to the latter the shock value that familiarity has
blunted and encrusted; of course, they do not achieve this solely
by an exceptional individual contribution, but are aided and sup-
ported both by a strong, specifically narrative tradition and by a
French culture that is quite accustomed to the most advanced
speculations in various fields of research – epistemology, psychology, education, etc. Calvino, on the other hand, has behind
him the calmer, more composed Italian culture which does not
afford him a wide margin of movement: if, therefore, he ventures
bravely to the very limit where objects grow large and press at all
points on the visual screen, clamouring to take the initiative, he
still does not have the strength to abandon the threshold of
'common sense', and in the end actually sees that legislation and
hierarchies prevail in the world of objects where they have cur-
rency. In other words, the writer remains attached to a universe
of usual proportions and is full of confidence in a familiar nature,
within easy reach, entirely verifiable. And most probably he will
come to believe that this equilibrium, this keeping things in their
place will guarantee the victory of rationalistic attitude over the
irrationalism of European decadentism; we, more pessimistically,
think that this is a victory of Italian 'good sense' (with all the
limiting connotations of narrow-mindedness and conformism that
are associated with this term) over more vital restlessness and passions. The trouble is that entrenchment in 'common sense' cannot
fail to condemn to futility and vacuity the subtle analytical considerations so effectively drawn by Calvino. Just consider the series
Amori difficili[1] and for instance *Avventura di un viaggiatore*
which as we have said can be vaguely compared to Butor's *La
Modification*: the protagonist's maze of tiny gestures, patiently
recorded and fixed, still remains marginal, suitably scaled down to
the world of 'common sense', never becomes of primary importance, nor assumes dramatic proportions (as happens, on the other
hand, in Butor). Calvino's analysis, therefore, does not go beyond

1. A group of stories in I racconti.

the ambitions and possibilities of a marginal treatment, charming, exquisite, finely-wrought, but incapable of capturing higher values.

For these reasons it is perhaps more appropriate to speak of *sguardo* in his case than in that of the young French writers because his view of things is linear, photographic, free of ontological implications or any attempt at a new phenomenalistic order: *sguardo*, then, that is to say an act of intermittent application consistent with a feeling of 'indifference' which makes him jump from one object to another with restless and erratic curiosity. Within this basic situation, though, Calvino is allowed very considerable freedom of articulation. Sometimes things stand out separately in profile, artificially, figuratively, emblematic and then we enter a zone of magic realism with excursions over the frontiers of fable; or else the catalogue firmly takes the lead – things mentioned one by one punctuate the story (*Ultimo viene il corvo – The Crow Comes Last*; *Un pomeriggio, Adamo – Adam, One Afternoon*[1]; *Furto in una pasticceria – Theft in a Cake-shop*), or again they form machines baroque in style; or linked in fleet, slightly absurd groups, they verge on the nonsensical, stopping short, however, to preserve a last trace of physical and natural reality and so avoiding extinction in a mere play on words. Calvino is the amused demiurge of this world where 'marriages and illegal divorces between things' are celebrated – to borrow a happy phrase from Bacon (an author recently vindicated by Anceschi in the field of baroque sensibility). Never forget, however, that his attachment to 'common sense' is always present and ready to intervene in order to prevent these juxtapositions from opening on to a new dimension of knowledge.

Alongside these patently obvious possibilities of articulation (as long as he is dealing with things) there are on the other hand grave deficiencies. Calvino's observation and his naturalistic enthusiasm for association of ideas completely lack dramatic force and pathos, they operate on a plane that passions scarcely reach or if they do, are filtered and purified. In this connexion we might speak of his

1. The title story of the collection published in English.

childlike 'innocence'. It is not by chance that many of the principal characters in his stories are either children or adolescents. In general, I should say that maybe the author portrays the state of childhood more than any other. Notice, however, that in contrast with Pavese, while childhood figures in his work the corresponding sentimental myth does not. If it did, it would load objects with painful emotion, vast connotative layers, obscuring them and destroying their direct relationship one to one with the words.

Moreover, in Pavese childhood is of necessity a state that now appears remote, as inaccessible as *Paradise Lost*. But in Calvino it can be directly experimented with and verified, in other words it is not a unique, irrevocable experience but the main, normal way of establishing contact with the world.

A logical corollary of this lack of drama in the *Racconti* is also their asexuality: not that there is any lack of gestures and revealing signs of sex motivations and impulses: on the contrary these are readily and avidly fixed with precise analytical power (as for instance in *Avventura di un soldato*), but treated in the tone of superior detachment and amusement of someone outside the particular key that characterizes and unifies them: and once again we are reminded of the childlike mind, quick to grasp the aberrations which sex causes in the conduct of adults, and to judge them with ironic superiority. Which again confirms the fact that things are the true dominating factors in Calvino's stories and that sexual implications, like any others are subordinated to them (*Va' cosí che vai bene*). Even the little psychological and pathological depth in his work can be explained by taking into account the reactions of a state that hovers between the childlike and the adolescent. The difficulties afflicting the characters in the *Racconti* all originate in a central crisis which arises when conventions, oppressive rules and adults' ways try to cloud and alter the clear outline of things, that is when they biasedly impede the fluid naturalness and availability necessary for unprejudiced contact with things. Also stemming from the same source are the scruples, problems, and guilt complexes that influence child and adolescent consciences on account of the brutal revelation of class distinction as stressed and repeated over and over again by adults with crystallized minds (*Pranzo con un pastore* – A Goatherd at Luncheon; *L'entrata in guerra*).

At this point it is plain to see that it is extremely difficult for Calvino to be *engagé* as a writer, if by *engagement* we understand a declared allegiance to a socially valid and politically practical ideology proposing a class-conscious form of teleology (today in our cultural circles this unfortunately is the significance given to the term *engagement*); no one thinks that a writer could be *engagé* for accepting one epistemology, one psychological conception, instead of another and that consequently an indication of his commitment might be the choice of certain technical instruments rather than others. Precisely because he has a 'nature' completely divorced from any ideology connected with the comic and curious trick of *regard*, Calvino was one of the first to break with the fictitious and stodgy atmosphere of our post-war realism : but he was not persuaded to break away by the awareness of his own talents, since, after rejecting the heavy Marxist-type ideology, he still did not have the courage to come out into the open but, swathed in a cloak of ambiguity, made repeated references to his position as rationalistic-illuministic. But as I have pointed out, although this ideology is more subtle and superficially, at least, more suited to the writer's gifts it is far from easy to trace it in his work. Take for instance the most successful experiment in this vein, *Il barone rampante*.[1]

From our previous examination we can immediately see the essential ingredients : firstly a naturalistic panorama of a vast country seen through the eyes of childhood (reminiscent of Nievo, but clearer and bolder in colour and line) : then the various associative ideas, vegetable ballet, baroque machine, swift, agile compositions of objects on the verge of nonsense. As for the eighteenth-century libertine and illuministic patina, this has a clearly chromatic, not an ideological or mental function : it is therefore an accessory, not a structural element – which demolishes

1. The novel published in English as *Baron in the Trees*.

the theory of a new ideological *engagement* professed by the writer.

There remains one last consideration, also of far-reaching consequences. Calvino, we have seen, moves at a level crowded with objects which sometimes take the initiative; his usual attitude is descriptive, like a catalogue, exploiting the possibilities that the juxtaposition of those objects offers. Hence one can appreciate how difficult it is for him to hold this light, porous material together, to channel it in a single direction, to carry it to a conclusion, a dénouement, a catastrophe. This explains the difficulties that Calvino faces in writing a novel and, conversely, his preference for the short story. It also explains the successive disguises he has adopted in the past, and doubtlessly will continue to adopt in the future, in search of a mould, a blue-print, a framework to help him organize the diffuse, detailed material that his eye catches. And finally it explains the unstable relationship, at times, of the analytical and structural aspects of his work.

For others (Robbe-Grillet is an example) can make this instability an intrinsic part of their literary personality: Robbe-Grillet's style is, in fact, generic, haphazard, banal so as to bring more forcibly to the fore the underlying minutely-meshed texture of perceptions. Calvino, on the other hand, remember, has no intention of severing the links with 'common sense' and is therefore forced to seek natural, convincing and homogeneous solutions. And it is precisely this that he finds particularly difficult.

Take, for example, the three stories at the end of the collection,[1] which because of their length aggravate the problem of absorbing organically descriptive details, plot and action. *La formica argentina* which in detail is full of amusing invention, and brilliant baroque complications, considered as a whole, tries to reproduce the unifying atmosphere of Kafka: but here Calvino at once comes up against various taboos – chiefly again the impassable barrier of 'common sense', which prevents him from expressing coherently and accurately an experience of the absurd: then there is his inability to dramatize which renders the whole futile, destroying all

1. *La formica argentina, La speculazione edilizia*, and *La nuvola di smog*.

the ingenious details with it. *La speculazione edilizia* is packed with subtle observations and local colour (the garden of the ancestral home, builder's yard activity, the growth of the new building) conjuring up a wonderfully clear picture. But over all there is a lack of clearly-defined aim and direction, the story gropes to an end, terminating in a spate of socialistic idealism (the intellectual's brotherhood with a group of workers who were formerly his comrades in political battles and their struggle with *parvenus* and the bourgeoisie which is a too obvious way of finding a respectable solution.

The argument does not change too much in *La nuvola di smog*: here too, rarely perceptive, is the inner shrine where the principal character goes to live; marvellous the reception of nocturnal sounds, the discovery of the fine layer of dust over everything. But, to spoil it all, comes the attempted, allegorical, ponderous and ineffective justification, the disjointed insertion of a love affair, confirming the almost complete inability of the author to deal with complex dramatic psychological situations.

The most satisfactory solution, and it is easy to understand why, is provided by the three autobiographical stories published some time ago in Einaudi paperback (*L'entrata in guerra, Gli avanguardisti a Mentone, Le notti dell' UNPA*). Here we find that the rhythm of experience in life, just as it was, gives structure to the stories. But Calvino cannot continue to rely on a direct and spontaneous manner of ordering things and events in the way that 'life was lived'. From this point of view, the three most clearly autobiographical stories constitute experiences which can scarcely be repeated, and so offer a solution that Calvino cannot, quite rightly, consider as ideal.

This study has come up against many snags, many blind alleys. In conclusion, however, this must be said for Calvino. His is a substantial achievement, his work is packed with presences and things which are meticulously described in a personal, original manner, ventilated by clear, keen perception.

Translated by Gwyn Morris

Italo Calvino

THE SIGN IN SPACE

The sun is situated in the outer zone of the Milky Way and (according to the calculations of J. H. Oort) takes some 200 million years to revolve completely round the Galaxy.

That's right, that's the time it takes, no less – said Qfwfq – once when I was passing I made a sign at a point in space, just so that I could find it again two hundred million years later, when we passed there on the next round. What sort of a sign? It's not easy to say because if you hear the word sign you immediately think of a something that is distinct from a something, whereas in this case there was nothing that could be distinguished from anything else; you immediately think of a sign marked by some tool or with hands, and then you take away the tool or hands and the sign stays, but at that time there weren't any tools or even hands or teeth or noses – those were all things that came afterwards, but much later. The form to be given to the sign, according to you, isn't a problem because, whatever form it has, it's enough for a sign to serve as a sign, that is, that it's different or the same as other signs: here too it's easy to talk, but at that time I had nothing to refer to which would tell me whether I was doing it in the same way or differently, there was nothing to copy, there was no knowing what a line was, straight or curved, or a point, or anything convex or concave. True I had the intention of making a sign, in other words I had the intention of viewing as a sign anything that I happened to make, so that, as at that point in space and not at another I had done something with the intention of making a sign, the result was that I really had made a sign.

And anyway as it was the first sign that had been made in the universe or at least in the round of the Milky Way, I must say that it came out pretty well. Could it be seen? That's all very well, but who in those days had eyes to see with? Nothing had ever been seen by anything, the question didn't even arise. But what it was was recognizable without risk of mistake, that, yes, while all the other points of space were the same and indistinguishable, this one had the sign.

So, as the planets went on in their round and the solar system in its round, I soon left the sign behind me in the endless fields of space. And already I couldn't help thinking of the time when I would be back at it again, and how I would recognize it, and of the pleasure it would give me, in that nameless expanse, after travelling a hundred thousand light years without running into anything familiar, nothing for hundreds of centuries, for thousands of millenniums, and then getting back and there it would be in its place, just as I had left it, rough and primitive but with that un-mistakable stamp, so to speak, that I had given it.

Slowly the Milky Way turned on itself with its fringes of con-stellations and planets and clouds, and the Sun with the rest, but on the edge. In all this merry-go-round only the sign stayed put, protected from every orbit (to make it I had leant out from the margin of the Galaxy so that it would be in the open and the rolling of all those worlds would not run into it), at any point that was no longer any point once it had become the only point you could be sure was there, so that all other points could be defined in relation to it.

I thought about it day and night; the fact is I could think of nothing else; or rather, that was my first opportunity of thinking anything; or better still, thinking something had never been pos-sible, first because there weren't things to think, and secondly because there weren't signs to think them, but as soon as there was that sign there came the possibility that the thinker should think a sign and therefore that sign, in the sense that the sign was the thing that could be thought and also the sign of the thing thought, that is, of itself.

So the situation was as follows: the sign served to mark a point, but at the same time it marked that there was a sign there, which was more important as points were plentiful whereas that was the only sign there was, and at the same time the sign was my sign, the sign of me, because it was the only sign I had ever made, and I was the only one who had ever made signs. It was like a name, the name of that point, and also my name that I had marked on that point, in other words it was the only available name for all that required a name.

Borne away on the side of the Galaxy our world sailed beyond furthest space and the sign was where I had left it to mark that point, and at the same time it marked me, I took it along with me, it lived in me, it possessed me entirely, it came between me and everything with which it was possible for me to attempt a relationship. While I was waiting to get back to meet it I could try to derive other signs and combinations of signs from it, series of the same signs and different countersigns. But already tens and tens of thousands of millenniums had passed from the moment I had made it (or rather, from the few seconds in which I had set it down in the continuous movement of the Milky Way) and at this very time when I most needed to have it present in every detail (the slightest uncertainty about how it was made cast uncertainty on possible distinctions about other eventual signs), I realized that though I had its broad outlines in mind and its general appearance, still, when I tried to decompose it into its various elements something about it escaped me, I couldn't remember any longer whether it was this way or that way between one element and the next. I needed it there in front of me so as to study it and consult it, whereas there it was far away, how far I couldn't think, because I had made it precisely to know the time it would take to find it again and till I found it again I wouldn't know. But it wasn't why I had made it that mattered to me now, but how it was made, and I began making hypotheses about this how, and theories that a given sign ought necessarily to be in a given way, or else proceeding by way of exclusion, I tried to eliminate all kinds of less probable signs, so as to arrive at the right one, but all these imaginary signs evaporated in the irresistible flow, because of there being no first sign of comparison. In all this worry (while the Galaxy went on sleeplessly turning in its bed of soft emptiness, as if moved by the itching desire of all the worlds and atoms which set one another on fire and radiated) it came to me that even my confused notion of the sign now escaped me and all I could conceive were fragments of signs interchangeable with one another, that is, signs within the sign, and every change in these signs within the sign changed the sign into a completely different sign, in other words I had completely forgotten what my sign was like and there was no point of reference to bring it back into my mind.

Did I lose hope? No, this forgetfulness was tiresome but it wasn't irremediable. Whatever happened I knew that the sign was there waiting for me, motionless and silent. I would reach it again, I would meet it and take up anew the thread of my reasoning. At a rough guess we must already have passed through half the course of our galactic revolution; we had to have patience, the second half always gives the impression of passing quickly. All I needed to think of now was the fact that the sign was there and that I would be passing by there again.

Day followed day and now I must be near. I was trembling with impatience because by now I might run into the sign at any moment. Here it was, no, a bit further on, now I'll count up to a hundred. . . . Perhaps it wasn't still there? Perhaps I had already passed it? There was nothing. My sign remained heavens knew where, behind, completely out of reach of the orbit on which our system was revolving. I had failed to reckon with the oscillations which, especially in those times, the forces of gravity of the heavenly bodies were subject to, which made them describe irregular and indented orbits like the petals of a dahlia. For a hundred odd millenniums I worried over my calculations: and they proved that our course touched that point not every galactic year but only every three, that is, every six hundred million solar years. When you have waited for two hundred million years you can wait six hundred; and I waited; the journey was long but after all I hadn't to make it on foot; on the back of the Galaxy I galloped on the planetary and stellar orbits as on the saddle of a horse with its hooves scattering sparks; I was in a state of ever-increasing exaltation; I felt I was advancing towards the conquest of the only thing that mattered to me, my sign and kingdom and name . . .

I made the second round and the third. I was there. I gave a cry. At a point where that particular point should be, instead of my sign there was a shapeless scrawl, a chipped and bruised abrasion in space. I had lost everything: the sign, the point, the thing that worked so that I – who was precisely the one of that sign and that point – was I. Now there was no sign; space had gone back to being a nauseating whirlwind of emptiness without beginning or end, in which everything, including me, was lost. (And please don't tell me that to make a sign at a point, my sign, and the obliteration of my sign were one and the same thing; the obliteration was the negation of the sign, and hence didn't sign or mark, that is, didn't serve to distinguish one point from the points coming before and after.)

Discouragement took over and I let myself be dragged on for many light years as though deprived of feeling. When at last I lifted up my eyes (in the meanwhile sight had begun in our world and, in consequence, life also) – when I lifted up my eyes I saw something I would never have expected to see. I saw it, the sign, but not that one, another similar one, a sign doubtless copied from mine, but which you knew immediately couldn't be mine, deformed and casual as it was and awkwardly pretentious, a disgusting counterfeit of what I had meant to sign in that sign, whose indescribable purity now at last, by contrast, I could evoke once more. Who had played this trick on me? I couldn't make rhyme or reason out of it. In the end, after a plurimillennial chain of inductions, I reached the solution: on another planetary system that was on its galactic revolution ahead of us, there was a certain Kgwgk (the name was only deduced later in the epoch of names), a spiteful fellow devoured with envy who had obliterated my sign with a vandalistic impulse and then with a vulgar trick had tried to mark another sign.

It was plain that that sign had nothing to sign except Kgwgk's intention of imitating my sign, with which it couldn't even be compared. But at that moment the desire not to give in to my rival outweighed any other consideration; I felt an immediate urge to sketch a new sign in space that would be a real sign and would make Kgwgk die with envy. It was about seven hundred million years since I had given up any attempt to make a sign, after the first one, and I set about it with zest. But now things were different, for the world – as I have already suggested – was beginning to provide an image of itself and to the function of each thing there was now the beginning of a corresponding form, and it was thought at that time that the forms had a long future before them (but it wasn't true: think for instance – to take a relatively recent case – of the dinosaurs), and so in this new sign I made you could feel the influence of how things seemed then, the style so to say, the special way everything had of being there in a certain way. I must admit that I felt thoroughly satisfied, and I stopped mourning for my first obliterated sign because this new one seemed to me enormously more impressive.

But during that galactic year you began to understand dimly that up to that moment the world's forms had been provisional and they would be changed one by one. And this awareness was accompanied by a feeling of boredom about the old images, so much so that you couldn't even endure remembering them. And I began being tormented by a thought: when I had left that sign in space it had seemed impressive and original and adapted to its function but, as I remembered it, I could see all its pretentiousness and its out-of-placeness, above all it was a sign of an antiquated way of thinking of signs and of my silly complicity with an order of things that I should have had the sense to detach myself from in time. In a word I was ashamed of that sign which worlds in their flight went on skirting for centuries, and giving a ridiculous spectacle of itself and of me and of the provisional way we had had of seeing things. Blushes of shame afflicted me when I remembered it (and I remembered it continually) which lasted through entire geological ages: to hide my shame I sank in the craters of volcanoes and my remorse made me sink my teeth into the ice caps that covered the continents. I was assailed by the thought that Kgwgk, who was always ahead of me in the circumference of the Milky Way, would see the sign before I could obliterate it and being the clodhopper he was he would mock and mimic me and, to show his contempt, would repeat the sign in rough caricature at every corner of the galactic sphere.

Whereas this time the complicated timing of the stars worked in my favour. Kgwgk's constellation didn't run into the sign whereas our solar system reached there punctually at the end of the first round, and so near that I could wipe out the sign with the greatest care.

Now there wasn't a trace of any sign by me in space. I could sketch out another, but now I knew that signs can also stand in judgement against those who make them and that in a galactic year tastes and ideas have time to change, and your way of looking on the early ones depends on what comes later, in fact I was afraid that a sign that would now seem to me perfect would make me look ridiculous in two or six hundred million years. Whereas to my distress my first sign that had been wiped out by the vandal Kgwgk remained beyond the reach of the change of times, it had been born before the faintest beginning of forms and had to contain something that would outlive all forms, that is, the fact of being a sign and nothing more.

Making signs that weren't that sign held no interest for me any longer; and that sign I had forgotten a billion years ago. So as I couldn't make real signs, but as I still wanted to annoy Kgwgk, I started making false signs, notches in space, holes, splashes, all sorts of little tricks that only an incompetent such as Kgwgk could mistake for signs. But he was kept furiously busy making them disappear under his obliterations (as I could observe in subsequent rounds) with a care that must have cost him a lot of trouble. (By now I was scattering those false signs in space to see how far his stupidity could go.)

Now as in round after round I saw his obliterations (I now sailed through the revolutions of the Galaxy in a lazy, bored way without aim or expectation) I began noticing something: that as the galactic years passed by, his obliterations tended to fade in space and below them what I myself had marked at that point revived, my – as I called it – pretended-sign. Far from displeasing me, the discovery fired me with new hope. If Kgwgk's obliterations obliterated themselves, the first that he had made, there at that point, should have disappeared by now and my sign should have become as evident as it had been in the beginning.

So once more I had anxious days of waiting. The Galaxy turned itself like an omelette in its red-hot pan, it itself was both the pan that was frying and the golden curled omelette; and I fried with it in my impatience.

But as the galactic years passed by, space was no longer the uniformly naked and vague expanse of before. The idea of marking with two signs the points where you passed, as I and Kgwgk had done, had occurred to plenty of others scattered on billions of planets in other solar systems, and I was continually running into one of these things, or a couple, or even a dozen, mere two-dimensional scrawls or solid with three dimensions (for instance polyhedrons) and even things put together in a more workmanlike way still, with the fourth dimension and all. So that when I get to the point where my sign is, I find five of them there together. And I simply can't make out which is mine. It must be this one, no it's that other one, this one looks too modern, yet it could be the oldest, here I don't recognize my workmanship, surely I couldn't have had the idea of making it that way.... And meanwhile the Galaxy hurried on through space leaving old and new signs behind it and I hadn't found mine again.

It wouldn't be exaggerating if I said that the galactic years that followed were the worst I had ever experienced. I went on looking and signs were growing thick in space, no one from any of the worlds who now had the possibility ever neglected to mark his trace in space in some way, and as for our world, every time I looked back, I now found it more and more crowded, so much so that the world and space seemed mirrors of each other for both of them were decorated with hieroglyphs and ideograms, and any of them could be a sign or not as the case might be: a limestone conception on basalt, a crest raised by the wind on the curdled sand of the desert, the arrangement of eyes in the feathers of the peacock (little by little life amongst the signs had made you see as signs the innumerable things that had been there before without signing anything but their own presence, it had transformed them into signs of themselves and added to the series of signs made deliberately by whoever wanted to make a sign), the stripes made by fire against a wall of broken rock, the four-hundred-and-twenty-seventh fluting – rather sideways – of a cornice in the pediment of a mausoleum, a sequence of streaks on a screen during a magnetic storm (the series of signs was multiplied in the series of signs of signs, of signs repeated innumerable times, always the same and always in some way different, because to the sign made on purpose could be added the sign that had happened there by chance), the badly inked stroke of the letter R in a copy of an evening paper happening to fall on a break in the fibre of the paper, one amongst the eight hundred thousand bare patches on a tarred wall of an interstice in the Melbourne docks, a statistical curve, brake marks on asphalt, a chromosome. . . . Every now and again a start: that was it, and for a second I was sure I had found my sign again, it made no difference whether it was on the earth or in space for between signs a continuity had now been established, without a clear borderline.

For now in the universe there was no longer a container and a content, but only a general thicket of signs placed on one another and stuck together that took up all the volume of space, it was a continual ever-so-minute speckle, an entanglement of lines and scratches and reliefs and incisions, the universe was one big scribble on all sides and along all its dimensions. There was no way now of fixing a reference point; the Galaxy went on with its turning but I couldn't count the rounds any more, any point could be the starting point, any sign piled on the others could be my sign, but it wouldn't have been the slightest use discovering it, for it was now perfectly clear that independently from the signs space didn't exist and perhaps had never existed.

Translated by Bernard Wall

Notes on the Authors

ALBERTO ARBASINO: Brilliant, with a quick wit sometimes deliberately frivolous, extraordinarily widely read and very versatile, Arbasino might be described as a *salottiere* intellectual. Angus Wilson has said of him that he is 'the youngest and cleverest of all the Italian critics today'. Well known for his interviews of literary people, he has been called by Paolo Milano the *magnetofono ben temperato*, the well-tempered tape-recorder (from Bach's 'The Well-tempered Clavier') – a nickname that has stuck. He travels abroad a great deal and contributes prolifically to newspapers and journals. He has a regular place on the literary page of *Il Giorno*.

Arbasino was born in Voghera, Lombardy, in 1930 and took his degree in law and political science. He now lives in Rome. His first two books, *Le piccole vacanze* (1957) and *L'anonimo lombardo* (1959) were collections of stories. *The Lost Boy* (1964) was a long story taken from *L'anonimo lombardo*. Two novels, *Parigi o cara* and *Fratelli d'Italia*, were published in 1961 and 1962. Then came *La narcisata, la controra* (1963): stories, and *Certi romanzi* (1964): essays. *Grazie per le magnifiche rose* (1965) is a collection of theatre pieces and *La maleducazione teatrale* (1966), essays. A film was made from one of his short stories, *La bella di Lodi* (1962). *Figaro Up Figaro Down* appeared originally in *Tempo Presente*.

GIOVANNI ARPINO: Arpino was born in 1927 and lived for a long while in Piedmont; he now lives in Milan. He was educated at Turin University. For many years he has worked as an editor. Stylistically he keeps a balance between experimentalism and traditionalism. His novel *Sei stato felice, Giovanni* was published in 1952 and was followed by his two books of poems, *Barbaresco* (1954) and *Il prezzo dell'oro* (1957). His other novels, which have been widely translated, are *Gli anni del giudizio* (1958); *La suora giovane* (1959, *The Novice* 1961); *Un delitto d'onore* (1962, *A Crime of Honour* 1963); *L'ombra delle colline* (1964), which was awarded the Premio Strega; *Un' anima persa* (1966). He has written children's books and has contributed numerous articles and stories to *Il Mondo*, *Botteghe Oscure*, *Paragone*, *Tempo Presente* and other literary magazines.

RENATO BARILLI: Barilli belongs to the younger group of Italian critics and writes on both art and literature for *Il Verri* and other similar journals. He was born in 1935 at Bologna, where he lives and lectures on aesthetics at the University. His first three books were *Dubuffet materiologico* (1962), *L'Informale ed altri studi d'arte contemporanea* (1964) and *Per un'estetica* *mondana* (1964). The essay on the work of Italo Calvino (compare Calvino on himself, p. 35) comes from *La barriera del naturalismo* (1964).

The theme of *La barriera del naturalismo* is that an invisible barrier has grown up between ourselves and reality. In the nineteenth century attempts were made in literature to provide keys and solutions to the human condition. In this century writers, especially at the present moment, have well and truly breached the wall. It started in Italy with Svevo and Pirandello. Moravia enlarged it. Sanguineti is the latest exponent. But after the war many young writers tried to return to naturalism. Calvino was in the position of being on both sides at once.

The Short Stories of Calvino, considered by Montale to be the best essay in *La barriera del naturalismo* when he reviewed the book in the *Corriere della Sera*, first appeared separately after Calvino's collected stories, *I racconti*, were published in 1958. Some of the stories mentioned by Barilli are to be found in *Adam, One Afternoon* (1957), which is a selection from *Ultimo viene il corvo* (1946) and also containing the novella *La formica argentina* (The Argentine Ant).

GIORGIO BASSANI: Bassani is among the most influential literary figures in Italy today. He is also one of the most widely read Italian authors abroad. At present Vice-President of Italian Television and Radio at Rome, he was for some years literary director of Feltrinelli. where he was responsible for discovering *The Leopard*. Previously he was editor of Marguerite Caetani's *Botteghe Oscure*. Born at Bologna in 1916, he published his first book in 1945: *Storie dei poveri amanti*. His talent became internationally recognized with *Cinque storie ferraresi* (1956) – in English *A Prospect of Ferrara* (1962) – which won him the Premio Strega. These five novellas were designed to present a composite picture of a large Italian provincial town, and of the gradual seeping into it of the poisons of Fascism and anti-semitism. The story selected here by the author, *The Snows of Yesteryear*, published in 1964 in *I maestri del racconto italiano*, is somewhat in their tradition. His novels, *Gli occhiali d'oro* (1958) and *Il giardino dei Finzi Contini* (1962) have also been translated: *The Gold-Rimmed Spectacles* (1960); *The Garden of the Finzi-Continis* (1965), and very well received by the critics. *L'alba ai vetri*, poems 1942–50, was published in 1963, *Dietro la porta*, a novel, in 1964 and *Le parole preparate*, essays, in 1966.

ITALO CALVINO: Although Calvino's talent is highly individual, he may be described as a true representative of modern European writing. He has sometimes, in certain moods, been compared with Ariosto. His prose is glittering and sparkling, and he has a special brand of humour and fantasy, mixed with a feeling for the grotesque and with an underlying irony and satirical edge. His first book, *Il sentiero dei nidi di ragno*, won the Premio

Riccione in 1947 and was published in English as *The Path to the Nest of Spiders* (1956). This was a direct result of his experience with the partisans between 1943–5. In 1964 it was reissued, with an important preface which was, in effect, a survey of all his writing; an extract from the preface is included in this book.

He was born at San Remo in 1923, the son of the curator of the botanic garden there, a fact which no doubt accounts for his interest in natural history and the superb way in which he can evoke the magic of scenery, gardens and wild things growing and living. In his three novels, *Il visconte dimezzato* (1952), *Il cavaliere inesistente* (1959) – published together in English as *The Non-Existent Knight* in 1962 – and *Il barone rampante* (1957, *Baron in the Trees* 1959) Calvino allows his imagination to roam among ranks of chivalry, convents, castles and courts. His last novel, *La giornata di uno scrutatore* (1963), is totally different from the others, in effect a sociological and political (left-wing) treatise. However in 1965 he published a collection of stories *Le cosmicomiche* – one being *The Sign in Space*, the last item in *Italian Writing Today* – and these, though science fiction and more 'difficult', to some extent follow the mood of his earlier fantasies; each story begins with a scientific premise, and each has as its protagonist Qfwfq, whose age is that of the universe itself.

In 1947 he joined the publishing firm of Einaudi, and he is now on its editorial board. He is editor, originally with Vittorini, of the controversial literary magazine, *Il Menabò*. An essay by Renato Barilli on Calvino's work, written after the publication of *I racconti* in 1958, is to be found on page 254; see also pages 272–3.

CARLO CASSOLA: *The Return of Michele*, from a forthcoming novel, appeared first as a short story in *Tempo Presente*. It contains many typical ingredients: first stirrings of love, ordinary people in provincial settings, the effects of war; all presented in the usual, somewhat 'bare' style. A new book by Cassola is automatically a best-seller in Italy, and his novels have been widely translated. He prides himself on always having been outside literary trends or schools.

He was born in Rome in 1917. During the war he fought with the partisans in Tuscany. At first he wrote short stories only and these were collected in two books published in 1942: *Alla periferia* and *La visita*. Other books of stories and novellas followed, in particular *I racconti* (1958) and *Il taglio del bosco* (1959), an important landmark in his career. His novels are: *Fausto e Anna* (1952, *Fausto and Anna* 1960); *I vecchi compagni* (1953); *Un matrimonio del dopoguerra* (1957); *La ragazza di Bube* (1960, *Bebo's Girl* 1962), the winner of the Premio Strega; *Un cuore arido* (1961, in America *The Arid Heart* 1964); *Il Cacciatore* (1964). *Tempi memorabili*, a novella, was published in 1966. He lives in Grosseto.

NICOLA CHIAROMONTE: An essayist and leading drama critic, Chiaromonte is co-editor with Ignazio Silone of the Roman monthly magazine, *Tempo Presente*, the nearest equivalent of which in Britain is *Encounter*. He contributes to *Il Mondo*, *Partisan Review*, *Encounter*, *Preuves*, *Merkur* and *Der Monat*. He also wrote for *Solaria*, the important pre-war literary magazine, as well as the anti-Fascist clandestine magazine *Giustizia e Libertà* and *Politics* (American). His only book has been *La situazione drammatica* (1959), which contains the piece in this book, being the major part of the text of a speech delivered to the Circolo Universitario Teatrale of Naples in March 1959 and revealing his very wide knowledge of his subject.

Chiaromonte was born in 1905 in southern Italy. From 1934–46 he lived in France and the U.S.A., on account of his opposition to Fascism.

UMBERTO ECO: Eco is one of the brightest figures to have emerged on the Italian literary scene during the last five years. As a critic he is the mouthpiece of the avant garde, through his essays and by means of magazines such as *Il Verri* or the manifestos of *Gruppo 63* and others.

He was born in Alessandria in 1932 and is now Reader in Aesthetics at Turin University. He made his mark in 1962 with the *Opera aperta: forma e indeterminazione nelle poetiche contemporanee*, essays on electronic music, cinema, television and literature, including a long essay on Joyce. *Diario minimo* (1963) is also a book of essays on social behaviour, with literary and philosophical parodies. His *Apocalittici e integrati* (1964), from which *The Structure of Bad Taste* is an extract, is a study of mass communication and culture – strip cartoons and the like ('Peanuts' is a current craze among the Italian intelligentsia). Recently he wrote an essay on James Bond (here one might compare Kingsley Amis's book, *The James Bond Dossier*). His conclusion in the essay is that one should not attempt to analyse books by Ian Fleming but rather the society in which these phenomena have such wide repercussions. *Le poetiche di Joyce* was published in 1966. He reviews regularly in *L'Espresso*.

LUCIANO ERBA: Erba is a solitary figure in Italian poetry, representing the younger, as against youngest, generation. He is a highly reticent person and completely outside any organized movement. He remains firmly aloof from the sophisticated, 'winnowed' styles popular with the avant garde poets. Born in Milan in 1922, he lives and works there as a professor of French literature at the University. His books of poetry include *Linea K* (1951), *Ippogrammi e metaippogrammi di Giovanola* (1958), *Il prete di Ratanà* (1959) and *Il male minore* (1960), where *Dignus est Entrare* and *In the Ivory Tower* appeared. He edited *Quarta generazione: Antologia della Giovane poesia* (1954) and has translated *Cyrano de Bergerac*.

BEPPE FENOGLIO: Among the most gifted of Italy's first wave of post-war authors, Fenoglio died in February 1963 at the age of forty. A reserved man, he worked in business (for a wine firm) and writing was therefore a spare-time occupation for him, accounting for his small output. His passion for honesty, clarity and realism caused him to be compared with Pavese. During the war he fought with the partisans, to him a fabled experience.

He was born in 1922 at Alba near Cuneo, where he also died. Many of his stories contain the same characters and settings. His first book was a collection of stories, *I ventitre giorni della città di Alba*, and was published in 1952. Two years later it was followed by another collection, *La malora*. A novel, *Primavera di bellezza*, was published in 1959. *Un giorno di fuoco* was published in 1963; this also was a collection of stories and included part of an unfinished novel, *Una questione privata*, from which an extract has been taken (see Calvino's comments on the book on page 42).

BRUNO FONZI: Although Bruno Fonzi has translated a great deal from a variety of Anglo-Saxon authors (Boswell to Hemingway, Mark Twain to O'Neill), he has taken to creative writing fairly late in life. Born at Macerata in 1914, he published his first book, *Un duello sotto il fascismo*, short stories, in 1961. His only other book, a short novel, *Il maligno*, about the effect of the evil eye on the inhabitants of a small village in Central Italy, appeared in 1964 and has been much admired. After living for a long while in Rome he is now in Turin, the setting of *Il Nord* – part, or rather parts, of a longer piece that was published in *Tempo Presente*, but with a new beginning specially written by Fonzi for this book. He is editorial adviser to Einaudi, the well-known publishing firm in Turin.

FRANCO FORTINI: A poet and critic, Fortini is an engaged Marxist, owing his artistic formation to Éluard, Brecht and Lukàcs. His poems sometimes have an elegiac quality, revealing a conflict between an aristocratic tradition and man's political predicament, as influences on thought and political action. The two formidable rather compressed studies of the work of Luzi and Sereni are part of a long essay, *Le poesie italiane di questi anni*, which was published in *Il Menabò* 2 (1960), and show Fortini's remarkable critical insight and love for poetry, with of course a strong political bias. The whole essay gathers together and weighs up the Italian poetry of the previous fifty years and as such is very important – probably one of the most important on the subject, together with *Passione e ideologia* by Pasolini, with whom intellectually he might be compared.

Fortini was born in Florence in 1917. Since 1945 he has lived and worked in Milan, where he works for *Comunità*, Olivetti's monthly magazine. Two books of poems, *Foglio di via* and *Poesia ed errore*, were published in 1946 and 1959, and *Dieci inverni, 1947–1957 – contributi per un discorso socialista* appeared in 1957. *Una volta per sempre*, poems, and *Sere in Valdossola*, memoirs of the Resistance, were both published in 1963, and *Verifica dei poteri*, essays, in 1965. He edited *Profezie e realtà del nostro secolo* (1965), and *L'ospite ingrato*, poems, was published in 1966. He has translated Éluard, Brecht, Gide, Goethe, Flaubert and Proust.

Poems by Luzi and Sereni will be found on pages 144, 145 and 146.

CARLO EMILIO GADDA: A writer unique in Italy and greatly respected, Gadda has an individual style, full of verbal acrobatics and the most scholarly allusions, even invented words. His use of Italian is very condensed, so a translator may have to use two or three words to convey the exact meaning. Behind his deliberate pedantry there is nearly always irony. In some respects he is like an Italian James Joyce writing in the style of Ivy Compton-Burnett.

Gadda was born in Milan in 1893. In 1918 he was a prisoner of war in Germany. In 1920 he graduated in industrial engineering and later carried on his profession in many countries abroad. He now lives outside Rome. He has published many books of short stories: *La Madonna dei filosofi* (1931), *Il castello di Udine* (1934), *L'Adalgisa* (1943) – all three being collected in *I sogni e la folgore* (1955) – *Il primo libro delle favole* (1952), *Novelle dal ducato in fiamme* (1953), and *Accoppiamenti giudiziosi* (1963), a selection of his stories between 1924–58. His novels are *Quer pasticciaccio brutto de via Merulana* (1957, *That Awful Mess on Via Merulana* 1966) and *La cognizione del dolore* (1963). *I Luigi di Francia*, essays, and *Le meraviglie: gli anni*, essays, travel notes and fragments of autobiography, were both published in 1964, and in 1965 his *Giornale di guerra e di prigionia* (first published 1955) was reissued.

P. A. QUARANTOTTI GAMBINI: Pier Antonio Quarantotti Gambini was never a very popular author in Italy in the general sense, but he enjoyed great esteem among a select readership. Several British publishers have wavered over taking on his books, none of which has so far been translated into English.

He was born at Pisino d'Istria in 1910 and died in Venice in 1965. He spent his childhood in Trieste, where later he worked as a librarian. The piece here comes from his last book, *I giochi di Norma* (1964), linked to two earlier novels, *L'amor militare* (1955) and *Il cavallo Tripoli* (1956); a further novel in this series appears to have been planned.

Gambini wrote forcefully and with a simple clarity. His most imaginative prose was usually concerned with the sea or with Trieste. The most successful novel was *La calda vita* (1958). Other books were: *I nostri simili* (1932), short stories; *La rosa rossa* (1937), a novel; *Trincee* (1942), a novella; *L'onda dell'incrociatore* (1947), a novel; *Sotto il cielo di Russia*

(1963), travel; *Racconto d'amore* (1965), a narrative poem, published post-humously.

ALFONSO GATTO: Gatto is a southern poet, with a highly lyrical style. His work often shows a deep feeling for his childhood. It has also always revealed, even when hermetic symbolism seemed to engage him, a profound desire to maintain a form sensitive to the social structure of humanity, and in this there is a parallel with Quasimodo's poetry.

He was born in Salerno in 1909. In 1938, with Vasco Pratolini, he founded the magazine *Campo di Marte*, directed against mass industrial culture. He was actively polemical against Fascism. Later he was in the Resistance. He now lives in Rome, where he is a journalist and art critic. His books (all poetry) include *Isola* (1932), *Morto ai paesi* (1937), *La sposa bambina* (1943), *Nuove poesie* (1950), *La forza degli occhi* (1953), *Osteria flegrea* (1962) and *La storia delle vittime* (1966), Resistance poems, winner of the Viareggio Prize. *Osteria flegrea* contains *The Spider* and *A Day where the Hour*, and is concerned with his search for an ideological reason for the evil of death. *Carlomagno nella grotta: questioni meridionali*, essays on social problems, was published in 1962.

NATALIA GINZBURG: Natalia Ginzburg is – with Elsa Morante – among the best known internationally of Italy's women writers. She has a deceptively simple style, with a trick of using the most 'ordinary' words to great effect. Born of Jewish parents in Palermo in 1916, her first marriage was to Leone Ginzburg, of Russian origin, a director of Einaudi the publishers, where later she herself worked. Leone Ginzburg died in 1944, probably poisoned by the Germans. In 1950 she married Gabriele Baldini, Director of the Italian Institute in London from 1958–61 and now Professor of English Literature at Rome University – presumably the subject of the frank and very vivid essay at the beginning of this book. Many of her full-length books have been translated into English: *La strada che va in città* (1942) under the pseudonym of Alessandra Tornimparte, and *È stato così* (1947), both novels being published together as *The Road to the City* (1952); *Tutti i nostri ieri* (1952, *Dead Yesterdays* 1956); short stories; *Le voci della sera* (1961, *Voices in the Evening* 1962), a novel. Her autobiography, *Lessico famigliare* (1963, *Family Sayings* in the U.S.A. 1966) won the Premio Strega. *Le piccòle virtù* (1963), essays, contains *He and I*. Her latest book is *Cinque romanzi brevi* (1965), a collection of all her novels.

MARIO LUZI: With Sereni and Gatto, Luzi is one of the chief figures of the Italian middle generation of poets. Once dominated by Ungaretti and Montale, he perhaps has not received the attention he deserves for his highly individual poetic voice. Luzi finds himself by extremes, plunging into continuity and discontinuity, but transcending the moment by keeping his mind in a state of moral tension, thus enabling it to 'return to the soul'.

He was born in 1914 in Florence, where he now lives and teaches French literature at the University. *Onore del vero* (1957) and *Il giusto della vita* (1960) are collections of all his poetry published in earlier volumes. *Biografia a Ebe* (1942), *Studio su Mallarmé* (1951), *L'inferno e il limbo* (1964), and *Tutto in questione* (1965) are all books of essays. *Nel magma* (1964) contained the two poems printed here. *Dal fondo delle campagne* (1965) is a further collection of his poems. He has translated Coleridge, among others. See p. 148 for an assessment of Luzi's work, by Franco Fortini.

DACIA MARAINI: Dacia Maraini caused a literary stir when her novel *L'età del benessere* (1962) was given the Prix Formentor. Published in English as *The Age of Discontent* (1963), the book's paperback cover describes it as 'the prizewinning novel that scandalized Rome. . . . *La dolce vita* at the other end of the social scale'. Alberto Moravia originally discovered Dacia Maraini's work and pressed for the award. This new, sophisticated story has a delightful, rather *Marienbad* quality about it.

Her father is Fosco Maraini, the well-known writer and explorer. She was born in Florence in 1936 and during the war was detained in Japan. Now she lives in Rome. Her other novel, *La vacanza*, was also published in 1962 (*The Holiday* 1966). *Crudeltà all' aria aperta*, poems, appeared in 1966. She has had stories published in *Nuovi Argomenti* and *Tempo di Letteratura*.

LUIGI MENEGHELLO: Meneghello is one of the most original writers to have emerged recently on the Italian literary scene. Both his books *Libera nos a malo* (1963) and *I piccoli maestri* (1964), and especially the first, are literary oddities, hard to put into a category. They are autobiographical, yet not quite autobiography. They also have qualities – such as modesty and irony – which are more usually to be found in Anglo-Saxon literature. *I piccoli maestri*, to be published in English as *The Outlaws*, translated by Raleigh Trevelyan, is about a band of young students in the northern Italian Resistance at the end of the last war, an experience which still arouses passionate feelings in Italy. The style is almost spoken, though the vocabulary is wide, and the humour is subtle and delightful.

He was born at Malo, near Venice, in 1922, read philosophy at Padua, and came to England in 1947. He is now Professor of Italian and head of the Department of Italian Studies at Reading University. He is represented here by three sections from *Libera nos a malo*.

PAOLO MILANO: Paolo Milano is one of Italy's senior critics, with an international reputation. He was born in Rome in 1904 and took his degree at the University there in 1927. At first he was chiefly interested in German literature, and he wrote a number of essays on the subject. He translated the works of such authors as G. E. Lessing, Thomas Mann and Georg Kaiser. From 1931-5 he was drama critic on the literary weekly *L'Italia Letteraria* and from 1932-8 editor-in-chief of the theatre monthly *Scenario*. In 1940 Milano went to the United States, where he lived in New York, teaching History of Drama at the New School for Social Research, and Comparative Literature and Romance Languages at Queen's College. He also became a frequent contributor of literary essays in English to leading American cultural magazines. Since 1955 he has been living in Rome where he is literary editor of *L'Espresso*.

His main works in Italian are *Lessing* (1930), *Henry James o il proscritto volontario* (1948) and *Il lettore di professione* (1961), a collection of essays. His most important work in English is *Dante*, published in New York in 1946.

ANNA MARIA ORTESE: A mysterious writer, because of her long silences and her aloofness from the literary world, Anna Maria Ortese has a curious and very individual style. In *The Lights of Genoa*, a newspaper article (from *Il Mondo*), which on its publication marked her latest re-emergence, she has chosen an effective, rather dreamy way of employing non sequiturs. She was born in Rome and has lived for long periods in Naples, Tripoli, Genoa, Venice and Milan. Her first three books were collections of short stories: *Angelici dolori* (1937), *L'infanta sepolta* (1950) and *Il mare non bagna Napoli* (1953), translated into English as *The Bay is not Naples* (1955) and the winner of the Premio Viareggio. *I giorni del cielo*, stories, and *Silenzio a Milano*, reportage on modern Italy, were both published in 1958, the latter winning the Premio St Vincent. Her latest book is a novel, an original and very strange fantasy, *L'iguana* (1965).

OTTIERO OTTIERI: Ottieri achieved literary recognition with his novel *Donnarumma all'assalto* (1959, *The Man at the Gate*, 1962). Published at a time when many Italian avant garde writers were concerned with industrial subjects (perhaps the most famous novel being Volponi's *Memoriale*), it is the story of the opening of a new industry in southern Italy, from the point of view of the personnel manager – a job which Ottieri himself holds at Olivetti's. His other novels are *Memorie dell'incoscienza* (1954), *Tempi stretti* (1957) and *L'impagliatore di sedie* (1964). *La linea gotica* (1962) is his notebook from 1948 to 1958. *L'irrealtà quotidiana* (1966) is described in the blurb as an 'essay in the form of a novel'. Ottieri was born in Rome in 1924 and lives in Milan.

GOFFREDO PARISE: Parise was born at Vicenza in 1929 and now lives in Milan. Like Moravia he is contracted to write one story a month for the *Corriere della Sera*. He has written five other novels – *Il ragazzo morto e le comete* (1951), *La grande vacanza* (1953), *Il prete bello* (1954, *The Priest among the Vines*, 1955), *Il fidanzamento* (1956) and *Amore e fervore* (1959). Following in the tradition of Fogazzaro, Piovene and other 'Scrittori del Veneto', these books were all concerned in some way or other with religion (see also *Deliver Us from Evil* on page 88 by Meneghello, one of the latest bright stars from the Veneto). With *Il padrone* (1965, to be published in English as *The Boss*), however, religion has been abandoned. The book took him three years to write and was awarded the Premio Viareggio.

PIER PAOLO PASOLINI: The most important Italian poet to emerge since the war, Pasolini is essentially a solitary figure in literature. He is a sort of *deus ex machina*, contradictory, debatable. Anything he produces, whether a book of poems, a film or a novel, automatically creates a stir. There is something omnivorous in the way his poems cover such various and contrasting fields of experience and comprehension. None of the younger poets in Italy can match him in content or technique.

Part of a Letter to the Codignola Boy represents Pasolini at a turning point in his life. He feels he can no longer be of any use to the new generation in pointing out fresh paths in literature or politics. The other poem concerns his own religious torment – and in this there is a parallel with Auden's present work; he is torn between Marxist beliefs and an increasing attraction towards the Catholic interpretation of life.

Pasolini was born in Bologna in 1922. Besides being a poet and a novelist, he is a film critic, film director and exponent of popular and dialect poetry. His *Canzoniere italiano, antologia della poesia popolare* was published in 1955. His books of poetry include *Le ceneri di Gramsci* (1957), *La religione del mio tempo* (1961) and *Poesia in forma di rosa*, from which these two poems are taken. His most famous novels are *Ragazzi di vita* (1955) and *Una vita violenta* (1959). *Passione e ideologia*, essays, was published in 1960. His latest publication is *Uccellacci e uccellini* (1966), the script of his film, with an essay on *cinema come poesia*. The best known films are *Accattone* and *Il vangelo secondo Matteo*. He now lives in Rome.

CAMILLO PENNATI: Camillo Pennati is a very individual poet. He is neither fashionably experimental nor avant garde, nor yet tied to any 'group', and his work is thus inclined to be unjustly overlooked by the critics in Italy. In his poetry he aims to celebrate the ambiguous intricacy and meaning of life as related to two landscapes: the human and the natural. The two poems chosen here are representative in that they show the poet being moved by nature and trying to grasp at its growing significance – but being rejected.

Pennati was born in Milan in 1931. He has had two books published,

Una preghiera per noi (1957) and L'ordine delle parole (1964), which contains these two poems; in addition the Keepsake Press in London has published his Landscapes (1964), poems translated by Peter Russell with parallel texts. He has translated W. H. Auden, Thom Gunn, Ted Hughes, Philip Larkin and Louis MacNeice. He now lives in London, where he works at the Italian Institute of Culture.

NELO RISI: Nelo Risi has a unique voice in poetry, with a highly developed wit and sense of humour not generally found among poets of the twentieth century in Italy. The three short poems included here are all from Pensieri elementari (1961). His first well-known book was Polso teso (1956). Civilissimo was published in 1958, Minime, massime in 1962, and Dentro la sostanza in 1965. Born in Milan in 1920, he now lives and works in Rome as a television commentary editor.

RENZO ROSSO: Rosso is from Trieste and writes of his native city with a passion and a single-mindedness that continue the tradition of Svevo and Saba. Born in 1927, he is a very idiosyncratic writer, though in Italy his one novel, La dura spina (1963, The Hard Thorn 1966) has caused him to be compared with Thomas Mann, for his breadth of vision, his preoccupation with Natur (the physical side of man) and Geist (the spirit). His only other book is a collection of short stories, L'adescamento (1959, The Bait and other Stories 1962).

EDOARDO SANGUINETI: Poet and critic, Sanguineti is attached to the avant garde Novissimi and contributed to their anthology, Il Verri, published in 1961. He and Umberto Eco are undoubtedly the most brilliant of this group. Capriccio italiano (1963) was his first novel. The piece included here is its opening -- ten out of the one hundred and eleven sections into which the book is divided – and first appeared, before publication, in Il Menabò. A translation of sections L–LVIII was included in Art and Literature 2.

Sanguineti was born in Genoa in 1930. He wrote a highly learned volume on Dante, Interpretazione di Malebolge (1961) and a brilliant collection of essays on contemporary literature, Tra liberty e crepuscolarismo (1961). Dante is an acknowledged influence on his poetical work: Laborintus (1956), Eroto paegnia (1958), both books published together in 1960 as Opus metricum. Other poems, K. e altre cose and Purgatorio dell'inferno have since appeared. He wrote the libretto for Luciano Berio's opera, Passaggio, performed at the Scala during the 1962–3 season. Moravia, an essay on the writer, was published in 1962, Ideologia e linguaggio, essays, in 1965, and Il realismo di Dante in 1966. In 1956, with G. Getto, he edited the anthology, Il Sonetto. He now lives in Turin.

LEONARDO SCIASCIA: Sciascia was born at Racalmuto, in the province of Agrigento, in 1921. His first book was an historical and sociological study, *Parocchie di Regalpetra* (1956). *Gli zii di Sicilia* (1960) consisted of four historical short stories. *Pirandello e la Sicilia* was published in 1961, as was *Il giorno della civetta* (in English *Mafia Vendetta*, 1963), a novella denouncing the Mafia as well as analysing its social, historical and moral problems, and the winner of the Premio Crotone. *Il consiglio d'Egitto* (1963, *The Council of Egypt* 1966) was another novella, based on an actual uprising in Palermo. *Morte dell' inquisitore* was published in 1964, and A *ciascuno il suo*, a novel, again a Mafia story, in 1966.

VITTORIO SERENI: Sereni is one of the main pillars of the Italian middle-generation poetical movement. At first very much under the shadow of Montale, his poetry has now achieved a meaning and a vision unmistakably his own. He is a poet of guilt and of fruition by means of a sharply focused memory. At times he is bitter and at times movingly tender. He has an intense desire that life should be restful, through fulfilment and love, but at the same time he is painfully aware of his own daily loss and pain – from which, and in spite of which, living can be turned into something worthwhile: a constantly repeated act of faith.

Born at Luino in 1913, he was one of the editors of *Corrente* and *Rassegna d'Italia*. During the last war he was for two years a prisoner in North Africa. For about a year he was in charge of the literary column of *Milano Sera*. Now he is a director of Mondadori, the publishers in Milan. He has translated Valéry, Pound and W. C. Williams. His books include *Frontiera* (1941), *Poesie* (1942), *Diario d'Algeria* (1947), *Frammento di una sconfitta* (1957), *Gli strumenti umani* (1965), all poetry; *Gli immediati dintorni* (1962), essays, and *L'opzione* (1964), prose. An essay by Franco Fortini on Sereni's work appears on p. 151. The two poems in this book are published in *Gli strumenti umani*.

IGNAZIO SILONE: One of the intellectual giants of Italy and internationally respected, Ignazio Silone was born at Pescina dei Marsi, in the province of Aquila, in 1900. The son of a small landowner, he was orphaned at the age of fourteen as a result of the Marsica earthquake. Before long he was involving himself in political agitation, first locally, later on the Socialist weekly *L'Avanti* and as editor of *Il Lavoratore* in Trieste, finally with Gramsci as a clandestine worker against Fascism. He was denounced and had to flee the country, settling in 1930 in Switzerland. In that year he broke with the Communist party and drafted his novel *Fontomara*, to be published first in German in Zurich in 1933 and soon translated into twenty-five languages (English edition also 1933). Since then, except by necessity during and immediately after the war, he has kept away from party politics. Indeed his whole subsequent career as novelist, essayist and co-director – with Chiaromonte – of *Tempo Presente*, reveals the essentially individual and non-sectarian nature, both social and moral, of his inspiration. He called himself Silone during his clandestine period and has since adopted the name legally, his original name being Secondino Tranquilli.

His novels are *Fontomara* (1933); *Il seme sotto le neve* (1940, *The Seed Beneath the Snow* 1950); *Una manciata di more* (1952, *A Handful of Blackberries* 1954); *Il segreto di Luca* (1956, *The Secret of Luca* 1959); *La volpe e la camelie* (1960, *The Fox and the Camellias* 1961). *Der Faschismus* (1936), and *La scuola dei dittatori* (1939, *The School for Dictators* 1939), were books of essays. *Uscita di sicurezza* (1965), which contains *Visit to a Prisoner*, translated by his wife, and which was the winner of the Premio Marzotto, is also a collection of essays, forming in effect an intellectual autobiography. Silone has also written a play *Ed egli si nascose* (1944, *And He Did Hide Himself* 1946).

CARLO VILLA: Carlo Villa is primarily a poet, noted for a special, rather biting irony. His work has appeared in *Il Menabò* and other literary magazines. A collection of his poems, under the title of *Il privilegio di essere vivi*, was published in 1962, with a preface by Pasolini, and reissued with further poems in 1964 as *Siamo esseri antichi*. He spent some years working on his first novel, *La nausea media* (1964), from which the extract here is taken.

Villa was born in 1931 in Rome where he took his degree in law at the University.

CESARE VIVALDI: Vivaldi is one of the latest protagonists of the avant garde poetical movement. His work has appeared in the publications *Gruppo '63*, *Il Verri* and other leading literary magazines in Italy and abroad. In *Striptease*, a rather Dadaist poem, he attempts to present the title-theme by means of a verbal jigsaw; he arrives at images as it were in competition with those reached by the electronic brain, used by a poet-member of *I Novissimi*, a group which produced its own anthology: *I Novissimi: poesie per gli anni 60* (1961).

He was born in Imperia, Liguria, in 1925, and now lives in Rome. For several years he was a political journalist. Both a literary and art critic, he has published several small volumes of verse, all of which are gathered together in *Dettagli* (1964), where *Striptease* is included. He is a translator of poetry, especially Latin, and has translated the entire *Aeneid*. He has also edited selections of verse from Rimbaud and Martial and has written a number of monographs on individual artists and groups of artists. In 1964 he edited the anthology *Poesia satirica dell' Italia d'oggi*.

PAOLO VOLPONI: Volponi's *La macchina mondiale*, from which an extract is included here, was one of the most remarkable Italian novels of 1965, though not quite so successful as his only other novel, the greatly praised *Memoriale* (1962).

Volponi was born at Urbino in 1924. He went to Rome in 1950, then to the Abruzzi, Calabria, Sicily and back to Rome, on sociological concerns. Since 1956 he has lived at Ivrea, where like Ottieri (see page 280) he works for Olivetti. His books of poems include *Il ramarro* (1948), *L'antica moneta* (1955) and *Le porte dell' Appennino* (1960), which won the Premio Viareggio for poetry. *La macchina mondiale* won the Premio Strega. He contributes often to *Il Menabò* and *Paragone*.

Other books in the new Penguin series Writing Today ...
are listed overleaf

The Writing Today . . . Series

An interesting new venture by Penguins which aims to inform the English-speaking reader of new developments in the literature of other countries.

The following volumes are available or in preparation

The New Writing in the U.S.A.*
African Writing Today
Latin American Writing Today
South African Writing Today
German Writing Today

*Not for sale in the U.S.A.